Stinging Fly Patrons

Many thanks to: Mark Armstrong, Maria Behan, Niamh Black, John Boyne, Trish Byrne, Edmond Condon, Evelyn Conlon, Sean Curran, Edel Fairclough, Michael J. Farrell, Ciara Ferguson, Olivia Gaynor-Long, Michael Gillen, Brendan Hackett, James Hanley, Christine Dwyer Hickey, Dennis Houlihan, Peggy Hughes, Nuala Jackson, Geoffrey Keating, Jack Keenan, Jerry Kelleher, Conor Kennedy, Gráinne Killeen, Joe Lawlor, Irene Rose Ledger, Róisín McDermott, Petra McDonough, Lynn Mc Grane, Jon McGregor, Finbar McLoughlin, Maggie McLoughlin, Ama, Grace & Fraoch MacSweeney, Mary MacSweeney, Paddy & Moira MacSweeney, Anil Malhotra, Gerry Marmion, Dáirine Ní Mheadhra, Lucy Perrem, Maria Pierce, Peter J. Pitkin, Mark Richards, Fiona Ruff, Alf Scott, Ann Seery, Eileen Sheridan, Alfie & Savannah Stephenson, Mike Timms, Colleen Toomey, Olive Towey, Simon Trewin, Debbi Voisey, Ruth Webster, The Irish Centre for Poetry Studies at Mater Dei Institute, Lilliput Press, Poetry Ireland and Tramp Press.

We'd also like to thank those individuals who have expressed the preference to remain anonymous.

By making an annual contribution of 75 euro, patrons provide us with vital support and encouragement.

Become a patron online at
www.stingingfly.org
or send a cheque or postal order to:
The Stinging Fly, PO Box 6016, Dublin 1.

New Writers, New Writing

The Stinging Fly

issue 33 | *Spring* 2016
volume two | €15.00/£12.00

IN THE WAKE OF THE RISING

COVER DESIGN

Fergal Condon

'... God has specially appointed me to this city, so as though it were a large thoroughbred horse which because of its great size is inclined to be lazy and needs the stimulation of some stinging fly...'

—Plato, *The Last Days of Socrates*

Next Issue Due: June 2016

The Stinging Fly
new writers, new writing

Editor
Thomas Morris

Publisher
Declan Meade

Design & Layout
Fergal Condon

Assistant Editor
Fiona Boyd

Poetry Editor
Eabhan Ní Shúileabháin

Eagarthóir filíochta Gaeilge
Aifric MacAodha

Issue Guest Editor
Sean O'Reilly

Printed by Naas Printing Ltd, County Kildare

ISBN 978-1-906539-53-5 ISSN 1393-5690

Published three times a year (February, June and October).

The Stinging Fly gratefully acknowledges the support of The Arts Council/
An Chomhairle Ealaíon and Dublin City Council

PO Box 6016, Dublin 1
stingingfly@gmail.com

Keep in touch: sign up to our e-mail newsletter, become a fan on Facebook, or follow us on Twitter for regular updates about all publications, events and activities.

www.stingingfly.org | www.facebook.com/StingingFly | @stingingfly

Editorial

There are many reasons behind the publication of this special edition of *The Stinging Fly* in the centenary year of the Easter Rising. Perhaps the most important one, I would say, is that any literary magazine, whether it likes it or not, is a product of the times in which it is made. Hopefully, it is also an inspirational and critical response to those times. So it was both tempting and necessary to put out a public call for submissions for this edition of the magazine, in order to engage with this year of national introspection, this year right now, 2016, this here moment. The issue would open up an alternative space for writers to re-read and respond to the events of that Easter Monday, the background and the legacy, and to the Proclamation itself, a founding document of the Republic, outside of the official events and memorials planned by the government of the day—which, as I write, is preparing to go to the people again. The writers were free to respond to this material in whatever way they wanted, in any shape or form.

This spirit of immediacy, the heat of the moment, is a vital energy for a magazine these days, as much as it was for the great variety of printed material produced in the years leading up to the Rising, and after. It was the time of the manifesto, the pamphlet, the bill poster and the public lecture, the articulation of the aims and objects of clubs and societies and groups like The Co-Operative Movement (1894), The Irish Literary Theatre (1899), Inghinidhe na hÉireann (1900), The Sinn Féin Resolutions (1905), The Constitution of the Irish Citizen Army (1913)—and let's not forget 1912, and Ulster's Solemn League and Covenant, and the pledge to use 'all means to which may be found necessary to defeat the present conspiracy to set up a Home Rule Parliament in Ireland.' Or outside of Ireland, the Futurist Manifesto (1909), Du Cubisme (1912), Wyndham Lewis's Vorticist manifesto and the first feminist manifesto by Mina Loy (both 1914).

Padraig Pearse is said to have been responsible for most of the words in the Proclamation, with some additions by Connolly and MacDonagh. The typesetter was able to identify Pearse's 'beautiful upright script' in the handwritten document given to him by Connolly in the secret printing press in the back of Liberty hall. Re-reading the Proclamation, and the story of the Rising which stretches back at least as far as the era of the Irish Literary Revival and the extraordinary output of its thinkers and writers who set about trying to create an identity for the paralysed country, a national imagination, can we rekindle any of the energy of that time and use it for ourselves in our own day as we look for a better way of organising this society?

And for writers, there is another question which the magazine hopes to ask in some way: what if anything is left of the tradition of Realism, and the original design of that form to hold a microscope or a mirror, cracked or not, up to the world in order to see it better and change it? Do writers today have any interest in social change, any belief at all in the transformative role of literary culture in the life of the nation or is the feeling of a shared reality crumbling with the ice-caps? And perhaps, it might be asked, do the technological revolutions of the last few decades offer a real alternative to the traditional publishing house just as the development of the mobile guerrilla printing press did for the radicals of a century ago?

History is a story told by the victors. Or a tale touted by an idiot, signifying nothing. Or maybe it's about the phantasies of men maddened by some woman's yellow hair or a nightmare the artist must wake out of. The Tricolours and the copies of the Proclamation have been sent to every school in the country at the same time as History has been removed from the curriculum as a compulsory subject. 'History,' Foucault wrote, 'becomes effective to the degree that it introduces discontinuity into our very being.' There is no easy chronological route back to 1916. Is the ideological function of the centenary an attempt to produce a sham experience of continuity, of dubious integration, power trying to legitimise itself before our eyes, on our screens, or is it the final nail in the coffin, the lock on the cemetery gate, the last dry wake for the dream of Sovereignty as this small patchily decolonised island launches itself, warp-speed, into the global future™?

'A passion-driven exultant man sings out/Sentences that he has never thought…'—that was Yeats on his quest for a new literature for a new country, for a pure de-Anglicised mode of expression. Ireland was to be made like any other work of art. Joyce opted instead for his (un)scrupulous realism. Style is everything, they would both agree. For each of them, literature was the zone of struggle to create a different type of reality than the one forced upon them. By re-imaging what I am now, and where I am, by refusing to be told, by hurting the words, I can also imagine how things might become. And in that sense, the work is always a contribution to change.

As for me, my first sight of The Proclamation was on the wall of a narrow hall of a house in the Creggan estate up on the hill in Derry, May of 1981. The house was the family home of Patsy O'Hara, the first of the hunger strikers from Derry to die on the fast for political status for republican prisoners, and I was waiting in that hall with my father in a queue that went out the door and up the street, to see the body of the twenty-three-year-old martyr in his coffin in the front room. My father was talking to another man—about racing pigeons probably—while we waited, and to pass the time I found myself reading this creepy stained page trapped in a gold metal-work frame on the wall. It had the look of one of those *Wanted Dead or Alive* posters from the cowboy films but the words made me think of the yarns we had to do in Irish class about garrulous, big-thighed heroes. I had time to read it a few times before we moved up the queue and I got my first glimpse into the living room where two people, a man and a woman, were standing to attention, wearing balaclavas and black berets at the head of the coffin, and a small grey dented fan was spinning silently on a shelf.

On the way home in the car I asked my father what it was, this Proclamation thing. He told me to pay it no mind, that it was a death warrant, and those men who had signed it were executed by the Brits. Just for writing it? I mind asking him, incredulous, a touch awed—I knew the cops and army would shoot you at the drop of a hat or a paving stone from a rooftop but this was a new one: you could be stood blindfolded opposite a firing squad just for writing your thoughts down—and he said, Aye sure that's what they wanted, to be ghosts, to bloody scare the people off their knees. And then he went off on his usual rant about why the people never do what you tell them to, only a good pigeon could be relied on not to act the maggot. I wasn't really listening; I was thinking about getting back to the house and writing some massive big words in the back pages of my school jotter.

Don't forget either, that only a few months after the first performance of the Proclamation at the GPO, the poet Hugo Ball, read aloud the first Dadaist manifesto in Zurich, which, in a rough translation, ends: 'Each thing has its word, but the word has become a thing by itself. Why shouldn't I find it? Why can't a tree be called Pluplusch, and Pluplubasch when it has been raining? The word, the word, the word outside your domain, your stuffiness, this laughable impotence, your stupendous smugness, outside all the parrotry of your self-evident limitedness. The word… is a public concern of the first importance.'

What, reader, is your new word for Freedom?

Sean O'Reilly
Dublin, February 2016
inthewakeoftherising2016@gmail.com

The Rage of O'Malley

Paul Lynch

He had been in the room no more than a moment—not even that, Art Cahill said later, his foot was hardly in the door—when we heard the bullet hit him. Perhaps it was not heard so much as felt, and perhaps what we felt was the messenger's astonishment, the sudden wheezing puff as if he had hurried here breathless to impart news of his own death. And I saw what brought the bullet, the cigarette mid-suck on his lips and how it fell like burning blood. He sighed then not the sigh of a man but an animal of strange aspect and who knows what sounds we make when we stare into our own end. I looked for the shape of my gun beside me and put my fingers in my ears. And strange how the moment opened then—I remember being glad I was not a smoker, an unexpected thought, for I had dabbled before with cigarettes, and I was aware suddenly of the weight of my empty bandolier, could hear Art Cahill trying to breathe quietly as if that could make a difference. And still in that moment I could hear the bullet's afterclap diminish in the street below and yet how it still echoed at some impossible level of hearing. And perhaps you can hear it still if you listen, that clapping that is the applause that heralds death and who wants to hear death and its welcome?

The messenger seemed to go willingly to the floor no different than a man going to his bed. He sounded as if he were making himself comfortable. I checked about myself for some unfelt injury. The dying man gasped and fell silent. Art Cahill said, keep quiet. I did not know who he was talking to. I looked towards the dying man but could see little in that dark but for his boot meeting with the dark around it so that what was divisible of the man and night was becoming hard to tell. I became certain I saw the boot wriggle and perhaps that wriggle was the reflex of dying. I must have lifted my head, for Art Cahill said, keep your head down. We knew we were pinned by a sniper. For a moment I tried to imagine what such a sniper would look like, a face greased dark no doubt and a single eye asquint on our position. And the night's calm about such a man who has in all attitude become the frightening truth of the hunter. And yet this same man surely shared the same thoughts I had, how each man asks himself, how did I get here and what now of this?

Night had become the city. We had watched hours ago the gas lamps flutter and vanish. There was fighting still though it was intermittent, almost forlorn, and it reached our position like a rumour of the day we had been a part of, a detail of some future conversation. Sometimes you could hear their machine-gun fire as a lone and faraway fellow laughs at some afterthought. What to do now? I wondered. The struggling hours in this storeroom above some printer's shop. The smell of kerosene faint above the sootdamp and the must of old cardboard and mould on the walls. We were out of ammunition and awaiting word. The dispatch had died with the messenger. Of a sudden, the messenger groaned and we watched him resurrect into a sitting-up position. I thought you were dead, I whispered. It was Art Cahill answered. I'm not touched at all. I'm not talking to you, I said, I'm talking to that fellow. I looked again in the dying man's direction. Who are you? I said. I don't know who he is, Art Cahill answered again, he just came in, he was shot as he was coming in, I only heard the door, they went and shot the messenger.

The dying man whispered and I could not catch his accent. He said, I do not want to die like this, it is not what I expected. I yearned to see the dying man better but thought about the sniper fixed on our position. Then Art Cahill leaned towards the dying man and said, I honestly thought you were dead. By any chance do you have the message?

Of a sudden the dead man roared, you stupid ass. And he rose to his feet and I saw his fists. How he began then to rage about the room, finding within him some last moment of strength. He kicked his heels at the walls and pulled into riot the quiet of stacked boxes. Smashed them to the floor. Smashed a chair on top of them. It was a wonder he wasn't shot again. The way he let loose from his mouth unheard-of curses like some *djinn* imprecating the dark to his bidding and then his breath left him. He stood staring at us and I could not see his eyes. With great slowness he lay himself back down upon the floor and it was then Art Cahill began towards him with matchflame. The carrier of last light held in the hands of the last carrier, I thought, and such are the strange things you think of. I could see the dying man was in civilian attire. Art Cahill said, tell me lad, who are you? What was the message? And I said, be careful with that matchlight or you'll pull another bullet in on us. Art Cahill blew out the match and in the flame's abatement I saw enough of the dying man's face and thought, pity the youth in it. Saw the blooming roseate of blood on his lapel. The dying man's cigarette still aglow on the floor and Art Cahill picked it up and took a long pull from it, put it to sit on the dying man's lips. Art Cahill said, who are you then, just so's we can tell your people? The dying man lay in an increasing quiet. The cigarette burned itself out. For sure, he had stopped breathing. We knew then he had met his death. I blessed myself. Art Cahill blessed himself too, I think, and I listened respectfully because a person's passing is an exchange of sorts that brings into the world a silence.

I thought again of the sniper as the accomplice of such silence. I was glad again I was not a smoker. I told myself not to raise my head but I did and took a look outside. Keep your head down, Art Cahill said. There was nothing to see of the street. Everything was tight with the same dark and I never felt more alive. I could guess the sniper's position, a factory building across the way with countless faceless windows. And I saw how the night had knit the building and the dark together so that it was not a building of this city but a building of some endless hell and hell is not what you were told but is a place where nothing speaks to your wishes. I drew with my eyes the shape of each window. I might have beheld the sniper and I might not and he might have beheld me, who is to know. I remember thinking you could find yourself fixed with certainty at one window only to find death from another.

Without a single word uttered we debated what to do, whether or not to disobey command and abandon our position. Finally, Art Cahill said, I wonder what his message was. I said, I wonder what his name was, terrible for a man to have to die with other fellows not knowing him, though he died a hero all the same. And Art Cahill said, they'll know for sure who he is tomorrow. I found myself climbing into the dead man's mind and his memories opened at the touch. Strange how such a thing happens and yet I could see images of a life, a young man taking tea and toast in a frosty room and I could sense his disappointments and desires, saw sunlight caught in a greasy window, was certain I could see a young man searching for his socks of a morning and I could smell his unwashed feet. And such a thought might have been an intrusion for suddenly the dead man roared out. Jesus fuck! What am I going to do now? He began to sit up again and I could feel him looking at us. This is not the way that I wanted it, he said. I had plans, didn't I? And what about my children?

Then, impossibly, he was up again on his feet, raging with what was left of his body, raging with what was left of his will. He pulled at the air and smashed what he could find. And Art lit a match and we saw his bleeding was profuse, that his blood raged out of him and covered his chest. I put my fingers in my ears. Then he became quiet and stood over us. Art Cahill asked him about his children and the dying man said, you ass, I don't have any children. And Art Cahill lit another match as if to evidence light upon the meaning of such words and it was then the dying man spat at us.

I pretended to myself none of this happened. It is a strange indignity to be spat at by the dying. A man on your own side. A man you could hear lying down a moment later to stare into his own end. The thought that a dying man can take with him nothing of such an act and yet I would be left to nurse the grievance. The man laughing in unreachable silence. Slowly, slowly, the dying man stopped breathing. And I became glad. I thought of all the men across the city who will have met their death gladly and with dignity, but not this fellow. I wished him dead for in death you cannot be anything other than what the living make of you and tomorrow we would report the incident and have him conferred a hero. His name would be spoken with reverence at hearthsides. People might even hang pictures of him. And I wished him dead because the truth is he had become an inconvenience. His indignation had become an indignity in itself. I listened for a long time to the night's silence until the dying man's silence was held in that quiet and I blessed myself again. Art Cahill cupped another match and we could see the dead man's body. How many times can a man die in one night I do not know but there are better ways to die. For sure I had wished him dead and now that he was dead I thought perhaps it was regrettable I had wished it. Art Cahill leaned towards me and whispered, if he gets up and roars like that one more time I'm going to kill him.

The hour before dawn is the loneliest hour. I thought again of the sniper and imagined his life, met details I could not know, all that a man hides in the privacy of his mind and yet I was certain of a few facts, that he too was growing weary in this lonely hour and that his elbows were sore and scuffed and that he dreamed of his family, that he dreamed of breakfast, a boiled egg and a kidney perhaps, that he dreamed of something to belong to. And that these facts belonged to him I have no doubt for he was as true to me then as I was to myself. And sometimes you can see it, how all men are the one kind, and it was then Art Cahill interrupted. He said, he never said who he was. Who? I said, for my thoughts were with the sniper. The dead man, he said. And at that, the dead man groaned. Sweet Jesus, Art Cahill said. Perhaps it was the dead man's ghost that rose again because a man with that sort of wound has no life left in him. And yet how he climbed slowly to his feet and how he raged again though he had lost all his strength. He staggered with his arms out like a drunkard. His roars had become whispers. Finally he stopped and stood to the wall like some fellow soon to become his own mural. And Art Cahill lit another match and pulled him out of the shadows. You could see how he stood holy in his blood. Art Cahill said to him, now that you are up, you never told us the message. And the dying man did not answer. Finally, he whispered, I could have had a life. Wouldn't that have been something? And then I said, but only out of politeness, because you want a man to meet his death feeling he has contributed somewhat to things, so I told him, haven't you done your duty? Won't your people be proud? And he roared out, what fucking use is all that to me? What can I do with it? And he sat down then and bowed his head and was silent for some time, and there are no words to give a man in such a moment. Finally he spoke. And when he spoke it was to answer an ancient question, perhaps the oldest of questions and it was the oldest of answers, the giving of a name for the last time. He said, my name is James O'Malley—but all my friends and family, they've always called me Jim. He spoke it twice. Jim. And then he died. And in the silence that opened I understood the man's rage but did not want to think of it, and I thought about the closing of a man's mind like that, all that private thought and feeling, all that yearning and sorrow, all that makes a man, and I saw it as the closing of an entire world and how does one world hold dominion over another? Outside came rising the dim light of yet another morning. And I began then to understand and then I didn't.

Now We Can Talk Openly About Men

Martina Evans

> … the blue, forked torch of a flower
> down the darker and darker stairs, where blue is darkened on blueness
> down the way Persephone goes, just now, in first-frosted September
> to the sightless realm where darkness is married to dark…
>
> —D.H. Lawrence

19 Ballydaheen, Mallow
September 1st-September 28th 1920

1

I was in a weakness. I couldn't stand up. I leant back against the wall like a drunkard. Was that Himself I'd seen on the back of a Crossley tender on Main Street? The truck lurched down the hill and out of the back appeared a pair of eyes. They pinned me, bored me. It was an outrage. A small Tan or maybe an Auxie, lounging in the back against the canvas with a bayonet pointed at my waist. The head off Himself in a cracked leather coat with goggles hanging round his neck. After twelve years. Could he have clambered out of the other side of O'Sullivan's Quay that night in Cork and run away with his bowler under his arm? We never found the hat although Eileen Murphy and myself searched high and low, tearing at the damp walls, our hands bright green from the moss.

2

Eileen Murphy was tough out and I should have listened to her that night when she said to shove his head down in the water with my boot. We were wrapped in fog by the brimming brown water, the Lee overflowing after the deluge. I wanted him to be taken by God with no hand in it at all myself but of course that was a Sin of Omission so I was a black sinner too. We should have called the constabulary the minute he slithered in. They say a drunkard has more lives than a cat. Lurching up the road every night, steamed to the gills taking the two sides of Blarney Street—horses and carts the whole lot and not a hair of his head damaged. His white collar shining in the greenish gaslight. How many times did he fall down and rise again like an Indian rubber ball? And what was there to stop him rising again? The body wasn't found. No one saw Jesus rise on Easter Sunday either. He is not here, for he has risen, as he said he would. Come and see the place where he lay and that is the Gospel according to Matthew. But Himself was no Jesus and he had plenty reason to run after what he'd done. The fog was thick and heavy as a wet wool overcoat that night, soaked us so we left drips all over the concrete kitchen floor when we came home. Eileen only fifteen but she'd already had a taste of his antics too. We bent over Flora, lying in the sheets I had embroidered with cherries and leaves, to see if she was still sleeping and she was. Now we can talk openly about men, I said, and now I wonder if I should have said anything, maybe it was Myself as well as Himself that turned Eileen hard as an armoured van, sent her out to join Cumann na mBan.

3

It was the Thursday I thought I saw Himself that the simmering madness got into me. My brain wouldn't run straight in its track anymore, only started lurching and shooting electric sparks up the right side of my face. We'd had a doing from the Tans in June the night of the attack on Eileen but this was worse. Because staring hurts worst of all. This fellow was morning-sober not like the Tans that night who couldn't see straight with the drink. One fellow had to hold himself up with his rifle, using it like a walking stick to stop himself from falling down. Trying to look a big man in front of Flora. The fellow in charge leant up against the wall for balance and left a green smear after him. I was scrubbing for days. But you never knew what way they'd turn. One minute a Tan might be sticking his head under the hood of a baby's pram, *what's 'er name, blue-eyed little dohling,* next he would be trying to—what they called—click with a girl, then you could turn a corner and a gang of them were stamping on an old man's fingers. Every day of the week, people ran like the chickens before them. Savage drivers but expert—the tenders, like motorised brooms, pushing carts and people and animals into the ditches—pirate patches over their greasy eyes, the hooks of their hands slashing the air, scraping walls and gathering leaves off the trees as they passed. Dark faces and stained fingers—people said they'd come from hell and that you could still smell the singe off them. I couldn't smell the singe only engine oil because they loved driving motors and couldn't stop even for themselves. They got tangled up with Hounds of Duhallow out beyond Burnfort on the Island Road and then, even the great Britisher, Mrs Pound said she was angry with Lloyd George for sending them because the language out of them you wouldn't hear it out of Turks and how lucky we were to have 17th Lancers, The Duke of Cambridge's Own, between us and the Cockney scum.

4

The darting pain ran up the right side of my face. If I could turn the clock back to Thursday the first, I'd have got off my chair faster. That was the cause. Getting frozen in a draft before the curfew, standing on my old green painting chair, pinning the vermilion blankets over the window for the blackout with Scissors No. 1 in my hand for protection. A pure perishing mist rose up from under the bridge while I stood there foolishly too long, clenching the scissors. The two rivers twining and separating in my mind like a pair of snakes—the Lee and the Blackwater—had I left my husband underwater in Cork only for him to resurrect himself in Mallow?

5

Captain Galway, Auxie, was an ex-officer with some queer ideas about whose side he was on. I didn't know if he was a gentleman at all and Mr Bloom was hinting the same. I had a fiery letter from Eileen. Someone wrote to her in Dublin. I couldn't believe how the news had gone, like a shot off a shovel through Royal Mail and Eileen was back down tout suite on top of me by letter. She was boiled up completely about the two of them walking openly in the streets of Mallow—Flora, in her three-quarter-length smashed strawberry coat and the Captain in his mould-green with the empty sleeve pinned to his epaulette. The whole town with their eyes outside their heads, killed from looking at them. Galway, blonde, too handsome. And people were scared of the Auxies too—even more than the Tans—their old eyes in their young faces under their black Glengarry caps, the ribbons fluttering on their necks. They hung off the side of the tenders, as mean as you like, in rifle green. Constable Doon complained to me about Flora cutting her hair. A woman's crowning glory, he said, avoiding my stern eye, looking down over his long moustache to the rifle tip between the two toes of his boots standing outside Broadview barracks. Well, that's the youth, I said, walking on with my messages. John Lucy's lamb chops were dripping out of my basket, he'd given me a free sheep's head as well, with instructions how to cook the head for a healthy mutton broth, he thought Flora had fallen away. The whole town was telling me that, calling on me to feed Flora after she'd cut her hair.

6

And had I saved her from Himself, only for Galway to arrive and drag her down? Tarred and feathered, she could be tarred and feathered, the words went round my head in a wreath. And I wasn't the only one. The Mahoney twins, always smelling of ham and hiding under their mud-green caps made their fingers into scissors and went snip-snap when she walked and the Tans were worse, shouting *Dolly, Dolly* every time she crossed the street with a message from Sullivan the solicitor. And when Sullivan started to defend Sinn Féin prisoners in court, I thought we would go up in smoke, tarred with one brush or another or both, our beds drenched with petrol some night by a red angry crowd.

7

On the Saturday He appeared again wearing brown boots laced up to his knees, standing across the road from the house by the Royal red postbox. Halfway through painting the parlour cocoa with cream on the wainscot, I threw open the window for the fumes and saw him staring in with his hand on His Majesty's Mail. Small as a jockey, like Himself, only sallow. But he could have gone abroad after his escape, fought on the sands of Gallipoli. Would he, could he claim me again and get the priests behind him to let him into my apple-green bed, every bit of silk double-stitched and finished to a high degree? The pain was kneeing into my brain from the night before, as if he'd opened my head like an egg and was spooning it out. If he wasn't Himself then who was he? He could be after Flora for espionage. And for which side? Didn't Sinn Féin make the girls spy for them? Eileen Murphy said they all volunteered but girls are easily forced. I pulled my eyes away and cast them down to the tongues of my brown button boots. I brought down the sash like a guillotine and whipped the bottle-green curtains across fast. Mrs Simm's crimson satin dressing gown was only cut out and I left it thrown across the sewing table, took to my bed with Mr Pym's linctus. The brown bottle stood in the table beside me, staining the broderie anglaise in the dark. I couldn't move, hardly breathe, my lungs shrunk to the size of two teaspoons tied around my throat.

8

I'd only just rocked off with the linctus, when the two of them came back and woke me and I had to get up out of my bed, wrap my sea-green shawl around me, feel for my carmine slippers with my heavy, heavy feet. It was my duty as a mother to go down to say good evening and pretend that I was civilised towards him and his mutilated arm. I didn't doubt that he had a mutilated brain along with it. None of those fellows came back normal. If Flora had a father, he'd call him in and demand a doctor's certificate but what could I do? Flora blushed every time she spoke to him in front of me. I wondered if the cause was me. Me, staring with my brown linctus eyes. It's a hard fact that not one of us can see ourselves from the outside. But something was not right. Yes, he was handsome, no one was in any doubt. Not real gentry but not one of those shrivelled yokes from the East End of London either. One of them outside St Mary's church on the Sunday, grinning over his bayonet with a monkey face. His bandolier strapped across his wrinkled olive jacket and his thighs no wider than rolling pins inside the black trousers. I couldn't bear to look at him. The officer class had the shoulders to carry the jackets. A bunched uniform was always an affront to my eyes because I was brought up in tailoring and with the highest respect for the tailoring laws. Captain Galway, he knew how to fill his uniform, apart from the left sleeve and it was the empty sleeve that had lured Flora. Sucked her up like a hungry straw.

Brothers – 7th May 1916

(all text taken from original document by Richard Kent)

I was called on this night at nine o'clock
by a military chauffer and constable with a motor car.
I hurried on my clothes, fear clutching my heart,
suspected the journey by night was no idle one.

At first I assumed it was myself alone he wished to see
but when we proceeded to my sister, sister-in-law, and brother,
my fears that news was bad
became certainties.

We drove through the black night pouring torrents of rain
challenged at intervals by armed sentries
until Kilmainham Jail loomed up
dark and grim before us.

Inside the gate we were kept in suspense
while keys and lanterns were got
and thence through dark narrow passages
only dimly lighted by candles carried.

Sentries stood idly about.
A prison warden could just be distinguished in the gloom.
We picked our way across to Éamonn's cell and soon
stood within, clasping his hand.

He was the same calm as always.
Not a sign was there that the advent of moon
and the probable cutting off of his young life
had the slightest effect.

His hair was ruffled
as though he had been thinking deeply,
running his hand through it.
I asked—'What was the news?'

'Oh the worst,' he answered nonchalantly,
then putting his arm around Aine and smiling
said—'And isn't it all for the best?'
'I don't think so, Éamonn,' she wound her arms around him.
'Oh I think it is, all for the best,' he said.

Two guards stood in the cell all the time.
In a corner was the plank bed,
nearer the door a small table
on which stood a guttering candle
and numerous letters complete for posting.

His mind had been disturbed somewhat
by a visit from the prison chaplain talking trivialities,
who insinuated something might happen during the night;
this conversation was unnerving
as he was quite prepared to die.

We stood aside while they
sat side by side on the lowly bed
talking
          talking
                    talking in whispers
just like the pair of lovers they had always remained.

Our allowance of twenty minutes was nearly spent
so we sat down in a little circle,
him the coolest of us all.
Our janitors were getting impatient.

At last the sentries—'Time's up please'—
made us stand for the final parting.
It was hard to realise
it was the last leave-taking.

Never demonstrative,
a simple handshake for us three
and a kiss for Aine
composed our last sad blessings.

On my way out the Commandant said,
no one had any right or reason to even suggest a reprieve,
that Eammon was to be shot in the morning,
and kindly suggested my going back and telling him.

He was standing upright in his cell,
back partly to the door, hands in his pockets
apparently thinking
                                        thinking
                                                        thinking.

I told him, his friend Father Augustine was coming.
He replied 'Oh, is that so?'
but in a tone that I since think meant
he knew all hope was gone.

Another handshake, still not a tremor,
and the door clangs between us.
Back into the rain and the night.
This was my last glance at my brother.
The candle was still burning.

Roll-Calls and Role-Play

Aidan Mathews

Little Brughas and Cosgraves, miniature Costelloes and Briscoes, sat side by side in my Jesuit prep school at Gonzaga College—here a Mulcahy, there a MacDonagh, and everywhere an impartial/pro-imperial Mathews—in the jubilee year of the 1916 Rising, where, with the help of truly revolutionary audio-visual aids (quarter-inch tape and slide-projectors), they studied a negotiated chronicle of the entire national story, from the fall of the Fianna to the rise of the Fenians, the declension of a recurrent martyrology which stopped short at precisely the point in the childhood of the twentieth century when their grandfathers and granduncles had lost the plot and started killing each other instead of their immemorial adversaries.

Not that the small and smelly posterity of the founding fathers needed formal notice, either from the settled culture or from the set curriculum, of deep family divisions and their dynastic stamina, as the fiftieth anniversary of Easter Week approached, and a fancy-dress fiesta, part-carnival and part-crusade, travestied the twenty-six counties in a carefully kettled riot of High Masses, low volleys, and a broad appropriation of the Christian Passion Narratives as the primer of Irish irredentism. (Nothing of the sort had been seen in the state since John F. Kennedy went without sex for three whole days during his triumphal tour of the truncated Republic, in what had been a 1963 dress-rehearsal of Cásca na hEireann.) The bad blood between the emerging bourgeois houses, which were otherwise identical in their liquidity, their postal codes and their cocktail cabinets, was no more novel and newsworthy in itself than the gravelled drives or the tradesmen's entrances of the centrally-heated homes where the surviving veterans deteriorated amongst their guerrilla reliquaries, their nebulisers, and the first colony of Filipina chaperones to arrive in South Dublin.

That much was basic and binary; and, if it was ultimately bogus as well, disguising a contented mutuality behind the antagonistic masks of the men who had fought each other fifty years before, it served admirably for three generations to camouflage the economic piracy of a unitary class behind the ideological privateering of apparent partisans, the lasting alliance beneath the trivial affiliations. The Greek and Latin patina that the Jesuit Fathers put on the Christian Brother's seed and breed in Clongowes and the Crescent in the years since the Civil War was a tactical part of the same strategy of stealthy cultural assimilation: gentrify the gun and vindicate the violence, forgive with a vengeance, but mute the demographic spectacle of the majority share-holders' monopoly on surplus capital by parading the wealthy phantom opponents as the cultic trophies of a cunning metaphysical decoy to distract the wholly destitute, who were insensitively plentiful across the country throughout the period.

Cathal Brugha's son, by way of example, wouldn't ordinarily be spotted chin-wagging cheerfully with W.T. Cosgrave's boy after outdoor Benediction on Sports Day, parents' three-legged race or no parents' three-legged race, for neither middle-aged, middle-class magnate could quite abdicate the mystique of his inherited victimhood, the pathos of his patrimony, or the operatic, OK Corral atrocities at the dark root of their red-brick reticence, although both parliamentary patricians were the equal beneficiaries of the same constitutional settlement that had consolidated a hundred, hugger-mugger clans as the new dominant class. Even Gonzaga's Ignatian motto *Semper Et Ubique Fidelis* (the template, as it happens, for Himmler's later *Loyalty is My Honour*) admonished the wavering. Only chancers chanced their arm at the feminine wiles of speak-soft reconcilement, and the hands that shook in the shaking of hands at services and sacraments were probably Parkinsonian. Equality of disdain had more dignity; that, and implacable courtesy toward the irreplaceable rival, the shadow-self, the criminal sibling, who would wait until the next millennium to be named in the *OED*, in a comical composite diminutive, as a frenemy.

It was perfectly natural, on the other hand (or fist), for General Mulcahy to reminisce with the ex-Taoiseach John A. Costello in the school gymnasium at the little light operas that the senior classes staged, for the latter would have known many of the principal political players, seventy-seven in all, whom the former had executed in a heated historical context, which, although early days yet, it was the eventual vocation of a new cadre of non-partisan Anglophone annalists at Peterhouse, Cambridge, to moderate and magnify; and they had so much grief and grievance in common, the two venerable silhouettes at the wooden horse in the college hall, the one as thin as Laurel and the other as fat as Hardy, that I sometimes wondered if their wives ever felt excluded from the stern joy of warriors sharing the spoils, like the tired spouses of talkative Spitfire pilots over ships' decanters in the Royal Irish Yacht club, just as I wonder now, fifty years later, how the young scholastics from the priests' house, where the community lived in a communist economy, so successfully predicted future homosexuals when they cast ten and eleven year olds in the female roles, rouging the right two cheeks in any class of thirty pre-pubertal boys: those freckled Os and Macs who would crawl out of a collapsed cultural rugby scrum and its dismal masculine mythology to strut and swagger at a Gay Pride pageant in the spiral streets of San Francisco twenty years later.

My own genealogy was vigorously mongrel, the majority strain in Ireland from the pre-Celtic Firbolgs to the Catholic bourgeoisie of the new Ascendancy, where I was a complicit cadet member of the aspirational *arrivistes*. Most of my mother's people had been working-class Papists from Queenstown, Cobh, who enlisted in the Royal Navy as able-bodied seamen (one of them, an Archdeacon, drowned at Jutland a month after the GPO and is buried there), although her uncle Seamus, from whom I first heard the oriental term *plenipotentiary* in a veranda after a funeral, had sat for North Cork in the second Dáil and voted against the Treaty in a ruminative Republican homily that I had partly memorised in the hope of the handsel of a Kennedy half-dollar. It was worth seven and six at the time in our animal coinage, and could buy many cordite caps for my imitation revolver.

My poor parents were always terrified that his own eventual interment might provoke a Provo guard of honour at the graveside, all blinkers and balaclavas, like his émigré brother Michael, who was a bit of a bandit over in America, a hornet in the amber of the ex-pat's slow-to-stop time-warp; but it was the elongated, El Greco figure of Eamon De Valera, sightless and stricken, who attended the requiem mass on the lurching arm of his aide-de-camp, and he was as ghastly an apparition in the Marian transept of the church as he had been when I first met him in the papal nuncio's railway-carriage at Kilcoole in County Wicklow, a stalactite in spectacles amongst cruciform fretwork panelling from the Eucharistic Congress, so that all the Irish I could muster in that slow-motion moment of disembowelment was a request for his authorisation to go to the toilet.

Inevitably, my dad, whose roots were Redmondite, delighted in this detail over Beefeater's gin and Schweppes tonic, as would my ancient uncle, a British Army chaplain at both battles of the Somme who wore a plastic poppy defiantly inside his Monkstown parish presbytery all day long at Armistice, and refused to the lethal last to celebrate the shortened, Second Council Eucharist in English; but my good godfather, who was a *patrino* and not a *padrone*, was mortified, for it was he who had spearheaded this strange commemoration, at a wind-swept shingle beach, of guns smuggled by Protestants to their social inferiors on a posh yacht in the year of the Great War between the three grandchildren of Queen Victoria, the Emperor, the Tsar, and the Kaiser.

This lovely man, who laughed like the Dalai Lama, had married, once upon a time, before breakfast in Westland Row, travelled by steam engine to Dingle town, by horse and cart to Dunquin harbour, and across out of Ireland altogether by a tipsily bucking currach into the Great Blasket, to honeymoon there, amongst rabbit-droppings and the roar of the North Atlantic ocean, for a full fortnight with Maureen McDermott, a doctoral student of Douglas Hyde's (she called him Duggie) and a good foot taller than her husband, in the house beside the home where a pipe-smoking storyteller called Peig Sayers was entertaining a couple of clipped Cambridge Marxists who were too courteous to tell her they were anthropologists with a purpose and a publisher's contract.

Like their Palestinian counterparts, the last of the islanders brought with them as they left for Springfield, Massachusetts, material tokens of their title deeds to the very scarcity they were forever forfeiting; and the present absentees of an era of continuous economic cleansing (half of all those born into Winterland since 1831 have fled it on foot), may also hold the replica keys to much of the real estate of Ireland, but they do not hold the locks, let alone the swipe cards or the sensor lights or the surveillance cameras.

If 60% of the properties in Corca Dhuibhne were vacant on the Feast of the Immaculate Conception in December 2011, when the last census was taken, that is not because the absentee landlords of the new dispensation were reciting a Jacobite rosary in the clustered Catholic parishes of a largely priestless diocese in penal Munster, but because the owners of these holiday homes, the residual legatees of the rebels who rose up, were opening their electronic gates remotely and reluctantly in the boulevards of South Dublin to scribble under porchlight *Not Applicable* or *Simply Spiritual* in the category marked Religion on the mandatory form that some student fellow in an anorak or a hoodie, even, had produced when the beam was broken, the alarm went off, and a non-shedding Shih Tzu snarled behind the stained glass window.

The south-facing *secondaires* along the eroded west coast of the country prefer, of course, a more nuanced affirmation of their standing nowadays. A concrete lattice fence, incongruous Pampas grass or Doric portico, a sad attempt in a paleolithic landscape at a suburban lawn, all of these proclaim the recidivist native who has never heard of Habitat and thematised interiors, while a wilderness of fuschia and a minutely reconstructed dry stone wall with a nineteenth century scythe propped prettily against it, signal the smart oligarchy, the current courtiers of the Three Louis's—Louis Le Brocquy, Louis Mulcahy and Louis Vuitton—whose shorthand cipher for the new republic on their double-fronted stationery is the acronym ROI, the French word for a monarch of all (s)he surveys.

The 1916 insurrectionaries (a jubilee term that replaced the use of Volunteers in much the manner that *itinerants* was ousting *tinkers* in the same euphemistic period) failed in their bid to hold the General Post Office, but their hereditary inheritors, none of whom would ever open a post-office account or stamp their own envelopes, barricaded themselves in the banks, which are redoubtable defences with ingenious loop-holes in the masonry. The artisans and civil servants had seized several symbolic strongholds (biscuit factories, a park with a duck pond, and canal bank lock-gates), but their children and their children's children made a shrewder sortie. They took the King's Inns and the Incorporated Law Society, the medical faculties in the university colleges, the chambers of commerce and the public utilities, the engineering contracts and the private connections, the gentlemen's clubs, the Georgian squares, the prestige streets on the new Monopoly board that climaxed, to my mother's misery, on the road at right angles to the one we lived on.

The inadvertent arson of the records' office in the Custom House in the preliminary skirmishing of a final rift in the rebel ranks (five years after Easter week had morphed into Holy Week, if not into the Triduum itself) might even have endorsed a reflex sense of solemn entitlement on both fratricidal sides; for the documentation which showed that the indigent lot of us were half a hundred years from cholera and the poorhouse sank out of sight in a blizzard of sooty snow between the two canals of the capital, the Grand and the Royal, as the files went up in flames. That pillar of cloud signified, in its way, a kind of carte blanche for the new proprietors in the next cycle of an eternal recurrence of resentment and desire.

When my daughter was awarded her parchment to practice as a solicitor in a ceremony at Blackhall Place two years ago, on the far side of the river that still divides Dublin, the keynote speaker turned out to be a Sinn Féin deputy with a Donegal accent, and there was a discreet restiveness in the room (which was a deconsecrated chapel), an infinitesimal rustling as he spoke, like the low-frequency stirring of a swarm of crickets on the cusp of the chrysalis by which the little species mutates ferociously into a plague of locusts.

It brought me back, in a weird wormhole, to my own boyhood, to an afternoon spent listening to long Latin speeches at a commencement in the Examination Hall of Trinity College, where a family member of mine who would never have dared set foot in those forbidden grounds while still a Catholic undergraduate at UCD's Earlsfort Terrace in the early thirties, was now being conferred with an honorary academic degree, alongside an odd-looking Asian called U Thant, and an important Irish pacifist who had made a strong impression on the non-aligned nations of the world, our missionary turf, at an all-night session of a UN conference.

This was Frank Aiken, whose violet autograph I wanted to add to those of Charlie Chaplin, Padraic Colum, Bunny Carr, and a British Legion P.O.W. on a walking-frame in the Stephen's Green Club who painted seascapes by numbers and had killed a Japanese officer, but not by beheading, and kept his steel Samurai sword over a marble mantelpiece, where you would expect instead to see a concave mirror that made hobbits of the household. I had seen this laureate in blurred black-and-white, standing at the rostrum in the General Assembly, mouthing inaudibly under his moustache, because the TV footage was a silent film with soft commentary from an unseen anchor in the studios of Telefís Éireann. I couldn't tell if he was a potentiary or a plenipotentiary, but he was surely a personage, in his red professorial robes, with the pump-action Latin accolade from the long-haired college rhetor in the pulpit beside the podium. After all, during the War of Independence, he had invented putting petrol into potato sprayers, and using them then, with a penny box of Maguire and Peterson safety-matches, to crack the windowpanes and incinerate policemen in their sand-bagged dormitory barracks.

Applause rose up around him, like a flock of startled doves, as he passed between the indignant portraits of loyalist provosts who would have quartered him at Tyburn between an Augustan satire and a Horatian ode, and out into the cobblestoned chic of Front Square for the press-corps' photographs under wheeling seagulls and the tang of breweries; and the sound of that tentative ovation—more truce than treaty, more ceasefire than surrender—was the very same twitching of rock pigeons, half a century later, as the strange Sinn Féin intruder with the Donegal accent began the conclusion of his oration on the lawful and the legal to the junior notaries in the chapel of the Law Society.

Neither the listeners' wariness, nor the welcome which disguised it, had faltered for a moment on either occasion. There was simply too much at stake for that sort of sentimentality. Because the instant of reciprocity, the recognition of one party by the other, of the incoming by the outgoing, of the have-not by the have-been, which concealed itself in the protocols of civil etiquette, meant more than the honest enmity of hostile forces bent on straightforward, manly annihilation of the Other. It signified instead the intricate, self-harming hospitality of conflicting factions in a mimetic monoculture which cannot ultimately hide the fundamental lack of a difference that makes the difference, at source, between their otherwise dissimilar twin identities; because, behind the perfume and the pedigree of all politics, high-church or low-church, left-wing or right-wing, military or mufti, there is always the ancestral slipstream of Caesar's wife: a residual odour of aboriginal violence, a whiff of the morgue.

For the victor, of course, the morgue will be rapidly refurbished as a mortuary chapel, if not as a cenotaph, the very whitest of sepulchres, with flowers to fumigate foulness, a glittering Egyptian needle at the nexus of all homelands, and all holy lands too. For the victim, there's a wooden spoon, it seems, but a wooden spoon with the potential to alchemise as silver, since the supernatural grace of a grudge ensures that its sediments harden, like a form of fossil fuel, through endurance and duration, compression and gravity, into igneous elements, flammable and explosive, when the victim will reconvene, in the next copycat cycle of secular history, more march than progress, as the sanctified victimiser.

When I went to university, I was taught by some of the tenured radicals to call this process positivist and/or dialectical, the latter term a mantra for poor Hegel, who worshipped the Antichrist in Napoleon Bonaparte; and they had a point, my mentors, even if the point was, from a forensic-pathologist's perspective, a blunt instrument. More moderate members of the Arts Faculty liked to encourage what they styled a Whig version of modernity, an incremental, rather than a combative, chronicle of our inevitable perfectibility; and they had a point as well, one with its own cruel cutting edge, as it turned out. The mild-mannered Jesuit priest who tried to teach those small-scale, second-generation, grandsons of the founding fathers in the octave of the fiftieth anniversary of the Easter Rising in 1966, preferred to speak of history as His Story, the male Lord's gradual and unfolding eschaton, a serial human narrative which the Trinity devours as an unputdownable page-turn, three persons thirsting for the next instalment at each cliff-hanging close of chapter. If this be the case, the Triune God has a weakness for penny dreadfuls and pulp fiction, or, in the French vernacular sense of the word *histoire*, for adulterous affairs and the tradition of betrayal.

What is good enough for God is surely good enough for me, and I too celebrate the precarious ordeal of the opulent world. Truly, it is very precious. Being well is wonderful, and well-being even more so; and I am, after all, a senescent baby-boomer, a member of the most sated (but still, of course, dissatisfied) generation in the entirety of human history. But, if I'm a knave, I'm not as much a fool as I had hoped to be. I see the blood-red threads of a collective psychosis in the split stitch of the polity in which I'm a privileged elder, who is not known to the police. I may have difficulties with Trinitarian thinking of all sorts, whether it be the Athanasian or the Marxist or the Freudian variety of this odd ternary mania, those necessary and ingenious theoretical makeshifts; but I can discern the transcultural universality of the pink triangle, the sign of the scapegoat, the body bag in the fluttering flag, the successful violence we call peace and quiet in the community; and, although I failed general mathematics in the Matriculation forty years ago (I was, of course, compensated), when it comes to the pink triangle, the person who wrote this paper is as accomplished a geometer as the person who is reading it now.

Nocturnal

Down in the village,
church and cemetery
keep silent vigil.

Cars are congregated
outside pubs, and the neon-
lit takeaway…

Out here, on the edge
of calculated farms,
newfangled bungalows;

amid weathered signposts
and uneven roads,
you and I blur

to climax: need
raising us fleetingly
beyond ourselves,

and the set seed.

Patrick Moran

Grip

When my father's hand
(calloused, huge) would grip
my pencil-holding fingers—

teaching me to write,
letter by letter—
was he charging me

with his own thwarted
longings, or urging
me beyond them?

Was he pointing me
towards an open road,
or looming cul-de-sacs?

Patrick Moran

Danny

Lucy Sweeney Byrne

Lucy is sitting on a flaking, purple chair outside the cultishly popular health food café in her local town, half-listening to a theory on how to live one's life well ('the simple things!') that her father has already expounded in detail the day before, and the day before that, when she gets the text from Aisling; Danny has tried to commit suicide. She's only there because her father offered to pay for lunch, and she finds it difficult to turn down offers which are free, especially if they pertain to food, or sex. This was, naturally, just food.

Lucy finds eating with her father unpleasant, because they've already said all of the things they have to say to one another, and new things aren't occurring quickly enough to sustain further conversation. Or, they've said all of the things they're capable of saying as father and daughter, which is about .001% of the things they hold. Still, she does find him easier to talk to than most people. She also finds it unpleasant because her father eats with great haste, as though at any moment he expects a bell to ring and his plate to be swept away. He only ever uses one piece of cutlery, the fork, and when he tries to scoop up the last scraps, he knocks food off the side of his plate, which makes her want to reach across the table and slap his munching face.

It's Lucy's fault that she and her father live together. She's twenty-five, and refuses to accept adulthood in any responsible, fiscal capacity. Because doing so looks, from her admittedly ignorant perspective, shit. She works little, and not well; much like the way she exercises, or plans for the future. She makes enough money to not die, and to drink supermarket wine on Fridays.

Her father is talking. 'It's important, to be happy, I think, to wake up every day with something you're looking forward to, some kind of treat…'

Lucy watches him as he scans the seating area for people he knows. He loves chatting to people, though he pretends to hate it, because she does, and he feels obliged to be more like her. Lucy regrets that she makes him feel this way. Sometimes she treats him as though he's an imbecile. And he's not. There are simply things she wouldn't discuss with her father. He is a staunchly logical and literal man. She'd never discuss her thoughts on contemporary art or philosophy, or attempt to describe the conceptual framework of the novel she's working on. He'd think it was contemptible bullshit. And he'd probably be right, which is another reason she wouldn't discuss it with him.

'You need to have balance in life, you see. It's important to work, I think, to have worked hard, for your sense of worth, for your little reward at the end of the day. For it to feel *earned*…'

Lucy's father is a drummer, and to him everything has a rhythm, which can be worked out, if you just take a moment and listen properly. He's aware of the existence of metaphors and symbolism and subtleties, but dismisses them as the refuges of the weak and pretentious. He sees this as a stance shared by comic greats such as Woody Allen and Larry David; denouncers of all things excessively heartfelt and hifalutin. She thinks he's mistaken. But there'd be no point arguing. And besides, winning for Lucy (because she naturally assumes she'd win) would really be a loss. She does love her father, and so wants to help maintain some of his self-protective walls. She believes this is what we do for our loved ones: fortify their delusions.

Unfortunately for her, Lucy can't help but share her father's loves, and his dismissive attitude to the wishy-washy world of art and the expression of *feelings*, and so she is a torn-up, Frankenstein's monster of a person, filled with immiscible contradictions and self-loathing. She goes to poetry readings in basements in the city, and scoffs and yearns in equal proportions until her insides feel like curdled milk. Afterwards, in small low-lit bars, she listens to painters and writers discuss the nature of artistic inspiration, and feels a contorted, knotty despair; a reaction to her intense desire to both contribute earnestly to the discussion, and simultaneously beat them up and take their lunch money. A sort of socio-creative masochism. But, as this seems to be how all great artists are posthumously described by their biographers ('conflicted'), Lucy hopes this means she has a fantastic forthcoming novel lurking inside her.

'You can be just as happy with a small thing as a big thing, in life, you realise. A good cup of coffee can be as good as a holiday, if you just look at things the right way…'

For Lucy, conversation with her father is like walking through a minefield they both know well. They're in no real danger; they can choose whether to misstep or not, and sometimes she deliberately does so, just to see the dazzling fireworks of guts when it all blows up. Lucy supposes that this is what is referred to as being close to someone. So close that their muted nasal breathing becomes a constant irritation, like Chinese water torture.

As they sit in the sun over their freshly emptied plates (alas), and Lucy's father wisely sermonises, nodding in agreement with himself, she interrupts, to tell him the news she's just received: that a friend from her younger years—Daniel, do you remember Daniel? He would have been at the house a few times?—has tried to commit suicide. He's in a coma, in a hospital, somewhere on the outskirts of Boston.

But then, of course Lucy's father wouldn't remember Danny. All of those pimply, hunched male friends were just a blur to him, to be treated with distrust. Potential defilers of his daughter and robbers of his DVDs and CDs, filing past with their heads down, up to Lucy's bedroom to drink and smoke weed and talk loudly about Tarantino films or the sound quality of vinyl until last bus time.

His immediate reaction is to be annoyed that Lucy was looking at her phone, but because of the gravity of the news, he checks himself. 'God, that's terrible.' 'Yes, it is.' She reads the text aloud, processing:

'Hey, so iv bad news. Danny tried to kil hmslf. He's in a coma, watr damge 2 his brain r smthng. This is al comin frm Sarah thru Jen, so bit vague. Apparntly he fel off a bridge ovr ther. So awfl.'

Fell off a bridge? Even after opening with the shocker of it being a suicide attempt (people love telling shocking news as a rule, Lucy thinks, as long as it isn't their own), Aisling still chose to use the word 'fell'. Too real to say 'jumped', maybe. Or were they (his friends and family, his girlfriend Sarah) holding out hope that it had been an accident? That he'd wandered onto a bridge and stumbled off, Laurel-and-Hardy-style?

Lucy's father lets out a 'how terrible' sighing sound and sits back in his chair. He rubs his mouth with one hand, while the other hand cups the first hand's elbow, which she recognises as the pose he unconsciously adopts when faced with something serious, and wishes to convey an appropriate physical reaction. 'God. I can't believe it,' Lucy says. Although really she can and does believe it.

Lucy finds herself wishing she'd kept in closer contact with Danny. She attempts, furrowing her brow slightly, to conjure up her already faded memories of him. Sessions, parties, cinema trips. Bus rides, swigging cans, shouting and singing down the back, on the way to gigs or nightclubs in the city. His dark brown eyes and sallow skin. His love of drugs, and his unwillingness to ever concede a point, no matter how clearly wrong he was. When they were fifteen, sixteen, Danny had been the guy they could always be sure would do the dare. One night he'd gone to the nearby petrol station totally naked and bought chewing gum. That had blown their minds.

Now that Lucy thinks about it though, there was definitely a sadness to him. Those black eyes, always up for anything, could be unnerving to be around, especially towards the end of a night. But maybe she's inventing that now; making a poetry of him, based entirely on this attempted suicide. Maybe that 'sadness' was just evidence of the fact that he was always, *always* high—or just bored, or preoccupied. Maybe he was just hungry. But then, he has now tried to commit suicide. He's in hospital with water damage to his brain. So he probably was sad, and maybe you could see it. Maybe, Lucy reckons, it's just that if you see a sadness in the dark depths of someone, it's unlikely you'll tell them. Or even give it that much thought.

Lucy and Danny were never that close, but he'd been good friends with her ex. They'd been in a mediocre post-punk band together. Danny played bass. Lucy had always thought he was good-looking, if not especially bright. And besides, he was shorter than her. Now Lucy wishes she'd been closer to Danny. She regrets not having taken some opportunity to kiss him. In the corner of a party someone had thrown because their parents were away for the night, or down the fields in summer, away from the light of the bonfire. But why? She'd never considered it before, so why now? Why does she suddenly regret they weren't closer? So that she could have helped him? Somehow prevented this? Talked him down from that bridge over the phone? Lucy has never been the type to do that anyway.

It's not that she wouldn't care, she reassures herself. She just wouldn't know what to say. It'd be so real, like live TV, she'd have no time to think of the right answers. Besides, she is not the person anyone would call. Except maybe her father, but he is far too practical to lend much thought to suicide. To Lucy, the sudden image of her father standing on a bridge considering the murky depths below is so absurd that she smiles, in spite of herself. She looks at him absent-mindedly as he scrolls through his phone, pretending to check for work emails but actually perusing Facebook. There is a line of white foam from his cappuccino in his moustache. This gives her satisfaction, and she says nothing.

Lucy wonders if she wishes she'd been closer to Danny, so that she could be more directly involved in what is an undeniably intriguing occurence?

The thought makes her uncomfortable. She shifts in her seat. Danny, by falling off that bridge, has inserted himself as a violent interruption into the flow of unremarkable events that Lucy's life was turning out to be. He has done a real thing. A significant thing. It's something all of their mutual friends will remember now, forever. 'I think it was when I was in the last year of my Masters, yeah, living in Edinburgh, the year Danny, off a bridge wasn't it…?'; 'Well I remember I was in the changing rooms in Topshop, uhuh, the one at the top of Grafton Street, when I got the text about Danny…' Lucy would love to do something all of their mutual friends remembered.

Lucy overhears a woman seated behind her tell her huband it's going to rain soon. Her husband grunts. Lucy imagines he might be reading a newspaper. The woman pauses, and then says in an ominous tone that she can smell it coming. Lucy shifts in her seat and folds her arms. Sure enough, at that moment shadows fall across the café's outdoor seating area and she hears the first droplets land, spattering the grey cement between the tables. The woman says, 'Ha, look now, told you!' and her husband says nothing. Lucy's father contracts his body, hunching his shoulders slightly and scrunching his nose. He is ready to go, but awaits her cue.

Lucy sits still. Although she is keen not to become cold or wet, she feels obliged to take a moment to think about Danny. She feels it would be indecent to get going too soon. It's probably already odd, she realises, that she hasn't even cried a bit. She tries very hard to think about him. To really consider the boy she knew. Danny, with whom she danced in stuffy, crowded living-rooms, talked with on train platforms and played basketball with on the courts behind their old primary school. She tries to picture him now, lying unconscious, on a lung machine (that breathing thing, whatever on earth it's called), with water swilling around his brain. A tiny creature in a sterile hospital room in the wide-open, sprawling United States of America. But she can't get to him. She is sitting here with her father outside this café growing cold and he is off somewhere, far away, and she can't get anywhere near him.

She watches the speckle-feathered thrushes fight for the last crumbs of scone on the table next to hers. The tanned, dark-haired waitress bustles over to gather up the plates and cups, shooing the birds with her dishcloth. Lucy watches her father as he attempts to catch the waitress's eye. He leans forward and back, trying to enter her line of vision, hand poised to wave. He has been shamelessly flirting with her for over three months now, and she has resorted to pretending not to see him, or responding in her native Spanish, feigning confusion. She escapes inside, and he wilts slightly, before resignedly turning back to the table.

Lucy can't imagine Danny doing it. Actually stepping off, falling through air. She wonders what it felt like. She could never ask him. She wonders how they got him out of the water. She wonders who found him, and how they got word to his family. Would they be flying over to him? Would he definitely recover? Would he have brain damage? Would Sarah stay with him, if he does? Lucy breathes heavily in and out through her nose, frustrated by the lack of information given in Aisling's text. She frowns as she scrolls down through it again. No, nothing more.

She tries again to reach for Danny. She closes her eyes, and pictures his physical body. His chest rising up and down, each of the thick, dark hairs of his eyebrows. She wonders if his skin would feel cool or warm, were she to lay her hand on his arm, his cheek? She wonders would they have washed his body? Would someone have lifted and sponged his heavy limbs, or run their soapy fingers back and forth through his hair? Or would he still smell like the river? Like sweat?

But Lucy can't seem to concentrate hard enough on any of it. He slips away from her and is replaced by the rain, the cold, the taste of coffee in her mouth. She knows it happened, but feels nothing to correspond with the knowledge. The fact just sits there in her mind, a lump of nothing. If she were shown a photograph of Danny, maybe. Or if she could listen to his mother or his girlfriend Sarah talk about him. Could see them tearing up. Then the reality of the image, their emotion, would surely seep into her. Lucy doesn't consider herself unfeeling. She reads poetry. She cries at sad films, and Trócaire adverts. Recently she'd sobbed watching a television show about mistreated dogs. Her father had rushed into the living-room, afraid something terrible had happened.

But now, nothing. To Lucy, Danny's just a notion. She feels no more than she would feel were he a stranger she'd read about in the newspaper, or a story heard on the radio. She checks inside herself, has a feel around, but there's nothing there, no matter how much she wills it. She'd love to be moved by this. She would give anything to be shedding tears, to require comfort, and to actually mean it. This is exactly the sensation Lucy undergoes when she watches the news and sees images of of death and carnage in foreign places. A strange sudden awareness of the lack of any feelings, where there surely ought to be some. The sensation makes her feel a little nauseous, and she unintentionally puts her hand to her stomach. Her father glances at her. He probably thinks it's grief.

'I can't believe someone actually went and did it,' is all she manages to say into the pause, as her father fidgets, growing restless, thinking of the next thing to be done in his day, but not wanting to be too hastily unfeeling. 'Yeah. It just goes to show, people…'

And he's off again, full throttle on a tirade of platitudes. Lucy recedes back into her own thoughts, picking up her cup and knocking back the last dregs of her coffee, nodding at moments when she senses a pause requiring affirmation. When he has finally finished imparting wisdom, Lucy—as a conclusive statement which works sufficiently well to mask that she wasn't listening—says 'It's all just too terrible to think about.' to which he agrees, nodding, 'Yes, yes.' Wise words all round.

There's a moment of silent respect. They linger, half gone already, thinking of the evening ahead. Large drops are falling regularly now, sploshing on the purple table and leaving dark round stains across her father's shoulders. An old man who had been sitting at a table near theirs, sighs theatrically, picks up his mug, and walks inside, holding his folded newspaper over his head. He gives Lucy an eyebrow arch and smile, as though to say, 'Typical rain, aye?' Lucy looks past him. She wonders what she should do about Danny. Send a card to the hospital? *Hi Danny, heard you fell off a bridge, hope you're feeling better, and that the weather is nice in Boston, xox.* A sad animal with a bandage on its head. *Get Well Soon!* Probably not.

She breathes deeply through her nose and sits up straight. Time to go. Her father is off to pick up a six-pack of Guinness, before meeting a few friends to jam. They are hoping to stage a gig in the town hall: songs from the eighties, with all profits going to a charity. They haven't decided which charity yet, but Lucy's father is leaning towards cancer. As well as drumming in the band, he's been asked to sing a few songs, and so has been practising around the house, slapping his hands on the armrests along with the music, or humming under his breath.

Lucy had intended to return to the library after lunch to keep 'researching her novel', which seems to involve a lot of online reading about atemporality and Taylor Swift's childhood. That morning she had typed 'Lena Dunham success how' into Google. But she quickly allows herself the excuse of this upsetting news to go home and watch a film curled up on the couch instead. She reasons that even if she doesn't, on the surface, feel upset about Danny, deep down this has no doubt affected her greatly, and so she ought to take the time to sit with it, and 'mind herself'.

*

That night Lucy sits idling on the couch while the end credits of *The Odd Couple* roll up the television screen. She has completely forgotten about Danny. She texts Aisling:

'Hey gurrrl, we should defo get brunch in town on Sun after Sat night. We cud go 2 the Rumbelly, sure it's jst around the cornr frm K8's place!x'

Just as it sends, a text comes through from her father:

'Hey Lu, told the lads wat hapend to ur friend. We thought it might be gud to do the gig 2 raise money for him? Wat u think? Hope u'r ok, it's very hard. Luv dad, x.'

Anxiety rises in Lucy's stomach. She had completely forgotten. Her father had been talking about Danny, and making plans to help, and she'd been thinking about the weekend. She worries that Aisling will get her text, and be disgusted at how she can think about something as trivial as brunch when their childhood friend lies fighting for his life all alone across the Atlantic. Lucy feels ashamed. She start concentrating as hard as she can on Danny, out of guilt, as punishment. As she's rinsing out her teacup, and returning the biscuit jar to the shelf, and brushing her teeth, and pissing, and washing her hands and face, she tries again to picture him. She wonders if he's bruised, or if anything is broken, or if, from the outside, he simply looks like he's sleeping.

As she cleans her retainer, she wonders why Danny did it. What was going through his head? What was the last straw, for him? Was someone rude to him on a train? Did he have a fight with Sarah? Did he get short-changed for his groceries? Or had it been growing in him, slowly, all these years? Should Lucy have seen it coming? She wonders if there's anything she could have done differently, anything a bit nicer she could've said. Then she thinks how egotistical it is of her to think she could've made any difference at all, and she sighs, pointedly. She pauses. Why can't she feel anything *real* about this? What's wrong with her? She look in the mirror forlornly, but it's no use. No tears come.

He must have felt so alone. He probably pictured Ireland and allowed himself to see all his old friends here having a great time without him. Like people in a Swedish insurance ad or something. Which isn't the case. People are just mildly unhappy everywhere, Lucy thinks. Geography doesn't make a difference. Although of course it can make things worse, if you're somewhere war-torn or disease-ridden or something. But when it comes to melancholia, she imagines one place is as good as the next.

She wonders if Danny had been drinking. Lucy thinks that if she ever tries to commit suicide, she will definitely have been drinking. Did he think about how they'd react? The 'folks back home'. As he was walking to the bridge, or planning it in bed the night before, lying awake in the dark, slightly too hot in the close Boston summer. Did it cross his mind? What did he think they'd feel, all of them back here? Did he think it would make a difference? Lucy composes a reply to her father, saying yes she's okay, just shook up, finding it tough, but that the gig sounds great.

She resolves, as she presses the send button, to be heavily involved, to do lots of fundraising, to really be at the forefront in raising money to help Danny. She pictures herself on a picket line with her fist raised, shouting passionately. She is wrapped up in gloves and a scarf and there is a poster of Danny's face strapped to the barrier before her. She will become his champion, and will make sure Danny gets better. People will wonder at her generosity, and Danny's mother will personally thank her, grasping both of Lucy's hands, tears welling in her eyes. Maybe, afterwards, she could even write a book about it.

Also, she resolves she will be kinder to her father from now on. He is a good person. She's too hard on him. Maybe he is wise, and she's the imbecile. She will buy him lunch next time. She will listen when he speaks. Then, as she is shutting the hall door, Lucy receives Aisling's reply:

'Eeeh, YES. Sounds brill. Also, wat'r u wearin Sat? Can't tel how dressy 2go, stressin bout it all day. P.S. Jst 8 an entire bag of jelly snakes :/'

Split Villanelle **[with Torn Tongues]**

Listen. Something [under] our tongues has broken.
We each feel this shared fissure, a fracture, lurking rupture
where something deep within us goes unspoken.

After exams, we throw away textbooks—loathèd, unopened—
and attempt to shed memories of useless vocabularies, cognitive clutter.
Still, something under our tongues is broken,

sharp, insistent. On these split tongues we are choking.
We swallow all the half-remembered syllables stuttered, spluttered
and still, something deep within us goes. Unspoken,

now, the hoarded words we learned by heart, the cursèd burden,
all the old stories and strange phrases we once tasted and turned
like something nearly-sweet under our tongues. It's broken,

the enforced bond that knotted us to that molten
language. Freed from inherited speech, we shudder,
relieved, but [in this silence] something deep within us goes unspoken.

Despite the relief of freeing ourselves from the curse
of being half-wrong in every borrowed word we utter,
[something] under our tongues [still] persists, [remains] [unbroken]
something deep within us, whispers itself and exists—spoken.

Doireann Ní Ghríofa

Marching Season

Grahame Williams

My brother peers through the wooden slats at his kitchen window and sees that it's me. Pipe bands play in the next street down; snare drums rattle under the shrill whistle of flutes. I never come home in marching season. He opens the door and coughs at the afternoon sun.

'Alright,' he says, half asleep.

'Alright.'

I step inside with his clean laundry heavy in my arms. The air is stale, warm with the smell of cigarettes and cat. God help him, this is how he lives. Mum bought him this house maybe three years ago. Now it's not worth half it was then. Money that was meant for the both of us. I dump the laundry on the granite worktop.

'Has she said anything to you?' he asks.

'No,' I lie. 'She only said she's worried about you.'

'Fuck sake. That's all she keeps saying.'

He shuts the door and I can barely make him out.

'Can I sit down?'

'Aye. Do you want anything? I probably don't have much.'

'Have you any herbal tea?'

'Sure just look in the cupboards. There might be some Mum got.'

I open one cupboard after another as he moves to one of the sofas on the other side of the room.

'Is it okay if I open the blinds a bit?'

He mumbles something and I twist the rod by the window to let light in. The middle of July and he still has Halloween decorations up. Paper skeletons are stuck to the wall above the toaster, limbs angled as if they're dancing. By the kettle a glow-in-the-dark skull lies on its side.

'There's no tea,' I say.

Hunched over in his shorts he lights a cigarette and, rocking a little, reaches to scratch the eczema on his leg. It's as bad as it has ever been. At 32 his legs and arms weep. I grew out of mine after primary school, but his clung on. Scabs cover his calves like countries on a map; tubs of cream and dented tubes of ointment litter the coffee table. He opens the E45, takes a three-fingered scoop of white and rubs it onto his just-scratched leg, the cigarette limp in his mouth. He always uses too much.

'Mum said you came round the other night with a bleeding nose,' I say and roll up my sleeves. The skin shows smooth on my forearms.

'Yeah, she probably thinks I've been snorting something and that messed it up. I haven't but.'

'What about the stuff you did take?'

'You don't snort it. I'm never taking that shite again. I'm serious. It's so bad.'

I sit on the sofa opposite him. He looks heavy, older than he is, maybe older than I am. Red and purple blotches cover his face and his hands shake as he puts the cigarette to his lips. Under his nose is a crust of brown blood. Nothing he doesn't deserve.

'So what happened?'

'I fell off that bloody stool while I was on the computer,' he waves his cigarette in the direction of the breakfast bar. 'I fucking whacked my head off it. I was sitting there and must have fell asleep and then boom and I was on the floor.'

'Is that really what happened?'

'Aye, I took a quick blast of the oxy when I got in from work. A slow release tablet it was meant to be. Usually it takes a while for it to come on.'

'What did you tell Mum?'

'I told her the truth. I told her I fell asleep and hit my head on the table. I bet she doesn't believe me.'

He drops the cigarette half-smoked into a can of Budweiser by his foot and lights another.

'I fell down the stairs the other morning too. I didn't feel anything though. Injuries, like.'

'That's not good if you're falling down the stairs.'

'That's what I mean. I am *definitely* never taking that shite again. No way,' he says, a slur at the word *definitely*. He looks at me.

'What do you think? Do I seem okay to you?'

'You don't seem too bad. Maybe a wee bit weird.'

He coughs and looks away. I'm supposed to say something else. I'm supposed to tell him about the letter.

They sent it to Mum and called him by his full name, Stephen William Bell. That's what she kept saying on the drive down from the International: 'They even know Stevie's middle name.' Usually when I land I just let her talk, she rabbits on about Stephen, his latest venture, what more money's been lost but this time she had something to say. I was waiting for her to call them cowards but she didn't. I guess you don't call them cowards when you're scared. She asked what I thought they wanted, what I thought they would do to him. I didn't know what to tell her. It was always the knees they went for, or it used to be, growing up here, stories of beatings on the local news before the sports report. But things have changed. Things are meant to have changed, with peace and all. The adverts at the International say *Our Time, Our Place,* next to pictures of people in canoes, laughing and carrying on, like life is normal now and always was. I said a warning was what it was. A warning. I said I'd sort it out. No need for Stephen to be troubled. Beloved Stevie.

He points the remote control at the TV. A blue-white comet swirls in the middle of the screen, fades and the room is lit by a paused scene from his game. He picks another controller from the table, angles it at a black box below the TV and the game starts again. 'I want to get one of them ones that does everything. One of them fancy controllers you can programme,' he says.

'What money will you use for that?'

'I've got some.'

On the screen he flicks through characters, cars, weapons, back to cars, back to weapons and finally settles on a menu that lists radio stations.

'What sort of music do you want?'

'Is there anything '80s?'

'There's everything.'

He chooses a station and a power ballad comes on, already somewhere near the end, the drums fast and drenched in echo. Leaning back in his chair, he presses a button on the controller and the view switches to behind a car he's driving.

'You can go literally anywhere in this. Do literally anything. And there's no police.'

'Can you go up and talk to people?'

'Except that.'

For a while he speeds through the city, crossing verges to drive on the wrong side of the road, running people over on the pavement, leaving them for dead. Every so often he gets out of the car, drags another driver from theirs and kicks them to the ground. His knees don't move as he pounds the controller. They shine in the light of the game.

'Remember when we did the drug deals with My Pet Monster?' I ask.

'That was ages ago.'

'And Charlie Sheen. I don't think we even knew who Charlie Sheen was.'

He scratches his leg, keeps his eyes on the game.

'Charlie Sheen. How come you always named them?' he asks. 'I don't think I did.'

'You did.'

He's right though. I was the one who named all our stuffed toys. I kept the good names for mine and gave his ones like Charlie Sheen and Pope John Paul the Turd. The only time I couldn't give them names was when they came with one already. My Pet Monster stayed My Pet Monster and Wrinkles stayed Wrinkles. I gave them voices too. Mine spoke smoothly, soothingly, almost like girls. His were nasty-voiced, with accents edged like knives. Something happens in the game that I miss, the screen goes black, fades in and he walks from the front doors of a hospital.

'Fuck sake. This didn't used to happen,' he says and looks at his hands.

I made up the games we played back then. The drug deals staged around the old house with My Pet Monster as the boss, Stephen's other toys his henchmen, hidden in cupboards and under beds, sprinkled with talcum powder as pretend cocaine, waiting with notes giving clues to where the next deal was going down. I even made the handwriting on the notes bad, as if his toys couldn't write properly, didn't have as good an education or weren't as smart as mine.

Charlie Sheen was My Pet Monster's lieutenant and he'd always be the second to last found, never with a note. The game was for Stephen to make him talk and tell us where My Pet Monster was. He'd have to beat him or shove his head down the toilet, do some kind of damage. Once he burnt Charlie Sheen's ear on the electric hob of the cooker. The brown fur shriveled and smoked but it didn't catch fire the way I thought it would. Mum stopped the game before things went too far and when Stephen was in bed she yelled at me. The trouble was always my idea, my fault, she said.

'How did you end up selling it?' I ask.

He thumbs the controller and his car changes from red to black.

'I ordered too much off the Internet one time. I must have been wasted or something. There's no way I could take that much. These guys from my old work were looking for some.'

'Was that all?'

'There was maybe some other guys down the pub. The Royal. That was all.'

'You shouldn't have been selling it.'

'I'm not stupid. I didn't mean to.'

'But it's all gone now?'

'Aye. I flushed the rest of it down the bog. Mum keeps going on about it though. I should never have told her I took it.' He changes the car back to red. 'She said she was going to give me her car. That's probably out the window now. It's a bloody old lady car anyway. You're lucky you don't have her living right next to you. You can leave and go home and not have her come round your house and hoke through your stuff and everything. You're lucky.'

'I've got the car outside.'

The letter says to bring him to a place on the inside edge of Strangford Lough, the old monastery ruin out on Nendrum Island. I can't remember if we've been there before or not. In the summer holidays Mum drove us to places on the Lough and around the peninsula, the empty beaches that would take an hour to get to, the whitewashed cottages turned into folk museums, the bird sanctuaries, the butterfly farm. I sat in the back and Stephen sat in the front with Mum, complaining he was bored and wanting to go home. He always sat in the front, her beloved Stevie.

'This fucking game,' he says, as there's a crash, the black screen and he walks out of the hospital again.

'Shall we go out and get some air?'

'What for?'

'It would just be good. It's a nice day.'

'A nice day?'

'Yeah. It's sunny.'

'You sound like Mum.'

'I do not. Come on. Let's go for a drive.'

'Could you maybe take me to the shop to get more fags?'

'Yeah.'

'Okay. Hold on and I'll get shoes and stuff on.'

He pauses the game, stands up and knocks over the Budweiser by his foot. Ash from the ring around the top spills onto the rug, the one that used to be in the dining room of the old house, the house Mum sold to pay for this place. As he goes upstairs I think about cleaning it up but I don't. He has to learn to look after himself.

On the shelves by the door are all his DVDs, the horror films and the action films. Near the top are the bigger-boxed Blu-rays of the same films. On the bottom shelf are the handful of books I've sent him for birthdays and Christmas. *The Wasp Factory* and *The Catcher in the Rye* and *A Prayer for Owen Meany*. I wrote inscriptions in each one saying why he should read it but there they are, all with spines uncreased. I did my best.

I wait for five minutes, then five more. He doesn't come down and there's no sound of movement. We're meant to be there in an hour and it's a forty-five minute drive if I take the long way. There's no question of being late.

'Stephen,' I call.

He doesn't answer.

'Stephen,' this time louder. There's still no answer so I go up to get him. The stairs are steep and narrow, no bannister on either side. At the top is a pot plant, green and healthy, with leaves that feather out towards the skylight. I check to see if it's plastic but it's real. Mum must water it when she comes to clean.

I stand by the open door of the bedroom. On the wall above the bed is a full-size cinema poster for *The Exorcist*. He's on his back on the bed, asleep, legs bent over the end, jeans on and trainers on but the laces hanging undone. I knock on the door and say his name. He turns his head to one side on the duvet and I see the crust under his nose more clearly. I want to press a wet cloth to it, to clean it, see how much of the blood will come off.

'Stephen?'

I step into the room and shake his leg.

'Stephen.'

'What?'

'We have to go.'

'Was I asleep?'

'Aye.'

'Ah, shit,' he sits up and looks at his shoes.

'Oh yeah, I couldn't get the laces done.'

'What do you mean?'

'I must have forgot how or something.'

'Can you do them now?'

He makes a sound as if he isn't sure.

'Here and I'll do them,' I say and kneel on the carpet. He falls back onto the bed.

The laces are bright white, the trainers new, black Adidas with the three bands in yellow. I tie the lace on each one, not sure if I've judged the tightness right. They seem loose so before I stand up I double-knot them and pull hard. His jeans are threaded thin over the top of his knees. They used to smash the kneecaps from the side or from behind to make it worse, back in the bad old days.

'Stephen. Wake up.'

'What?'

'Wake up.'

'I think I want to stay here.'

'Come on. It'll do you good to get out.'

Outside the drums and flutes have gone. The bands will be gathering at the park up in the centre of town. In their place is the squall of seagulls and the emptiness the sea gives to the air when there are no clouds.

'Bloody hell,' Stephen says as he slumps into the passenger seat and flips down the sun-visor.

'Do your seatbelt.'

'We're going to the shop yeah?'

'Yeah.'

I press the button that locks the doors. This is the car we learned in, the one we did our tests in. I had to take mine five times; Stephen passed with his first. Mum was so pleased about that she took us for dinner at the Italian place on the ring road and asked him to drive. In the restaurant they sat at their carbonaras and laughed at me, at all times I failed, like when the windscreen misted up, I didn't know how to work the de-mister and the instructor told me to pull over because we couldn't see the road. How was I supposed to know that? Nobody ever showed me. I learned it all the hard way. On the way home from the restaurant Stephen ran into the back of a Calor Gas lorry at a set of traffic lights, not used to the weight of the three of us in the car and the extra time it took to stop. I wanted to hug him that time but I was glad it had happened. Mum shook her head like it was my weight had caused it. When people ask why I left that's what I think of, although it's never what I say.

I take us in the opposite direction to where we're meant to be going, towards the outside edge of the peninsula. To drive the whole length of it and back would take maybe an hour and a half. When I'm home and I don't want to think, this is where I drive, out and away from the town, so nobody knows where I am—a road that feels like it's running away from everything, where if you're moving you can hide.

'What shop are we going to?' he asks.

'The Maxol garage out at Ballyneill.'

'That's bloody miles away. Why can't we just go to the one in town?'

'It won't take that long. I want to drive.'

'We should go to the one in town.'

'We're not going there.'
'Where are we going then?'
'Ballyneill. I just told you that.'
'As long as we go to the shop. Could I borrow some money?'
'Yeah.'
'What are we doing at Ballyneill?'
'We'll go for a walk on the beach or something.'
'A walk on the beach?'
'Aye. It's a nice day.'
'Okay. I might need to borrow twenty quid.'

The sky is tall and in the distance over the sea is the thin grey line of Scotland. When we were kids that was the place people ran away to, where they went when they were told to leave, after they'd had done whatever was done to them. More stories we heard on the news. The night Mum rang and told me about the letter she talked about people we knew in Aberdeen, about sending Stephen away to them. I said don't be stupid, I'll speak to them, I'll sort it out. What about those fellas you played football with, she asked, the lads who wanted to become ministers. Couldn't he claim sanctuary in a church? I'll sort it out, I said.

Where the road widens and dips to run closer to the coast we pass the Copeland Islands, islands with houses on them nobody lives in, places used to graze sheep, where you can get boats out to in the summer. We go through Groomsport, Donaghadee, Millisle and I know I need to turn inland if we're to make it in time. I look over at Stephen and he's asleep again, head back on the rest, mouth open. The Maxol garage passes on our right. They'll give him a warning and that will be all. A warning will do him no harm. Things have changed.

Mum once got stopped for speeding in Ballyneill. The cops let her off with a talking to and after that she always slowed right down coming into the village. Each time I reach Ballyneill that's what I think of, driving by the house where the police chief constable used to live, the walls still topped with barbed wire and security cameras at the gates, wondering if there were more police around here because of that house. Someone has to stop us.

I stamp my right foot down and keep it down. The red needle rises and the road ahead is clear. *Welcome to Ballyneill* a sign says. *Please drive carefully*. We pass fancy houses with big white conservatories, houses with tennis courts. Speeding up, a boat yard, bungalows, the beach. Stephen sleeps on. On our right a golf course is coming up, a zebra crossing in front of it. Orange lollipop lights flash and a group of boys with golf bags wait, jostling each other. One has a red and white Titleist bag. Such a wholesome game. I swerve onto the wrong side of the road towards them and they push back onto the pavement. The boy with the bag trips into the hedge. A car comes towards us, flashing its headlights and I have to brake and veer back onto the right side of the road.

'Jesus, Stephen, would you wake up?'

The village ends after more bungalows and a sign that says *Thank you for driving carefully*. I pull over. An old man on a bike hammers on the passenger window. His eyes are slanted in anger. He shouts at us, makes a sign for me to put down the window and I give him the finger. Stephen rolls his head, disturbed by the noise but doesn't wake up.

I turn the car around and shift through the gears, foot full on the accelerator, hand on the horn. Ballyneill blurs past a second time. The golfing boys make wanker signs at us from the other side of the road. We're thanked for driving carefully a second time. We pass the police chief constable's house. Nobody stops us.

Slowing down, I check the rearview mirror, indicate and turn inland.

Away from the sea, trees close in over the road and we're almost in the dark, cutting across to Newtownards. My hands feel light on the wheel and slip with sweat, the speed of the car not quite under my control. We're well within the limit but it feels like we're moving too fast.

'Stephen?'

The sky greys.

'Stevie?'

We reach Comber and I pray for the traffic lights to turn red so I can stop, lean over and shake him but they don't. It's one of those days where the lights stay green, one of those lucky days. 'Stevie?' This is the road we used to drive to get to our grandparents' house in Downpatrick, a town Stephen and I both hated for no good reason at all. Cowpatrick we called it. I called it.

In the middle of Lisbane town I turn left onto the old quarry road. After a while it forks and I slow down to see which direction to take. To the left is Castle Espie, the bird and nature place, where you can go and get married and have your picture taken by the water with the reeds and swans in the background. A brown tourist sign for the monastic site points to the right.

Rain flecks the windscreen and I have to check where the control for the wipers is. The rubber screeches on the glass at first, smearing the drops and blurring the way for a moment. The digital clock on the dashboard shows we have five minutes left.

The road narrows to a single lane stretching across a causeway. We're out on the Lough now, water on both sides; a red-edged sign says the road is liable to flooding. Ahead of us is the island, covered in trees stood straight, no wind to move them. There's another sign for the monastic site and parking. I check to make sure the doors are locked and stop the car on the causeway. Rain scars the passenger window by Stephen's head.

'Stevie, wake up.'

I punch him on the arm. He shifts. I punch again, hard. I used to be able to hit him like this and get away with it.

'Jesus, Stevie. Wake up.'

'What?' He opens his eyes. 'Where are we? Have we been to the shop?' He looks at his feet to where the blue plastic bag with cigarettes and crisps would be, touches his hand to his arm.

'Sorry, I forgot.'

'I need to go to the shop. Was I asleep?'

'Yeah.'

He looks at the clock.

'The whole time?'

'Yeah.'

'Fuck. It must take a while to get out of your system. I'm never taking that shite again.' He looks around. 'Where's this?'

'It's Nendrum.'

'What? You said we were going to the shop.'

He kicks the bottom of the glove box. Then he kicks it again and kicks it again.

'Fuck sake. I knew this is what you'd come for.'

'What do you mean?'

'Fuck sake. Do you think I'm stupid?'

I twist the control for the wipers but they're already on full.

'It's not me. Mum asked me to take you. She didn't know what to do. She didn't have a choice.'

'What do you think's going to happen?'

'You haven't done anything that bad. Nothing's got out of hand yet. You'll get a talking to.'

'You don't live here. You don't have a clue.'

'I don't need to live here.'

'I won't be able to walk.'

'Don't be fucking stupid. It's not like that anymore.'

'You don't know anything about it.'

'It'll be a warning. A talking to.'

'I'll not be able to walk.'

'It'll be okay. And I'm here.'

'No. No, no, no, no, no.' He puts his hand in his pocket, pulls out a handful of tablets, shoves them in his mouth, winces and swallows. The digits of the clock change. He rubs his eyes and the eczema shows raw around his wrists.

'Come on. It'll be okay.'

I start the engine and ease the car forward.

The surface of the road changes at the end of the causeway, becomes rougher and the car lurches as the wheels drop into craters in the old tarmac. Loose stones pelt against the underside, rattling like the start of a hail shower, like a drummer getting ready to play. I pull into the car park.

Parked by a row of bins is a red 4X4, the left-hand side splattered with sun-dried mud. A replica Rangers shirt is suckered to the back windshield. Two men are sat in the front. I park as far away from them as I can and turn off the engine. I unlock Stephen's door.

'You have to go up there,' I point to the steps that lead to the ruins of the monastery, a metal handrail running up the side.

'I don't want to go, Aaron. Don't make me go.'

'You have to. Come on. They only want to talk to you.'

'Are you coming?'

'I'll wait here for you.'

He scratches his legs with both hands so his jeans bunch above the ankle. The denim is damp, stained from the blood and weeping of his eczema. He's crying.

'Will it be okay?' he asks.

'It will. I'm here.'

The digits of the clock change.

'Take an umbrella.'

I hand him Mum's umbrella from the pocket under the steering wheel. He undoes his seatbelt, wipes his sleeve over his eyes and looks at his nose in the mirror on the sun-visor before opening the door. It swings wide and the smell of the Lough fills the air, sea-salty and stagnant.

He closes the door and walks round the front of the car. It's like all the times I dropped him off for the extra maths classes after school, when I was home from university. He walks the same way he did back then, feet dragging in his new shoes, a lean like he needs someone to look after him. My brother.

When he reaches the bottom of the steps he puts up the umbrella. The pattern on it is a Monet painting of water lilies, a shimmer of pinks and blues. He looks back at the car and I look away. The doors of the 4X4 open and the men get out. The driver slings a sports bag over his shoulder.

Grace Gifford's Wedding

The gaol chapel was lit by a single candle placed
on the altar
behind the priest in blood red robes.
I was led
up a stone corridor past a cast iron door, a chill
despite the May day. I was told
I could not see you beforehand.
When they brought you in, pale and spectacled
they removed
the shackles, your raw wrists
a reminder of violence. We were flanked
by two witnesses, soldiers, the priest
clasping his hands, his back
to the false windows, no sky, no moonlight.
The pews were empty, no family—
just us, the priest, the windows, the soldiers,
our shadows.

This will be brief, they said; no talking, no touching.
I wore a plaid dress, white collar and sleeves,
fake flowers on a straw hat. We read
our vows like children. We signed
our names on the register. I felt guilty
to know you had money.
Me, a spinster, and you, a gentleman.

Our marriage, the beginning
of our life
ended in the morning
in the stonebreakers' yard—

I imagined you
small beneath the unscalable stone walls,
my blind imbecile, the seagulls
mocked you. Twelve soldiers
held their rifles, aimed at your marker: six standing,
six kneeling. Such order.
Such perfect symmetry.

I still have your letter:
'You will marry me and nobody else.'

You, a martyr. Me, a widow.

Lauren Lawler

How Do We Know What We Know?

Catriona Crowe

Ireland has a depressing record of archival self-destruction. Having spent the best part of a century making the case for a dedicated archival repository (the Public Record Office, opened in 1867 at the Four Courts in Dublin), filling it with administrative, legal, ecclesiastical and demographic records, dating from the 12th to the 19th centuries, for almost 50 years, and creating a scholarly environment where researchers could examine archival evidence on which to base their assertions, the people involved in this endeavour had to witness it all being blown to smithereens on June 30th 1922, when a Free State shell hit an anti-Treaty mine brilliantly located in the basement of the building.

Apart from all the other extraordinary records charting the history of Ireland over seven centuries, we lost the census records for 1821, 1831, 1841 and 1851, the record of those who lived here before the Great Famine. Anyone who has walked in the beautiful deserted village on Achill Island, a pre-Famine settlement now being excavated, will weep for the loss of the names and details of those who lived there before 1845. You could say that Ireland's archival heritage was a material casualty of the decade of centenaries in which we are now involved.

On our small island on the edge of a powerful continent, and next door to a large imperial power, we embarked in 1912 on a decade of diverse thought processes, activities and interactions, often diametrically opposed to one another, which resulted in outcomes as varied as the establishment of a modern highly defensive Unionism in the northern part of the country, the birth of a modern trade union movement, mass participation in the most murderous war yet seen in the world, and the achievement of the franchise for some women. We saw the creation of a founding myth for our state, involving heroism, hopelessness, high ideals and self-sacrifice, the elimination of the political party which had enjoyed overwhelming nationalist support for three decades, the creation of a new nationalist party whose roots spread in many different directions, a vicious civil war, and most importantly, the deaths of almost 36,000 people, and injuries, many seriously disabling, to many more.

*

How do we know what we know about this turbulent and transformative period? Good trustworthy history depends on the availability of a variety of good primary sources from which to build a narrative. As it happens, a plethora of relevant high quality sources have recently been released, many of them free-to-access online.

*

In 2003, the records of the Bureau of Military History were released to the public after a long struggle to make them accessible. The Bureau was established in the late 1940s with the purpose of collecting statements and documents from participants in the events of Ireland's revolutionary period, 1913-1921. Participants included people like Ernest Blythe, Kathleen Lynn, Louise Gavan Duffy, Sean McEntee, Dan Breen, Robert Brennan, and the widows, sons and daughters of many of the key players who died during the period. Because the statements are in their own words, they are vibrant and immediate in a way that official documents cannot be. There are 1770 statements in all, running to 35,000 typed pages. There are also 300 collections of contemporary documents, 600 photographs, and 12 sound recordings, including one of Maud Gonne sounding impossibly aristocratic. Incidentally, the prime mover of this valuable project, Eamonn De Valera, never made a statement himself to the Bureau, an omission which has led to all kinds of speculation as to the reasons for his restraint.

The collection has transformed the study of the period. Charles Townshend, author of the best-selling recent history of the 1916 Rising, *Easter 1916; The Irish Rebellion,* writes about the statements in his preface to the book: 'The biggest change in recent years has been the final release of the participants' accounts assembled by the Bureau of Military History… suddenly, instead of a few dozen accounts, we have many hundreds.'

Because the statements dealt with peoples' recollections of their actions quite a while after they happened, they are relaxed and give a flavour of the writers' personalities, so we get, for example, Louise Gavan Duffy's account of confronting Patrick Pearse in the GPO in 1916:

> I said to him that I wanted to be in the field but that I felt that the Rebellion was a frightful mistake, that it could not possibly succeed and it was, therefore, wrong. I forget whether he said anything to that or whether he simply let it go. He certainly did not start to justify himself. I told him that I would rather not do any active work; I suppose what I meant was that I would not like to be sent with dispatches or anything like that, because I felt that I would not be justified. He asked me would I like to go to the kitchen. I could not object to that, and I went up to the kitchen at the top of the back of the building.

Or Vinnie Byrne, one of the key members of Collins's Squad, describing in chilling detail his many activities, using phrases like 'we plugged him' or 'we let him have it', 75 pages of violence or thwarted violence, underlaid with the classic soldier's unquestioning belief in the rectitude of his orders. Byrne didn't waste time with moral questions, and forty years later he is as cheerful and unrepentant about the deaths he caused as he says he was when doing what he was ordered to do.

The Bureau statements, photographs, sound recordings and sample contemporary documents were recently made available online free to access, at www.bureauofmilitaryhistory.ie, and the statements can be searched by person, place, subject, or browsed.

As far as I know, no other country possesses an oral history of its revolutionary period of this scope and magnitude. Its free online accessibility allows anyone who is interested to look at first-class primary sources, and to make up his or her own mind as to what happened. This is just one example of how digitisation of archival records, and their appearance on the internet, is transforming and democratising the study of history.

*

A more reliable and much larger archive for the period is currently being prepared for release to the public. The single biggest archival project related to the nationalist side of the decade of centenaries is the Military Service Pensions Project. The collection comprises ca. 285,000 files dealing with applications for pensions from survivors and dependants of those killed during the period 1916-1923, under various Army Pensions and Military Service Pensions Acts, 1924-1949. They provide hitherto unavailable and verifiable information about the conduct of the 1916 Rising, the War of Independence and the civil war. These applications are much closer in time to the events they describe than the Bureau records, and required a very high level of verification, in the form of references from three superior officers. Many people who should have got pensions didn't, because of this high standard of proof.

The Boards of Assessors who adjudicated as to who should be granted pensions gathered together supporting information as to activities during the period, resulting in Brigade Activity Reports on military actions and rolls of IRA membership at different times during the War of Independence. As well as the pensions files, there are files relating to the 80,000 people who got medals. Some of these medals are now to be found fetching high prices at Adam's Auction Rooms.

The collection will be released online, free-to-acess, in phases up to 2023. The first release consists of ca. 2500 files, accompanied by contextual administrative material, brigade activities reports and membership rolls, and a detailed archival catalogue. All this was launched in January 2014, and a second launch took place in October of that year. While other material may come to light relating to the nationalist participants during the decade, none is likely to be of the scope and importance of the Military Service Pensions files, and it is imperative that the project to process them continues to its conclusion.

The pensions files give us unparalleled access to social and economic information about claimants, as they disclose often dire financial circumstances, and that bureaucratic inertia could often cause problems for those seeking pensions. Witness the following correspondence between William O'Brien, general secretary of the ITGWU, and the Minister for Defence, Richard Mulcahy in 1924, about the delay in dealing with Lily Connolly's application for a pension and Mulcahy's irate instruction to his department to get on with it:

> Irish Transport and General Workers' Union
> 35 Parnell Square
> Dublin
> 6 February 1924
> Dear General Mulcahy,
> Some months ago Mrs. James Connolly applied for a pension under the Army Pensions Act but so far has not had any word about her claim, and has no idea when it is likely to be dealt with. She has found it rather difficult to make ends meet during recent years, and at the moment is rather embarrassed for the want of some ready money. She has one daughter who is a medical student in her last year, and it is hoped that she will be qualified in the next six to eight months. Perhaps you would be able to inform me… whether it would be possible for her to get a payment on account…
> Mise le meas.
> Wm. O'Brien

Aireacht Chosanta
Bearraic Phortobello
Baile Atha Cliath
8 February 1924
To Army Finance Officer:
Attached is one of the type of cases I was speaking to you about, and one which it is utterly inexcusable has not been dealt with by us long ago:
1. It should not take one day to get evidence that JAMES CONNOLLY was executed in 1916!
2. It should not take one other day to verify that the Applicant is his widow!
And those dealing with the matter of such pensions might have some appreciation that if a woman loses her husband and has a family she has been through very difficult circumstances and is actually in very difficult circumstances at the present time—whatever bit of luck even may come her way.
Is there any chance of having a first payment of pension in this particular case made inside seven days, namely, before 15th February 1924?
Beir Beannacht,
R. Ua Maolcatha
Aire Chosanta

Lily finally got her money on 3 April 1924.

And here is Margaret Skinnider's account of being wounded as a member of the Citizen Army in 1916. Skinnider was a Scottish-born member of Cumann na mBan who was active in the College of Surgeons garrison in 1916 under Michael Mallin. She was shot while trying to set some houses in Harcourt Street on fire to cut off the Army's advance. Her autobiography, written in 1917, a bit early, is fetchingly titled *Doing My Bit For Ireland*. She died in 1971.

> On Wednesday night going on to Thursday morning, I was wounded. Before that, Joe Connolly, now the Fire Chief, and I wanted to go to bomb the Shelbourne Hotel. The British had got into it that time, and when we asked Mallin for permission he said he wanted something else done first, and asked me to go on a job to Harcourt St. I was in charge of five men, and Tom O'Donoghue, now a priest, was also in charge of five men there. We went… to the foot of Harcourt St. on the left-hand side, now a fruit shop and then a photographic supplies shop… [William] Partridge was in the little detachment I was in. He used his rifle, and with the butt-end of it broke in the door; his rifle went off and a flash went out. There was firing then from across the street; it may have been from the Sinn Féin Bank, with the result that Freddie Ryan was killed and I was wounded. I got three wounds.

Again, the free online accessibility of these records has provided a huge quantity of high quality information to any interested person, in Ireland or elsewhere.

*

It is also imperative that resources are devoted to excavating Irish records from The National Archives (TNA) in London, where many were taken in 1922, and kept closed for long periods of time. Many were also reclassified into existing British record series, thus making their retrieval difficult. Records of particular interest include court-martial records for 1916, search and raid records for the War of Independence, and Cabinet records for the entire period. Discussions, after some initial difficulties, have now opened with TNA on the subject of their co-operation in making these and many other records of Irish interest more accessible. The great era of digitisation in which we now exist should make it possible to repatriate these records electronically rather than physically, thus avoiding contentious discussions along the lines of those about the Elgin Marbles. The National Archives, in partnership with Universities Ireland, will shortly be placing online and free-to-access the court-martial records of the 1916 leaders. We see this as the beginning of a programme of improved access to records relating to the Irish decade of centenaries held in London. Here is Patrick Pearse's statement to his court-martial:

> My sole object in surrendering unconditionally was to save the slaughter of the civil population and to save the lives of my followers, who had been led into this thing by us. It is my hope that the British Government, which has shown its strength, will now be magnanimous and spare their lives and offer an amnesty to my followers, as I am one of the persons chiefly responsible, having served as C in C and President of the provisional government. I am prepared to take the consequence of my act, but I would like my followers to get an amnesty. I went down on my knees as a child and told God I would work all my life to gain the freedom of Ireland. I have deemed it my duty as an Irishman to fight for the freedom of my country. I admit having opened negotiations with Germany. We have kept our word with her and as far as I can see she did her best to help us. She sent a ship with arms. Germany has not sent us gold.

Universities Ireland, an umbrella body for all of the universities on the island of Ireland, has created a steering committee to oversee academic activities, including archival initiatives, in relation to commemoration. Its first public event was a conference on Historians and Public History, held in the Royal Hospital at Kilmainham in June 2012. The attendance hugely exceeded our expectations—450 people, with more turned away. There is obviously great public hunger for intelligent, serious debate about this tumultuous period. Speakers included Diarmaid Ferriter, Keith Jeffery, Jay Winter, Paul Bew, Margaret O'Callaghan, Ann Dolan, and a panel of speakers from North, South and Britain on archives. Audience participation was vibrant, well-informed and curious. It was a good beginning to the many discourses which will evolve over the next ten years.

Further conferences have dealt with the 1913 Lockout (The Cause of Labour), World War One (The Road to War), and ordinary lives (Life and Death in 1915). There will be others on female suffrage, the War of Independence, the Treaty and the Civil War, also hopefully on less obvious subjects, including funerals, both state and personal, competing political philosophies, and comparative studies with other revolutionary societies.

*

The National Archives of Ireland (NAI) has many valuable records relating to this decade, in particular those of the first Dáil, 1919-21, including the full record of the Anglo-Irish Treaty negotiations. NAI will shortly be launching online ca. 6500 compensation files for damage to property in 1916. All levels of Irish society are represented—from claims for householders' curtains destroyed by gunfire in North Strand, gallons of milk taken by Crown forces in Foley Street, Repertory Company theatrical costumes destroyed by fire in Sackville Street, to claims for the loss of valuable jewellery left for repair and subsequently destroyed in various jewellers around the city and luxury goods such as furs and silk lost by hotel visitors. The collection includes detailed inventories of goods and furnishings destroyed in some households and in commercial premises of all types and sizes, from single traders working out of back rooms, to Clery and Company for the rebuilding of their world famous department store on Sackville Street.

NAI is also cataloguing the much bigger set of compensation claim files which cover the War of Independence and the civil war. Half of the catalogue can be found on www.nationalarchives.ie. And the rest will go up early next year.

*

One of the big archival lacunae in Irish history relates to land records. The big three collections are:

1. The Irish Land Commission, ca. 1590-date;
2. The Land Registry, 1891-date;
3. The Registry of Deeds, 1702-date.

Between them, these three collections cover most of the land transactions in Ireland for the decade of centenaries, and for centuries before and after. One of them, the Registry of Deeds, is open to researchers in its original home in the King's Inns, but the records are quite difficult to use, are in need of conservation, and could do with a digitisation programme. This last they are contemplating, but with a commercial operator, which may lead to unsatisfactory access for scholars other than genealogists. I will return to this question later. The records in the Registry of Deeds record the history of major land transactions from 1702 on, and therefore fill one of the yawning gaps left by the destruction of the Public Record Office in 1922.

The Irish Land Commission, established in 1881, was the body responsible for redistributing land from landlord to tenant under the various land acts. By 1923, 75% of the land of Ireland had changed hands under its auspices. You could say that the real revolution had quietly taken place without fuss, or much fuss, while the other one was happening with a great deal of fuss. The records of this momentous undertaking, which number millions, were preserved until 1992 in a purpose-built repository behind what is now the Merrion Hotel in Dublin. The sale of what had been the Land Commission offices by the government necessitated the destruction of this repository, it having no obvious value to a luxury hotel, and the National Archives was called in to save the records in an unseemly hurry.

They ended up in our warehouse in Bishop Street, accessible only to the increasingly superannuated staff of the records branch of the Land Commission, despite many requests from people like Martin Mansergh, who should have had some clout, and Professor Terry Dooley, who has a distinguished record on investigation of Irish big houses. The records contain not only the Fair Rent books for the whole country for the 1880s, but original deeds to properties to be transferred dating back to the 16th century, and a whole subset of Church Temporalities Commission property records dating to the late 18th century. In other words, a treasure trove. The records were moved from our warehouse to another warehouse in Portlaoise some years ago, where they are, if anything, even more inaccessible than they were before.

The Land Registry was established in 1891 to register the sale of all properties in Ireland on a compulsory basis, thus largely superseding the Registry of Deeds. As a young archivist in the late 1970s, I found myself assigned to evaluating these records. The Land Registry files the deeds submitted to them, and relevant particulars are entered on folios, which, with their accompanying maps, are available to the public on payment of a fee.

What are not available to the public are the deeds, or instruments of transfer, which underlie the information in the folios. In the late 1970s, I got to see these documents, hundreds of thousands of them, stored in a warehouse near Smithfield. What they contained astonished and disturbed me: the overwhelming majority dealt with the transfer of land from parents to children, and very many of them contained clauses guaranteeing the parents a seat by the fire, a bed to sleep in, and provision for food, such as the milk of a cow or a proportion of the potato crop. Did this mean that if such instructions were not legally recorded, the older people of Ireland would be put out of their homes by their own children? These could, of course, be legal rubrics employed out of habit, but all kinds of sources, particularly literary ones from writers like Tom Murphy and John B Keane, tell us that the social reality underlying Irish rural life differed greatly from the fantasy version promulgated by Church and State.

These three great collections, dealing with one of the most serious issues in Irish history, land and its ownership, have a great deal to contribute to our understanding of the kind of society which emerged in 1922. The continued inaccessibility of two of them, and the limited accessibility of the third, make it impossible to properly evaluate these events and their political, social and economic consequences.

*

Earlier, I mentioned a possible tension between genealogy and scholarship, and I want to elaborate a little on that. Genealogy is now a huge industry, with websites like Ancestry.com making fortunes out of people's desire to locate their ancestors. In Ireland, where the 1901 and 1911 censuses have been placed online free of charge, the response has been overwhelming: 1 billion hits since 2007, and 20 million unique visitors. The reason for these numbers is that the site is free; you can research your own ancestors, but also gratify your vulgar curiosity about their neighbours, or research the physical fabric and building usage of a rural townland or city street. You can find people staying with relatives and try to work out why—holiday, fosterage, education, employment, kidnapping? You can search by any of the fields used in the census: name, age, sex, townland or street, district electoral division, county, religion, occupation, relationship to head of family, literacy status, county or country of origin, Irish language proficiency, specified illnesses, and child survival information. This means you can search for particular occupations, nationalities and religions in particular places—how many Methodist butchers were there in Cork? how many French governesses in Dublin? how many Plymouth Brethern in Rathmines? The answer to the last question, by the way, is 18. Hours of harmless and instructive fun.

But also incredibly useful for literary scholarship. Joyce studies, for example, have been transformed by the census. I've now lost count of the articles on Joyce which reference the census online or which have originated directly from it. As we know, Joyce did not balk at mentioning real people and places in his fiction, and being able to find them in an almost contemporaneous archive is expanding contextual possibilities for literary scholars. For example. Alf Bergan, who shows up throughout *Ulysses*, and was a close friend of John Joyce, James's father, can be found in the 1901 census, aged 22, living in Clonliffe Road in Drumcondra with his widowed mother and five unmarried sisters. His occupation is solicitor's clerk, just as it is in the novel. Alf's moment of glory comes when he recounts seeing the dead Paddy Dignam in Capel Street in the afternoon, when he had been buried that morning.

In terms of literary uses for these records, Gene Kerrigan's recent novel, *The Scrap*, has fruitfully used the statements in the Bureau of Military History to construct a vivid and accurate narrative of the 1916 Rising. Many Irish fiction writers have used archives as bases or jumping off points for their work; they include Sebastian Barry, Colm Tóibín, Lia Mills, Roddy Doyle, Anne Enright and Eoin McNamee. And Brian Friel's *Translations* is firmly rooted in the history and archives of the Ordnance Survey in early 19th century Ireland.

*

As can be seen, a lot of progress has been and is being made in opening up serious archival resources to scholars and citizens. The results are apparent in the many excellent publications which continue to appear throughout the decade, including Roy Foster's *Vivid Faces* and Lucy McDiarmid's *At Home in the Revolution*, both of which made superlative use of diary and memoir material from the time, particularly women's writings, and both of which are in themselves wonderful sources for creative writers who are interested in what history has to offer them.

One of the most useful for those interested in the subject of the historiography of the revolutionary decade is Diarmaid Ferriter's *A Nation and Not a Rabble*. The first third of the book is devoted to listing and analysing the sources available at different times since 1916, and the uses made of them by historians. He also looks at memoir and diary material, like Dan Breen's *My Fight for Irish Freedom*, published in 1924 and influential as one of the heroic narratives of the period. Ferriter knows Irish state archives better than most other historians, and part of his achievement has been to excavate considerable social history from official files. This he uses to excellent effect in his narrative of the decade, the second part of the book, and his exploration of previous commemoration events, the third part of the book.

Creative writers have a lot to gain from exploring these sources; archives can be overlooked as potential material for fiction, drama and poetry. None of us knows where the initial spark for a novel, a play or a poem may come from. Perhaps the rich tapestry of historical records, with all of their flaws, ironies, truths and deceptions, may be one other place to start.

Oak

I'd like to spend Easter 2016
bird watching on the Isle of Wight.
I will not be remembering shootings or blood. I will kill no bird.
I will not hunt and I will not cry. On Monday I will set base camp
and patch my tent from the Plough and Stars.

A kindly man will tell me that westerly winds are prevailing and
I should pitch under a large shadowy oak tree and stretch out a
candy-striped wind-breaker across my extraction point.

I will heed his warnings.

I will indulge my Mick and me fantasy behind the furze bush,
then I will wet my lemony green tea behind the shadowy oak tree.

I'd have no trouble shooting people, dressed up in my ghillie suit.
Saving someone is far harder than shooting them dead. Save or shoot?
Roll up! Roll up! Meet ya half way? Any chance of a luck penny? Isn't war a hoor?
The very best with the power-sharing, though powerful people don't much like to share.
Good Luck with the hurt-remembering, dead-finding, place-scavenging.

I will slowly sip this tea as penalty.
A punishment, my own gentle firing squad.
I don't much like lemons, they gash my tongue.
There'll be no jaw jacking, just supping.

When night falls on the Plough and illuminates the Stars, I will low crawl
from the canvas, I will tell of echo to the Nightjar, share nibbles of shame with some
Woodcocks, the Long-Eared Owl will hoot at me to *give over about Victor*,
and by dark I'll delight in a Less-Spotted Woodpecker, knowing she can
damage just gentlygentlygentlyalphabravocharlie tapping
until
the
tree
dies
and
we
can
all
relax
deep
into
the
dark
bark
hole

Elaine Feeney

Aiséirí

Patrick McCabe

On and off, I'd been intimate with Connie so I knew that most of the *Cosmo* stuff was nonsense. ('Sleeping around but cool with it, Eddie, you know?' she'd routinely yawn with a crafted nonchalance.) But there couldn't have been any suggestion of traducement—which is as it should be, whether for a country and its citizens or a brace of self-consciously mutinous individuals coquetting in the gloom of a seventies bedsit.

Or arguing about art and politics in the Pembroke, debating the latest production in The Cellar, the little theatre Mairead Curtin had founded.

The Socialist Workers' Party met weekly in the CIE hall in Marlboro Street. The decade was exclusively ours—we were certain of that. Connie would always be on hand for a spirited rendition of The Internationale—taking impressive command of the rostrum with that sturdy voice we all admired.

'It's ours for the taking,' we told ourselves.

And meant it.

But the seventies came and went, as did a Marlboro Street hero of the time, a charismatic advocate of the approaching revolutionary decade—defecting first to the right and then, before we could satisfactorily vent our fury, inconveniently dying.

I don't know how to put it—I suppose it would be accurate to acknowledge a gradual disaffection. But the truth is, essentially, that I had recently fallen in love with another woman—a pal of Connie's, as it turned out, also a party member—Olwyn Price, who was beginning to make a name for herself as an artist.

I had met her first in Wynn's Hotel, across the road from the magazine office where she worked part-time, a listings periodical for which she also occasionally drew cartoons. It had happened pretty quick, and unexpectedly—among the whiskey-reddened priests and overfed countrywomen, the wives of farmers and rural politicians, who made up the greater proportion of the clientele at that time. The hotel was close to my place of employment—just across the bridge from O'Connell House and the road traffic division of the Department Of Transport.

We had both been attending a massive PAYE march. She'd come breezing through the door of the hotel with a bulging folder of files under her arm, tossing back her corkscrew hair as I brought her a gin and tonic. She'd always had a reputation for forthrightness, of which I'd been unaware when I fell for her. She moved the folder and rested her chin on her fist as she stared at me. 'I'll come straight to the point,' I heard her say as she contemplatively clinked the ice in the glass. 'There isn't any point in us continuing like this. Because I don't love you, Eddie.'

I met her on and off after that but didn't spend any great deal of time with her until my father's funeral in 2005. She had travelled specially up from Dublin. I'd like to say, like you so often read in stories, that she looked as beautiful as ever—or that she was even more attractive, in a kind of distant and glamourous way—but it wouldn't be true.

She had ended up teaching—from which she had taken early retirement—citing exhaustion, she told me. Not to mention disappointment, that much was evident, with her artistic career—which, having flourished briefly in the early to mid-eighties with a number of highly regarded exhibitions, had eventually stalled.

Before obscurity claimed her, or so I inferred.

That day of the funeral was one which might have been selected specifically for the occasion, direct from the pages of a nineteen-fifties short story—with soft rain sweeping in swathes across the cemetery, as all the old soldiers of the Fianna Fáil party lowered their heads, displaying their medals on suits of blue serge. She had known my father, Olwyn—even if just a little. The old warrior, I remember she had called him with gratifying respect and affection—before finally departing and heading back to the city.

In The Errigal Hotel afterwards—through the great picture window you could see the rain lashing the sides of the majestic granite mountain—my father's brother Laochra was animatedly relating some of his celebrated stories—in his way, just like Matthew, an old battler too. 'I'll never forget the night Mattie Bonner riz the roof! Proceeding to declare, after a couple more whiskies, that he personally would have no problem going over to bomb the House Of Commons. 'To hell with Churchill and all his Irish lackeys! There were no turncoats for the likes of Commandant Bonner—whatever else he might have done, he went to his grave never having sold the pass!'

As a very young man, aged only fifteen, my father had fought in the 1916 Rising, and in the War Of Independence and Civil War later on. We'd been brought up on all of it. Which was how my brother Brendan had become involved. We'd had many arguments—mostly about my growing leftist tendencies.

'There isn't any room for such luxuries, I'm afraid,' was a not uncommon utterance of his around that time.

He had always been impulsive, Brendan—arguably naive. Although maybe in retrospect that's unfair. Anyway, eventually, when the Troubles broke out again, after Derry in 1972, he became deeply and seriously involved.

Once he had called to my office in Dublin—unmistakably in a state. That was the night I hid the pistol. Although 'never again' I told him and meant it. It was things like that that kept us real close—even though I considered his commitment misguided. With it turning out the firearm had belonged to a friend from Tyrone—soon to be a hunger-striking colleague. One of the lucky ones who didn't die, a Hugh McGeeney from a townland called Lavey. Which was, and remains, a place where they viewed things rather uncomplicatedly. That they'd been fucked for years and now were fucking back.

When he put his name forward as a candidate for the proposed hunger strike—or should I say put their names forward, for McGeeney was equally as enthusiastic as my brother—to be honest I found myself devastated, and the coming dread I sensed had returned that wet grey afternoon when Olwyn had sat across from me in the hotel lounge bar and coolly, unflinchingly announced as she licked the Rizla paper: 'You see, the situation, Eddie, is—I just don't love you.'

I hadn't bothered going back to the office, deciding instead to drink and wander aimlessly around the city, right through the day and into the night. Mimicking as I did so the compulsive, map-less journey of the protagonist of a movie I picked up along the way—a disturbed schoolteacher played by Diane Keaton in *Looking For Mr Goodbar*, an uncompromising and transgressive exegesis of self-loathing and uncertain identity.

*

My brother had ultimately decided that he had no option but to commit himself and become involved in the struggle for liberation, as he had no problem calling it. Eventually setting up a stall in the Dandelion Market, flogging his personally authored pamphlets about James Connolly and the necessity of 'cleansing' and left-wing revolution. A federalist solution was the one he favoured most, he would insist, with his speech unconsciously echoing that expression of clipped certainty and truncated delivery that so identified 'colleagues' of their persuasion during those years—combined with their regulation livery of vented leather jacket and flared denim jeans, a separate tribe of Northern sympathisers.

He would give me regular lectures in The Buttery in Trinity, where we met occasionally after he'd called into the office. 'It's like the old man used to say,' he announced once more with unshakeable conviction, 'that as sure as grass grows and rivers flow there will never be peace in Ireland until Britain relinquishes her illegitimate claim to our territory.'

They had fired a volley of shots over my father's grave and an old civil-war comrade had affectionately clasped my hand as the two of us stood there. 'I seen that man,' I remember he began, 'I seen him defying a Brigadier, a right bastard, who was shoving a red-hot poker into his face. Do your worst, your father spat back, for you do nothing but further undermine your already untenable position. I despise you and your illicit authority. That was what he said, Matt Bonner. I heard it myself. And it fair shook the Tommy.'

Brendan had always been proud of that story and I'd heard him repeat it many times. Then in 1971 or thereabouts he had become involved with another splinter group—Aiséirí, they called themselves, pledging themselves anew to the time-honoured faith of rebirth and resurrection.

'Rebirth!' he declared, 'and this time we'll finish it. Aiséirí, Edward! That's all that matters now—with the Irish nation once and for all reborn!'

He had composed and published a number of small pamphlets for them, detailing the precepts and principles of their cause.

'A necessary purgation,' he had growled at me one night, drunk, 'and them that's not with us, let them be advised to stand aside!'

I remember sitting there half-dazed one evening after a particular arduous day at work, in front of a one-bar electric heater when I turned towards the window of the ground floor flat and saw him standing outside the window—

unusually furtive, disturbingly agitated. I would lose my job if they found him there, I told him. As he leaned forward in the chair, drawing repeatedly on the cigarette as he stammered: 'Of all the things to happen, Eddie. Of all the things to fuckin' happen, you know?'

A policeman had been wounded in the bank raid.

He hadn't been arrested—not on that occasion. When it had all blown over, he had re-emerged on the scene and could generally be found in his usual spot—in the Toby Jugg pub, a brass and burnt oak place directly across from the market where he kept the stall.

McGeeney would show up there the odd weekend too, having driven all the way down from Tyrone. 'Ah, the reluctant nationalist!' he'd snort impatiently with derision when he'd see me. 'Boys, but your father would he feel let down!'

These were the days just prior to the Dublin-Monaghan bombings when the conflict seemed remote and reasonably contained. With the streets of the secure southern city ringing out nightly to the sound of ribald, sabre-rattling ballads popular at the time, including: 'We're on the one road!', 'Four Green Fields', and the more conciliatory 'The Town I Loved So Well'.

Olwyn had been gone from me close on a year when I heard the news about McGeeney. He'd been apprehended with a consignment of explosives on a backroad in South Armagh and taken to Castlereagh Barracks for interrogation, before eventually receiving a sentence of twenty-five years.

It was after that I committed what can only be described as a brazen act—calling up Olwyn on the night of his conviction, shamefully courting her sympathies—trading on another man's wound, as my father might have had it, quoting his hero Ernie O'Malley.

'I'm becoming really worried about Brendan,' I said, 'this is really getting fucking serious. Do you think that maybe I could come around and talk about it?'

I ought, of course, to have known—and perhaps I did—that she'd instinctively intuit my shabby motivations. 'It's selfish, she said, 'you doing this—thinking only about yourself in such circumstances. It's beneath you. And as well as that, unnecessary. I'll always be your friend, Eddie—but the fact is, I'm seeing someone else.'

I had wound up that night in the company of Connie and Big Janis, an American who flitted around the fringes of our circle—arguing over some inconsequential drama production or other. In this case a Gaelic language version of Samuel Beckett's *Krapp's Last Tape*, which Mairead had mounted against all advice, to her eternal regret. 'If The Cellar Theatre', wrote *The Evening Herald*, 'wished to radicalise and reclaim this great playwright, they might have engaged the services of an Irish speaker who could actually act.' There was subsequent talk of closing the theatre down but, as so often before, it never happened and we continued with our regular weekend meetings in The Pembroke Inn.

I continued to wonder who Olwyn's new lover was, regularly telephoning O'Connell Bridge House to inform them yet again that I wouldn't be making it into work. Preferring instead to walk over to Drumcondra, where I knew she was lecturing part-time in the evenings. I only caught a glimpse of her once—climbing onto a bus, with her hessian bag swinging out behind her.

So often I could sense her presence beside me, with the prominence of a missing tooth—as I did now, in the dim afternoon interior of the Abbey Street cinema the two of us had used to frequent. Absurdly, I found myself reaching out to touch the absent hand. As *Mr Goodbar* again continued unspooling—taunting me, it seemed, with the suggestion that I might possibly consider exchanging places with Diane Keaton—join her in her obsessive and compulsive hunt for ecstasy through self-abasement, in the parlous domain of midtown Manhattan, trawling one murky singles bar after another.

It was while I was mopping the film of sweat off my brow turning all these ideas over in my head that I suddenly felt the entire cinema quake to its foundations—stumbling blindly out of my seat as the lights blazed on, with the harsh sound of sirens already tearing up the calm of early evening. I emerged into a city in the process of being remorselessly devastated. A woman stumbled past me holding a shoe as I shrank back into a nearby doorway, a steel girder falling to earth in front of me. Across the street, a department store window caved in—then came the sound of yet another explosion, only this time duller. As a young policeman pleaded through a loud-hailer: 'There may be other devices! Please go home. Please will youse for God's sake go home?'

As though intoxicated, I picked my way through the mounds of blackened masonry and just sat there, blankly, in the corner booth of a deserted café. Outside the fire engines raced past in a crimson blur. I lost all track of time.

It transpired that over four hours had elapsed when I eventually got back to the flat in Rathmines, finding the landlord standing waiting for me in the hall—observing me darkly as I turned to close the door behind me, still over-alert in the aftermath of the catastrophe. Just as he was, suppressed and wired standing there in the shadows.

'Your crowd!' he hissed, 'a ring of steel around the border is what we want!' Special Branch had been watching the flat for months, he told me—with my simply being Brendan's brother enough to validate such a degree of attention.

'I'll have to ask you to leave,' he concluded, 'I'll want the keys by Saturday at the latest.'

That was the end of the romance with Northern nationalists. Even the snug in The Toby Jugg was not immune. As I was to realise only a few nights later, at the ballad session which was normally lively and spirited by nine o'clock, with renditions of 'Only Our Rivers Run Free' and similar anthems raising the rafters. Now there wasn't a sound to be heard. With everyone, it seemed, reaching for their drinks in slow motion, glassily endeavouring to comprehend the enormity of what had happened—already halfway to being corpses themselves.

'Here is the news read by Maurice O'Doherty.'

I lifted my eyes towards the flickering screen. The Red Hand Commandoes—a loyalist splinter group—had issued a statement vowing to 'extirpate all remaining Fenian scum, every Irish treasonous rat that remained in Dublin. Make no mistake: there will be more bombs,' they said.

As, with the pint glass almost splintering in my hand, sitting there in the dim corner of the bar, I experienced a vision of Olywn Price hurrying anxiously out the gates of Scoil Mhuire as another bomb blast rent the air and the hessian bag went flying and I heard her call out helplessly: 'Eddie Bonner! It's you I want!'

As, across the landscape of a credulous, over-heated mind, a comically fictive ambulance rushed towards the scene. As the real-time newsreader confirmed further details of yet another casualty, an elderly lady who had only just passed away in the Royal Victoria hospital.

'Our sympathies go to her friends and family,' said the priest who had been first on the scene of the explosion. 'I just hope that the people who did this can live with themselves. And are happy with the consequences of their blood-and-death cult. For that's what it is. Rebirth? Death, I call it. Death and suffering, for that's all it ever brings.'

*

Brendan had lasted forty-seven days on his hunger-strike. I had received the news in the middle of the night.

The reception arranged in the aftermath of his interment had been impressively dominated by Dessie Milner—subsequently a European minister—with his kiss curl and trademark grin very much in evidence as he moved effortlessly through the crowd, immaculate in his cream-white suit.

At one time he and Hugh McGeeney had been inseparable. But now—after his participation in the ultimate sellout, when the country had been offered on a plate to a cabal of international financiers and bondholders, his former colleague would willingly have put a bullet in his head.

'That was the day it ended for me and Dessie Milner', he had told me, 'what I like to call The Day Of The Traducement—when I saw that fleet of black Lexus cars coming in and out of Government Buildings after they had signed the deal with our so-called 'European partners'—effectively bankrupting the fucking place, Eddie—and then to deny that any kind of deal had been done! When he knew the fucking truth—when he knew what had happened was we'd been bullied into the ground by the Troika and we took it, like we always seem to do in the end—time backs aching for the lash. Our day will come, my old mucker used to say—well, it has. And it's gone, and along with it the ghosts of the idiot dead—committed patriots and fucking-well innocents alike.'

After that day in 2008—what he insisted on calling 'The End Of Ireland'—I had begun to visit him regularly up the mountains.

Old habits die hard, sighed Hugh McGeeney lugubriously, poking away at the insides of a watch—a horologist by trade, those skills had proved most useful indeed during the course of the Troubles.

When he had initially heard of my forthcoming plan, he told me that he thought that I'd been drinking or taking 'something'.

But I didn't flinch.

'I'm going to take the whole thing down, McGeeney—blow the shit out of it, once and for all. A proper Aiséirí, I guess you might say. Government Buildings—one last big strike.'

He nodded for a bit and then lapsed into a brooding silence. Then, raising his head, gazed challengingly, piercingly into my eyes, sighing wearily as he swilled from the can of cheap beer.

'You're just like him, aren't you? You might as well be fucking Brendan

Bonner's twin. Just as obsessive as he was when it comes to it. Like I say, old habits die hard—the faith of Laochra Bonner, ancient old warrior, lives on. It's not just his face that you've got. One big fucking strike—man fucking dear, some mothers do 'ave 'em!'

A kid, if Olwyn and I had been so fortunate, I found myself thinking as the two of us stood there—she had planned to call Rosa, after her heroine Rosa Luxembourg. There had been talk at one point, also, of maybe buying an artisan dwelling—perhaps in The Liberties, which was fashionable then. But there wasn't going to be any artisan dwelling—or any children called Rosa either.

I had left the Toby Jugg that afternoon in another brandy-and-Guinness fuelled stupor, almost managing to get myself into a fight with the police. All I can remember about the details of the dispute is the officer in question giving me a vicious shove—actually close to breaking down himself, I now realise.

'Just, for Christ's sake, go on fucking home—don't you know the sort of times we're living in? Please!'

But I didn't—go home, I mean. Instead I boarded the Belfast train—at Amiens Street, Connolly, climbed aboard the Enterprise for Belfast.

York Street, Bombay Street, Cawnpore Street, all these winding arteries of empire, I kept thinking—in the middle of my bemusement somehow managing to lose my way—Fraser Street, Trillick Street, Kashmir Road—before finding myself right back where I started.

It eventually became a bewildering maze. Before, in a bar beside a car park—typically deserted and showered in glass—I found myself talking about the music of Bobby Darin to an old-time rocker of sixty or thereabouts—a fitter, he told me, by the name of Victor.

'There's good and bad on both sides,' I heard him continue. 'That's the way it is in this unfortunate conflict. Sooner or later we're all going to have to get together. I'm just an old-time rocker, my friend.' He laughed heartily, turning his head to display his ample sideburns. 'But, like I say, at the end of the day I've always had a soft spot for good-time crooners like Wee Bobby Darin.'

I leaned across the jukebox, selecting the disc of 'Beyond The Sea', while my new friend smiled appreciatively in warm recognition. Then the door suddenly swung open and an equally rotund associate was seen to enter, around the same age. Who told me he was pleased to see me and heartily welcomed me to his 'wee city'.

I barely acknowledged him—listening to Bobby as I stared off out across the abandoned parking lot, with its glass splinters swaying—like Bobby Darin's silver ocean.

'What takes you up to wee Belfast?' asked the pal.

'Maybe I'm searching,' I returned with some stoicism. 'Like Diane Keaton—you haven't by any chance seen her around?'

'He's funny,' the pal chirped. 'I'll give him that—he's funny. But you don't have to worry, friend—we'll help you. We'll help you find this woman of yours. Because we know plenty of dolls like that—don't we, Victor?'

'We do indeed,' replied Victor. 'Maybe.'

I remember there was a paper—*The Irish News*—lying on the counter as we ordered our final drink. It carried a photo of Dessie Milner on the cover, grinning away, but with the trademark white suit not yet in evidence. 'We will not stop—yes our campaign will continue until the day finally comes—and come it will, make no mistake. When this divided country, this ancient land which has been so cruelly sundered will at long last be reunited.' His glittering steel eyes were unflinching beneath the kiss-curl.

At what point the woman had joined our company I couldn't say. She reminded me immediately of the comedienne Barbara Windsor—bouffant-haired starlet of so many British comedies. She sat on my knee with her arm around my neck. Where exactly it was they had taken me, I couldn't, not with any degree of accuracy, say. It was somewhere in a backstreet in the eastern part of the city. Victor was in the process of fixing more drinks. 'Molotov cocktails,' he laughed good-naturedly—before crouching down and reaching deep inside a cabinet. 'He likes Bobby Darin,' I heard him say—as his associate nodded appreciatively. Victor had found his bottles, he declared, which he then set assiduously about uncapping.

'Who sings about lovers way out on the ocean,' he smiled, holding up the opened bottles. 'Way out on the ocean there and on golden sands. Watching them sailing, you know, wee honey? Watching the what's that go sailing, honey, do you think?'

'Ships,' giggled Barbara Windsor, perkily. 'Ships, Victor.'

As his associate struck me forcibly—just once—with a single perfectly-judged blow of the wheelbrace. Clearly he had done it before, I remember thinking—and the last thing I saw was her and Victor holding hands. 'Ships,' she repeated, as everything folded and he whispered: 'Mrs Goodbar. Here she is!' And a blackness of extraordinary immensity overtook me as I was swept up by a sea of glimmering silver that seemed to flow through all of time and infinite space.

'Welcome to Manhattan,' I heard Diane Keaton softly whisper, 'on this profane altar now at last you're free.'

'Look at me! I'm a queen!' Barbara Windsor was bleating, giddily sporting a rudimentary newspaper-crown. As Victor interrupted and impishly wagged an admonitory finger. 'No!' he corrected. 'Not just a queen but the Queen of all England! One that this Fenian fucker is going to pledge allegiance to. Aren't you, Irish? Going to fall on your knees before Her Majesty?'

'Oh! I like it!' Barbara squealed as she began trembling giddily. 'I really do like it, being the queen! It's fab!'

Chips were shoved into my mouth one after another. 'The wee man adores me!' Barbara tinkled—at which point I passed out anew. But not before seeing Olwyn standing wiggling before me. 'Look!' she was saying, 'Look, Eddie, there it is—the future!'

With my father, out of nowhere, appearing then, attired splendidly in slouch hat and bandolier, completely transfigured. 'I've just heard,' he was saying, 'Edward, son, I've just been told this minute. That everything we fought for has been vindicated. What wonderful news. How our enemies now will hang their heads when they hear that our every demand had finally been acceded to. Aiséirí! Our day has come! And it's a happy man who stands here this day, before returning to sleep forever soundly in his grave!'

Victor and his associate had administered further savage beatings, as Barbara Windsor The Queen looked on disinterestedly, consuming the chips from her crumpled greasy bag. 'All you had to do was say whatever they asked you to,' she sighed impatiently. 'Why did you have to be so stupid?'

They had simply demanded that I curse the Pope and pledge consummate fealty to Her Majesty, head of the armed forces in Ireland. 'Never!' I had obstinately repeated, invoking the shade of my father, wincing before the Tommy's glowing poker.

'If I didn't know better I'd swear that Irish wants to die!' I heard Victor snarl. 'Why would anyone want to die?' a now visibly agitated Barbara Windsor responded with her back to the wall. 'No one could be as stupid as that—not even a Catholic!'

'Did you hear that?' snapped Victor, as his pal caught my hair and hauled my head backwards. 'She says that no one could be that dumb, not even a

Taig! Now do what we say. Say you're forever a subject of the Queen!'

As I thought of Roger Casement and his black-draped casket arriving on a bier, with a volley of shots ringing out defiantly above his grave. My brother and I had been at the repatriation of his remains in 1966.

'Never!' I spat.

'Ooh cheeky!' giggled Barbara, but you could tell she was on the verge of tears. 'Please!' she said to Victor, 'please, baby, will you let him go—it's already gone way too far!'

They threw me out the back door of a car and left me lying on a patch of waste ground. When the doctor examined me he told me I was lucky to be alive.

At work I never referred to the Belfast episode—lying that I had been in a car accident down the country. If I did become a lot more withdrawn in myself, which I assume was the case, it wasn't remarked upon. Not even by Devanney, who just continued, every so often, to look up from his paper, muttering derisively as he gave it an impatient shake: 'Look who's just decided to join us—laugh-a-minute Les fucking Dawson!'

'Their inheritance is that of the robber barons of the gilded age,' Olwyn used to say. 'And just like them they take their sense of entitlement for granted.' Before throwing on her coat and heading down to yet another meeting—at SIPTU headquarters or in the CIE hall. On that particular occasion, though, it was the Teachers' Club in Parnell Square, as I recall. She and some colleagues, she explained as she searched for her keys, were committed once and for all to the amalgamation of the three teachers' unions. 'Let the barons beware, for the coming tide will wash over them. Believe you me, this decade is going to be different. There is something inevitable about it, Eddie. So watch out, Soldiers Of Destiny, Warriors Of The Rearguard, and every other sly running dog of capitalism, exponents of self-serving mendacity and sly populism.'

One by one she itemised them, crossing the floor—none of which mattered a great deal now. She called back that she'd meet me in The Buttery at two. We'd lived together in that little Rathmines flat for over a year—a typically spartan attic, with a drab lace curtain and cold-water tap, stacks of black bicycles lying in the hall.

There had always been something of the priest about you, she said, with qualities which might have been useful in politics—had I been interested. I guess she was right for after we parted I might as well have taken a vow of celibacy.

One night in The Toby Jugg, though, sometime in the early eighties, I happened to fall in with an American—high cheek-boned, hailing from some unremarkable Midwestern state. There could be no denying her affections and as we danced blearily to Blondie in some late night club I had to admit that the feelings were mutual.

But, unfortunately, when I awoke in the dawn light back at her place, the face I set eyes on was that of Olwyn Price.

I had once written a schoolboy essay—entitled 'Sacrifice at Easter'—a precursor, I suppose, of my much-anticipated 'final strike' on Government Buildings. Yes, my 'vanity project', as Hugh McGeeney had taken to calling it—the one I'd continue to outline for him in comprehensive detail. 'Aiséirí,' I said, 'only this time a proper, co-ordinated revolutionary act and one which has every prospect of military success—with me, effectively, assuming the role of the very first Irish suicide bomber.'

In that much-praised school composition, I had cast myself as Padraig Pearse—with an accompanying sketch illustrating the barrister-turned-schoolteacher surrendering to Christ as a choir of angels called out his name. Against a background of green, white and gold, depicting him splayed cruciform against the heavens as the life force finally began to ebb—like Diane Keaton in a darkened cinema, in night-town Manhattan—crying out in a delirious excelsis, at once sacred and profane.

Afterwards, privately, the incident in Belfast continued to take its toll—with one purported 'sick day' turgidly following upon another.

With me remaining alone in my city centre flat, oscillating between the twin images eliding across my subconscious—that of Olwyn dismissively shaking her head: 'It was never destined to work between us, Eddie—and even if it had you'd have probably destroyed it—wilfully, I mean. Because you only respond to what you can't have.'

And that of my father arriving up beside me—anxious but proud as he laid a familiar, protective hand upon my shoulder: 'Us Bonners, son, in the end we always show them—unyielding, you prevailed! I'm proud of you, son, that we should live to rise again!'

I'd do the best I could to forget them—Victor, his pal the fat one and Barbara Windsor. But then in the night they'd arrive up with scrupulous precision, standing there by the side of the bed and regarding me with voided, indifferent eyes. A state of affairs which continued long after I had sold the mews. Now finding myself lying there as a matter of course—awaiting them, in the capacious suburban house I'd eventually purchased in Rathfarnham.

They rarely disappointed.

'Somewhere beyond the sea,' I'd hear Victor whisper, and then he'd be gone.

Hugh McGeeney gave me whatever advice he could. 'Whenever I find myself beginning to get troubled or edgy about things that happened during those years,' he told me. 'I only have to dwell on the face of Dessie Milner—and after that, all I can do is laugh myself to sleep. Did you know it was him in the car the night we stiffed McElligott?'

McElligott, I knew, was a British agent, an informer of many years standing.

'It was Dessie Milner, and no one else, who gave the order. They dug him up recently, McElligott—the committee for the disappeared or whatever they call it.'

And as I thought of the clouds of grey smoke rising from the soon-to-be devastated Edwardian majesty of Government Buildings, I couldn't keep from thinking about how the dead, whether of Dublin or Belfast or anywhere else, are routinely at once recruited and reduced.

'Everyone is a victim in this conflict,' I'd heard Milner attest on more than one occasion. 'Everyone—without exception.'

And lowered my head in sympathy with the traduced departed.

'We're used to it,' I imagined I heard them murmur, 'we have become habituated to these tediously enervated, reflexive calumniations.'

As I thought of Dessie Milner—in an unfortunate tableau which continued to arrive unbidden in my mind—picking his way through yet another recently bombed town centre. Before bending down as if in the process of preparing to hear the dying man's confession. Not that he was alone, of course—for he most certainly wasn't, with a fleet of sleek black Lexus cars discreetly parked, chauffeurs at the ready to collect his new associates, discreet and polite in their smart overcoats and tinted glasses. Who listened patiently as he explained to his moaning, baffled, soon-to-be-former constituents:

'There's no need to worry—for you will not have given your lives in vain. And the Ireland you dream of, fear not, it will eventually come to pass. Except, perhaps, in a different way. What? What's that you say?'

As he covered his face to conceal his exasperation, with the little ginger kiss-curl dropping decadently across his forehead, before a black-suited official discreetly tapped him on the shoulder. 'Certainly,' he whispered in response. 'Just give me one more minute will you—I think this fellow's on his last legs.'

*

It must be emphasised, however, that whatever appraisals might come to pass in its aftermath, at no time had my decision to execute a 'final, conclusive and cathartic revolutionary act' been arrived at lightly—my private passion play as I liked to think of it. Tossing and turning nightly as I apprehended a bloated cloud of black and grey smoke rising above Government Buildings in glorious, unrepentant triumph.

No, 'Sacrifice at Easter' was anything now but a would-be therapeutic, fantastical diversion—it was nothing if not real and very soon would become an extremely formidable reality.

With the complexities of ordnance remaining the sole responsibility of Hugh McGeeney. As he demonstrated yet another bewildering assembly of wheels and spindles, chuckling away softly to himself as he did so. He went through the process a number of times.

'What escapes me, comrade, is why you should even care. Because the sell-out, my friend, has been and gone a long time now. They published the letter in the paper last week—from the ECB to the Irish government. In which they threatened to see that a bomb would go off in Dublin—if this sovereign state was not seen to comply with their stipulated wishes.'

'We'll soon see about bombs!' I laughed.

As did he.

It turned out to be remarkably simple in the end—and for anyone like us brought up on a farm and familiar from an early age with tractor parts, machinery and the like, even more so. A tiny device was attached to the underside of the intended vehicle, and when the car containing the bomb mounted a small incline, the device exploded. The tilting caused water in the switch to be mixed with mercury and this in turn set off an electrical current and detonated the bomb. McGeeney even sold me the second car—the one which was the intended 'operations vehicle' as he would have called it back in the day. Once it had been primed, it could be parked close to the bookshop in Duke Street, not far from Government Buildings, where I could pick it up.

'Go raibh míle maith agat, mo chara,' I heard McGeeney saying, as he stuffed the remainder of the notes into his wallet, 'but I hope you know that any of this won't bring back the brother you used to know, and worse than that in two or three weeks the whole thing will be forgotten—that is, if you succeed with your little vainglorious one-man revolution. That's something I've learned to my cost. You might have a chance, however—providing you don't clash with *Celebrity Doctors*.'

It might perhaps have turned out differently had Dessie Millner not been the central figure in an important news report—relayed that night at the very same time as my putative assault on the system—being hoisted aloft by his jubilant supporters at some municipal function or other. Or had I not received a phone call informing me of the recent death of Olwyn Price—from ovarian cancer, in London, where she'd lived for many years.

After that I just remained there, sitting—ossified, half-dazed from the brandy. And all I could see was her climbing again into the car, before turning for just a moment to vow one last time that 'the seventies would be socialist'.

As Dessie Millner cleaned his gun and bent down to inspect an arrangement of inert and expressionless figures—smiling at the cameras and parting his hands in imprecation as he began: 'There is no question whatsoever of betraying the Irish people. All of these rumours are mischievous and irresponsible—the fact is, my record stands. And I can safely assure anyone who fears that things might be otherwise that our national sovereignty shall never be impugned. Not on my watch, a chairde: go raibh míle maith agaibh go léir!'

In recent times I go out very little—with just the occasional visit to the shops, for cigarettes or perhaps *The Irish Times*. Which carries daily financial reports in which the country is reported as 'behaving well.'

I had the same dream again about my father last night. With the shots being discharged in a volley over his grave, and all his old comrades together in their blue suits under the trees. Before, to my astonishment, I watched as he clambered across the lip of the oblong hole—in his civil-war green, complete with slouch hat and brown leather bandolier, clawing his way past the still-moist mound of earth. At first he had appeared unusually composed and placid but then his expression altered dramatically.

'What's wrong, Eddie?' I heard him plead anxiously. 'I'm really worried about you—please will you tell me you're okay!'

And, with that, he was gone, supplanted by a pen-waving Jeremy Kyle, in the process of berating a feral, dissembling youth for over-indulgence in unprotected sex with a variety of women.

'Have you no sense of moral or civic responsibility?' the strutting host demanded shrilly, waving the pen in front of the boy's face.

Maybe one day it will happen—that they'll interrupt Jeremy Kyle, and a dramatic newsflash will proceed to describe in great detail the extraordinary exploits of the first home-grown Irish suicide bomber. Who, in what looked like a moment of madness had blown up Government Buildings, himself perishing in the process.

'First reports would seem to indicate that the perpetrator was a sixty-two-year-old civil servant male.'

And for two or three days, strident debates will follow with round-the-clock coverage: the camera homing in on my dead father's medal, and the only surviving copy of Brendan's seventies pamphlet, its single-word title stamped in green on the cover, against a background of white and gold.

Aiséirí.

'The seventies will be socialist,' Olwyn said.

I'll get the odd letter from Connie still and once Big Janis called when she happened to be back in Dublin. Kay Sherry recently retired as president of the National Women's Council, after many years of distinguished service.

Mairead Curtin I lost contact with long ago.

The suburb is leafy and quiet—almost to an unearthly degree. People call at odd hours and I've been thinking seriously of disconnecting the doorbell altogether.

Only last weekend there was a representative from Sky, offering me a 'knockdown package'—I can't remember for what.

It's the Maze Hunger Strikers' anniversary this coming Easter. Perhaps I'll find the courage to do it then, expire at the head of my own private insurrection. Yes, see my little hymn of oblation and redemption through to its ultimate, necessary conclusion: Sacrifice at Easter.

Unmindfully waiting for *Countdown* to begin, in the company of the seasoned, insouciant dead.

Remembering at a Civil Union

'A terrible beauty is born.'—W B Yeats, 'Easter 1916'

We wanted to remember how far we'd come
after twenty years of being together
as man and man fighting
to be relaxed about it;
remembering when you were ill
being asked if I were next of kin;
remembering the apologies
(even in Italian)
that a room was double not a twin.

Now sitting before an officer
of the Irish State and being asked
if we would care to light candles
(like at Hanukkah or Mass)
or exchange rings,
as though it were a wedding,
which it is not.

And so instead we asked to read:
a poem by Rilke and an excerpt
from a seventies manifesto
of the Gay Liberation Front.
We wanted to remember how far we'd come
in the forty years since then.

But must they now approve
the script and wording of the past
for fear it sits uneasy with this place
and time in which we rise
and so define ourselves?
Manifestos (it is said)
belong at factory gates,
at corners of a street,
or on steps of public monuments
inciting violence and struggle.

There's no provision for appeal,
the senior registrar is resolute:
nothing political can be read.
But it's history now not politics:
few remember politics.
It's history you remember:
the shout and the embrace of it,
the creative dignity
of kissing in the street.

That's beautiful it's like
The Proclamation at the Post Office,
Yeats's recurring line…
Can we read that?
There is silence, I think I've lost him:
he doesn't know the text of that,
after all he wasn't even born
and a hundred years is a long time:
try to celebrate.

Anthony Hegarty

Transition Year

Gavin Corbett

The game was a piece of shit dropping slowly off a stick. It was ten minutes into the second half and the players were strutting around. Entitled. 'End of a long hard season,' said Byron, like he invented it. His face was wise and sore and just laughing at the shitness of it all, wise because he thought that only he understood what it meant. He was tracking Rooney. James often wanted to punch Byron, because he wanted to call him out sometimes, but he couldn't, it just translated as wanting to punch him. James, his face was like Winston Smith's in the rat cage in *Nineteen Eighty-Four*, he was sure, if he'd been able to see his own face. Because they'd spent money on this shit. They were in the middle of exams and they'd spent money on this shit. He kept repeating it until it meant nothing. He looked at Rooney's raw head and thought, that's the thing you do, you get angry at footballers who make a million a week. Did he feel angry? Aidan, who was sitting beside James, kept turning his toes inwards like he had bone disease. He'd spent most of the game looking at his shoes. You get angry at people who spend two hundred on a pair of New Balance. Not that he was angry at Aidan and his New Balance, he was merely making an observation about Aidan, how bored he was. He could not hate Aidan or Wayne Rooney like he hated Byron. Man, he did not hate Byron. That's what you do too: life was a competition and you didn't take out the top dog, you took out the guy most like you, because that was your role he was taking. Once you thought about that, everything was simple and ridiculous. You felt okay to hate, or that it was okay to hate, but you could not hate. The thought itself became something and put itself in the way. You thought about it, it was the Byrons of this world you should be teaming with.

He did that thing he always did when he was bored, and only knew he was bored when he noticed he was doing it: he blew out his cheeks till he could feel his vein with his tongue. He imagined inflating his head so much that he floated among the white tubes of the roof. Even the stadium was bored: it was like a dried dead louse behind glass. James imagined moving one hand over the other along the tubes, into the network, and climbing up on one of them and banging it with a hammer, making all the tubes clang. Or klang—better.

'Why do we keep calling it the Aviva Stadium and not Lansdowne Road?'

Aidan looked at James as if James had just come out. Actually he didn't look at James, he kept his face on the game. 'What?'

'Like, Lansdowne Road is better. As a name. More classy, as a proposition.'

After a second Aidan's face relaxed. 'Yeah, but Aviva has "viva" in it. It's… joyous.'

James gave a disbelieving tut, inviting Byron, who leaned forward the other side of Aidan but looked straight across to James. 'The media isn't allowed say Lansdowne Road. If a journalist said Lansdowne Road instead of Aviva, the FAI and IRFU would ban every journalist from that organ.'

'Organ. Bullshit,' said James.

Byron shrugged. 'That's the policy.'

'Ah bullshit, like, we're not the media. We don't have to call it the Aviva.'

'D'you care?'

'I prefer Lansdowne, Hanno, it's the classier proposition.'

'Fair enough,' said Byron, sitting back in his seat. Then he said, 'Ah, you couldn't revert. This stage, no one remembers the old name.' He looped his thumbs into invisible elastic braces and said in the poshest Downton accent: 'Lens-daaauuuun Rade.' James found it funny.

But James remembered the old name, that's why it came naturally. Or it could have been that these last two weeks he'd read it and heard it so many times. A big thing in the build-up had been what happened the last time Ireland played England at home. 'The old Lansdowne Road,' they kept saying, 'the old stadium', like old was bad. The old stadium was made of wood and nails. Old was bad: this was true. The whole thing was degraded. The colour was weak. Something about the red in the Union Jacks. The hooligans sang "No Surrender"—it was like they were making a point about the North. The papers said the seats they threw were missiles. Everything was given glam names in all those struggles. You read about the IRA and how they were the world leaders in bomb making, and it made you proud, and then you looked into it, and those bombs were made of wood and nails too. You read about these elite fighters, but the pictures showed beer guts bursting out of old army tops, spilling over jeans, and one guy's army top was different to the other guy's, from a different army, put through the wash more times.

In a clip he saw on YouTube, guards in riot gear were stooped behind a low concrete wall. They were waiting for the hooligans to come down. You could see, even through the shine of their visors, and in the way they jiggled their clubs, that they were loving it. James, too, he found himself getting really into it, like it was happening live. The hooligans were skinheads, and they were wrapped in Union Jacks and looked racially a different species. They sang 'No Surrender, No Surrender, No Surrender to the IRA'. When you hear something like that, look at the faces of the people singing it, you can't help it, your blood literally boils. You sit forward with your nails dug into your hands. He was sitting forward now, with the remembrance, and now he was alert, though not quite. The air was so dead, and there was no movement. Back in those days you knew your enemy, and your cause. You listened to the English fans here today, and the best they could muster was 'Oh Sepp Blatter, he paid for your ground'.

James was capable of tuning out all the noise and hearing, now, the English players joke among each other. Byron going, 'System, system, system.'

Byron said to Aidan, 'I just need a break from all of it.'

'All of what?' said James.

Byron looked up from Aidan. His face calmed and then he crossed his eyes at James. He said in a Scottish accent, 'The murder machine.'

'Fair enough,' said James.

'Fair enough to what?' said Byron, uncrossing his eyes.

'That you would want to do that.'

James and Byron were going into Transition Year after the summer while Aidan was going straight through to Fifth Year. Transition Year was a year out of school, in effect. They would canoe on the Boyne and help out disadvantaged kids.

'The thing is, I actually believe in education, seriously,' said Byron.

'I believe in angels, seriously,' said Aidan.

'I mean… yeah. But it's a grind. There is actually a system.'

Where was he getting it from? He waited for Aidan to jump in, then couldn't help himself: 'What are you talking about, man?'

Byron didn't stir.

Seriously, though. Where was he getting it from? Yeah, there was a system, but no one played the system like Byron. James's mother even said about him:

he's a very mature boy. He was the class representative in second and third year. The staff loved him. He once personally formed a cordon around Mister Mahon when he tried to fish a condom out of a drain; he held back a hundred boys. Earlier, the man in front of Byron had asked him to take his feet off the top of his seat, and Byron had lifted his hand as if to say, 'Sorry, Buddy', man to man, and took his feet down, and that was Byron all over.

He was getting it from Mister Poole, probably, because that was Mister Poole. The students' friend. Mister Poole was young; even looked young. In the yearbook, when James was in second class in the junior school, Mister Poole had been in Fifth Year in the seniors. He could fill your head with shit, because he had a way. Because he was young. He had that rapport with everyone—'Call me Dan.' And he had this shit in him himself. He had ideas, ideals. He liked music. But it was the way he talked. He would be the class master for the Transition Years next year, and Transition Year would be no different from any year to that point; a step along the system, but a doss, James was sure.

'So—' said James, 'when you say murder machine, that's what you're saying: school, right?'

Murder machine was one of Mister Poole's sayings.

'Ja,' said Byron.

'It's not exactly murder though, is it, I mean.'

'Depends on your definition.'

'What's your definition?'

'They try and strangulate you slowly. They train you up to fit into their world and then you just crank away for life. And then you rust and fall off and die.'

'What?'

'They kill your soul.'

'Get out of it, man.'

'You don't think so?'

'Yeah, but. You of all people, Hanno, come on. You were the one saying you didn't care this place was called Aviva. You're the one all geared up to be a fucking…'

'What?'

'I dunno—a banker.'

'How in fuck does that make me a banker?'

'If you say fuck the system you can't just take the system lying down. You got to do something about it and take action.'

'Two separate things, mate.'

'Lads, lads, I'm trying to watch the game,' said Aidan.

James let Byron go on, but he didn't.

'You're struggling, man,' said James.

'Sport's a corporate shill. Has been for a long time. As long as you know that, everything's fine. I'm talking about the system at a more basic level.'

'He says school should treat people like children more,' said Aidan.

'Sh'tup, you,' said Byron. 'I'm saying school should have a better attitude to ideas and imagination. They see imagination as childish. They don't think adults with big ideas is a good thing, because they see it as childish. Because only children will listen to big ideas, only children have the patience. You see it in their attitude to Transition Year, giving the gig to Dan Poole. Guarantee you he was the only taker. Nothing wrong with a bit of time out though. Tread on our dreams and you tread on us.'

'Dan Poole is a child,' said James, but no one reacted and he repeated it, and the crowd let out a roar, and no one reacted again.

He waited for everyone to sit back in their seats. The players reverted to tapping the ball around sideways.

'Do you think Dan Poole is a pederast? Remember the time he said he was a pedagogue, and there was a wave through the class? Do you think he was trying in a fucked-up way to admit something?'

James was not saying Dan Poole was a pederast, but sometimes Dan Poole could be inappropriate. Like: why did he take James and Cormac Taney down to the sheds that time? It was not a good idea to make lads uncomfortable like that. It was unwise behaviour, even if Dan Poole didn't know what he was doing. They were made uncomfortable in ways they couldn't put a finger on, not that they ever said. Not that James would ever mention it now. That would be making discomfort where there was none. But you know what they say. You should say. Maybe they were uncomfortable just because they were aware of certain protocols. James remembered. The second the doors opened they felt uncomfortable because they were invaded by BO. And there was something uncomfortable about the two canoes there, like coffins. Dan Poole said he did not have the trailer that could carry two canoes, that he could only take one canoe on his car at a time. But he said he would get the Transition Years to build the river coracles of the ancient Irishman, which could be stacked on top of each other on a car roof. James remembered him running a shot-putt ball through his hands, dropping it one to the other and back up, like water in a water wheel, and then letting it slip with a bang to the thin wooden floor, but not jumping, because his mind was in another world. There was something dreamy about him—Byron was right—and that's what would get Dan Poole in trouble. The remarkable thing was no one ever said anything about him. He was just ultimately too sound. Fair enough. Your mind gets poisoned with the news these days, badness.

Contrast with poor old Father Deegan. He didn't remotely act like a pederast and people said it about him all the time. It was an occupational hazard, thought James. If you choose to become a priest, or stay a priest, what else can you expect? But on every level he was a normal human being. There was cruelty in that. You try your best, and just because of what you are = pederast. He was into his football—there was a rumour he'd been the chaplain for Celtic. He could have been at the game. James had seen someone, far off to the left, in the curve, near the back of the stand, that might have been him. Father Deegan had a very distinctive-shaped head, yellow enough and disproportionately small enough that you could in theory identify it from a hundred metres. There was continuous movement in that area of the stand that was probably heat. It played tricks with your eyes, and the yellow head might not have been him. Maybe James and Byron and Aidan were unofficially banned from the game; after all, they should have been concentrating on their Junior Cert right now. James had a fantasy. The stadium as it was now did not exist. It was a concrete stump with rain seeping down the walls. Father Deegan was standing at the side of the pitch staring up into the crowd. Then he climbed into the crowd waving a stick.

James saw someone he didn't recognise.

'Who's that?' he said to Aidan.

'Harry Arter,' said Aidan. 'He came on for Whelan.'

'Never seen him before in my life. Where do they get these people?'

'Bournemouth.'

James's eyes drifted to the empty banks of seats. It made it look like the people on the far side were sitting on a green grassy hill.

'This is such a shit game,' he said again.

'I dunno,' said Aidan.

'You don't think?'

'It might get better.'

'It's gonna take something incredible for that to happen.'

'I think something incredible is gonna happen.'

'Rooney will break Bobby Charlton's goal record with a hat trick.'

'Or a creature from mythology will turn up. Or a lead zeppelin will drop from the sky and kill everyone.'

James's granddad had been banned from going to soccer games. He told James once how the bishop warned everybody against going to a match between the Republic of Ireland and CCCP. It was a double warning—against foreign games and communism. He went to the game anyway. Fuck Ireland. Up the Republic. No—fuck the Republic. Up the Stickies. No compromises. The Republic was illegitimate. Granddad Tuite was a political man his whole life. He had a fit when James's dad said he was going to send his boy to the Marists. Granddad Tuite had had the shit beaten out of him by the Christian Brothers. James's dad told him to relax, that the Marists were not the Christian Brothers, and that only the laymen taught. Father Deegan was the only priest in the school, and he wasn't a teacher, and James wasn't even sure if he was a Marist. His job consisted of saying masses. There was only one time when he ever took confessions. They went in one at a time with a couple of lines learnt off. That was it for confessions, probably for ever. There were protocols in place now with regards child welfare. James and the rest of them were fifteen. Legally they were, he guessed, adolescents, children. Seventeen and up and they were out of school and adults and the world was free to smash them. He looked down at the shining butts of his hands.

Fuck the world.

Fuck the Aviva. Fuck Twix.

'You know it operates off fear, the whole insurance business?' James said to Aidan.

Father Deegan was a happy, happy man. He actually suited the word gay. He would have been Mr Viva in the Aviva right now. That Mexican wave earlier, that was him. He would have started it. But people only started Mexican waves when they were bored. Father Deegan found joy and amusement in the smallest gust of wind.

James grabbed a pinch of Aidan's shoulder.

'Here,' he said. 'Let's get a Poznan going.'

'You what?'

James was already half-stood up, half-turned around. Byron was staring, only half-amused.

'I'll give you all the cash in my wallet if you can get a Poznan going,' said Byron.

'How much have you got?' said James.

'About a hundred. And thirty euros of Microsoft points.'

'Well you join in so.'

'You need Aidan to make the link.'

Aidan was sitting there with his arms crossed and a Roy Keane scowl on him.

'You get up and Aidan will get up.'

'Why would I do that? I don't want to lose my money.'

'I wouldn't have asked you to join in only to gouge you.'

'Sit down, James,' said Byron.

James looked at the woman to the right of him. She was unamused. She was not giving James any encouragement. Mere encouragement would not have been good enough anyway. That was not how the Poznan worked. She needed to let James's hand on her warm sticky pink Helly Hansen, ye-hoo.

Fuck it.

James stretched to full height and felt beautifully light-headed. Maybe he'd try drugs in the next year. He tilted back his head and yawned, closing his eyes. When he opened them again he was looking straight up into the white bars and it all had a purple blissed-out tinge.

Constructivism.

The people in the rows above were considering him. He must have looked like a tool. Fuck 'em. There was a whole row of pretty-hot girls in 98FM T-shirts. Their miserable faces dragged at and cracked their happy make-up. Below them a fatberg melted into folds. Just looking down at James caused the fatberg's folds to pour and ooze. He was trying to look irritated but his big folds just made him look sad. Christ.

James sat down again. Nill-all still. Null. Negative. Void. Reichs canceller. The atmosphere now was like a crypt. The English fans weren't singing anymore. The only truly happy-seeming man he knew was Father Deegan. He supposed priests were freer now to do what they wanted. They were left alone because protocols prevented them from doing their old duties. Maybe this would be a new time for them. They were happier people now and wouldn't commit crimes. Imagine the old days. Day after day, their heads filled with the sins of the world. Their ears pressed to grilles like food stuck in drains. The sins going in their ears like worms. No wonder there were so many bad apples. But it would do a person good to have someone to upload your shit to. You knew it would be taken away even if you didn't know what happened to it. And that was enough. The net result being that people were happier in the old days. And priests had been bad. Now people were unhappy, and priests were clear and mellow.

James imagined himself spissing a wide gloopy spiss on a grille, and a wasp billowing about where the spiss splashed and entered. An ear scoured around beneath the grille and made sniffing sounds. The sunlight came in warm jelly cubes just like now, and it was pleasant to loll there. He would flick matches off the side of a box at the wasp. They would flare and then extinguish on impact. In the movies the grilles were black. He supposed that was meant to represent hell.

'Well this is a waste of an afternoon,' he said to the boys.

'No shit,' said Aidan.

'If I was you I'd be really fucked off,' he said to Aidan.

'Why me especially?'

'Because me and Byron have the doss year ahead, but you're head-down straight into the murder machine. You need to be getting every ounce of value out of this summer.'

'Don't you start. And it won't all be a doss for you.'

But pretty much it would. James's brother Jordan had done Transition Year three years before. There were the normal lessons, of course—Maths, Irish, English etcetera—but everything was turned down by four or five speeds. Mainly the year was about personal development rather than personnel development. This was another of Mister Poole's sayings. This was why James was doing Transition Year.

James asked Byron if he had any more of the Lucozade left. Byron passed it to him, and James took a few slugs.

'Shit, what's in this?'

Byron turned slowly to face James, his eyebrows ramped. 'Eh, Lucozade?'

Bollocks it was only Lucozade.

Part of Transition Year involved work experience. Jordan wanted to become a journalist, and he got a placement in the *Sunday Independent*. At the start of the week Jordan was allowed sit with the journalists at a meeting where they decided what articles to write for the Sunday ahead. One of the women said, 'Well, Jordan, have you got any suggestions?' Jordan's suggestion was: 'I think you should always put inverted commas around the word queen.' Apparently the whole room just completely cracked their shit. One of the journalists asked Jordan what gave him that idea. He said, 'My granddad.' 'What's your granddad, a Shinner?' said someone. The rest of the room shushed the journalist who said that, but Jordan went on, saying, 'Probably, I don't know. My granddad's political.' 'Do we know him?' someone said. 'I don't know,' said Jordan, but he said 'Nobby No-Clarke Tuite' anyway, and it turned out pretty much the whole of the room had heard of him. 'A Sticky,' they said. 'Sure, half of us were in the Stickies at some point.' Anyhow, he had a great old crack with them. But of course, when he got home he was all stressed out about this word Sticky.

'Sure it's Lucozade?' said James handing the bottle back across Aidan.

'Eh, like, yeah?' said Byron.

'I'll give you an idea how much of a doss Transition Year is,' James then said to Aidan. 'When Jordan was doing his work experience, he used to come back with actual titty pics of Georgia Salpa that wouldn't make the paper that week. That was work experience for him. He went through titty pics. And he was paid in sticky Georgia Salpa titty pics.'

'What are you going to do for work experience?'

Just as Aidan said that the whistle peeped and everyone lifted out of their seats almost before the peep had finished. Byron swatted his eyebrows up and down as if to say, 'And that, my friends, is that.' Then he led the way to the end of the row, up the steps, and through the bars and hot-dog stands. People were weary, some people were happy.

Out on the balcony they decided to hang back for a while. The crowds were a bit much. Everybody was streaming from the exits at once.

'You know what they call those exits officially?' James said to the lads.

They shrugged.

'Vomitoriums. It comes from the Romans.'

Mister Poole would do Classical Civilization with them for Transition Year. This was something James was interested in anyway, and he'd read ahead on Ancient Rome. On all history. James was an addict of Wikipedia's history pages. They leaned on the smooth concrete parapet taking in the sun and watched the crush of green hats and scarves from above.

'There's going to be a bloodbath down there.'

'Hillsborough,' Aidan muttered.

'The worst bloodshed of 1916 was in those streets. A couple of hundred British got massacred somewhere near here. Hard to imagine. The wealthiest part of Dublin, the biggest houses, and it was right around here in front of people's gardens they all got minced. I don't think I could sleep at night knowing it.'

'Look at this,' said Byron. He took his ticket stub from his pocket, held it up in the fingers of two hands, and ripped it into little pieces. Then he let the pieces flutter down to the heads below.

'What's that all about?' said Aidan.

'I dunno,' said Byron. 'A sacrifice.'

James swept the top of the parapet back and forth with the bare skin of his arm. It was like nougat. The burger vans had fired up again. On the way in the smell of meat and onions had been delicious. Now, it was like it was in bad taste. He didn't know what he'd do for work experience, that was the truth. He thought that maybe he was exempt. He wasn't sure what this had meant: a few weeks ago, after the mocks, Mister Poole had taken him aside. James was to look after the play for the year. He was to devote his time to writing a play that was going to be put on the next Easter.

Why James? Because James was a sensitive boy, that's what Mister Poole had said. The words sat in James's medulla oblongata like sick. Man, he supposed he was sensitive, but it wasn't a thing you'd ever say to yourself, and he didn't like other people to say it. When people see it in you, that's a weakness, right? But sensitive was a good thing, right?

And what sort of play? Well, that was up to James entirely. Mister Poole would talk about it with him in greater depth once the year started. He suggested this, that and the other—something like *The Plough and the Stars*. It didn't matter. For now, James was to know that he was marked out for the job. He was to start thinking about it over the summer. What if James only wanted to write about fantasy?

'Make a move?' said Byron.

They slid away from the wall. Fantasy. The escalator down was like a trench cut through concrete. Descending was like cattle descending to the slaughterhouse. Maybe he would write about the murder machine. No—bullshit. He looked ahead and down at Byron's head. The sunlight making his hair flare red. If he said 'murder machine' then Byron would always have that on him. If he said 'murder machine' then Mister Poole would think he was one of his boys. Murder machine;—murder machine was their thing. But what if he came at it from the future? A future where everything was robotic metal and the cleanest concrete. No, that wasn't what he meant by future. When he thought of the future just there he had thought of a time when.

'You'll never beat the Irish! You'll never beat the Irish!'

'Ooh! Ah! Jeff Kenna! I said ooh ah Jeff Kenna!'

Damn it it was gone. But the word 'future' puts things in your mind the second it appears. It was gone before he'd had it—the idea. It would come back. And the word 'when'. 'When' did it happen or 'when' will it happen? It referred to all times except now. His dad said now was all times. That the future was already here. If someone had said thirty years ago that the Internet would be a thing he would not have believed him. But here we were. There we are. But it's just the word 'future'. You think of it and a whole fixed idea comes into your mind. And the other idea is gone. Anyhow, there was a while to go.

Dragon's Teeth

Derry, 2016

A superstition certain sculptors hold:
the shape emerging, breathing from the rock
was 'in the block' all along, inherent,
awaiting the patient paring back of stone.

Sean, I'm not doing very well at all
in writing down my thoughts about the Rising
(for the magazine that you're guest editing).
Or its wake. The poem is stubborn in its stone.

I'd like to be on-message, poetry-wise,
about the beauty born and all of that,
but I'm stuck on account of some mental blocks
and I'm getting nowhere: dead end: STOP.

What we need now is another blockbuster
with Liam Neeson, where it all *ends better*.
Imagine! The only trouble is—I can't,
stuck as I am at these concrete blocks,

these rocks in a hard place. I can only
apologise. Or blame the ancestors?
It might turn out I'm a chip off the old
O'Doherty block after all. Uncle Joseph

knew the shock of Partition for nationalists
in the north, the years to come of apartheid state
and the rest—but no, *let's not get into that*.
Write, instead, about squat pyramidal concrete

blocks on a back road up to Grianán. *Step out*
of your vehicle, artist that you are, and confront
your obstructions, wonder what strange
forms might yet be freed from stones like these.

Colette Bryce

*Dragon's teeth: military; concrete anti-vehicle obstacles used on secondary roads over the Irish border.

#Rising

Val Nolan

Adam Baxter @OccasionalScribbler 24s
A twitilogical narrative is a bell curve which starts on the right
#NotGoingToDoBetterWorkThanThatToday

Relive 1916 Rising @Relive1916Rising 56s
Fifteen people – including all seven signatories of the Proclamation – are executed @KilmainhamGaol by firing squad between 3 & 12 May.

Hayley McKee @HMcKee 1m
@MarkMyWords Seems like a lousy way to leave things, but I guess that's that.

Adam Baxter @OccasionalScribbler 1m
Curious how most people choose to focus on Twitter's character limit, ignoring how we've become a culture forever looking backwards.

Mark Harrison @MarkMyWords 1m
@HMcKee Seriously?

Met Éireann @MetEireann 1m
Stormy weather will continue to move across the country tonight.

James Philips @PhilPhilHurray 1m
@aaroadwatch If only it had been that easy a hundred years ago!

Mark Harrison @MarkMyWords 2m
@HMcKee Here? Like this?!

AA Roadwatch @aaroadwatch 2m
DUBLIN: City Centre restrictions have been lifted after the #1916 #Rising commemorations.

Ted Brothers @Tbrothers1985 2m
Gonna start a support group for those of who missed the #1916 parade and feel bitter about it. Maybe one for the protestors too.

Hayley McKee @HMcKee 2m
@MarkMyWords I mean I think we should break up.

Adam Baxter @OccasionalScribbler 2m
Of course everyone's Tweetstream is a weird (sometimes v weird!) & unique snowflake, so I wonder how today looked to someone who's not me…?

Mark Harrison @MarkMyWords 2m
@HMcKee What do you mean "a break"?

Jo O'Neill @Joeill 3m
RT @rtenews No real consensus on whether today's #1916 commemoration was a PR triumph or a tragedy of stage- and statesmanship.

Hayley McKee @HMcKee 3m
@MarkMyWords I think maybe we should take a break.

Hayley McKee @HMcKee 3m
@MarkMyWords NBD?! Did you have to peel yourself off her to say that?! How am I supposed to trust you anymore?

Sandra @SandyCrowley 3m
Torrential Rain Man #IrishUpAMovie @MetEireann

Declan Hegarty @DeclanHegerty 3m
@Relive1916Rising Blackadder? Has anyone told Rowan Atkinson? Sounds like a pretty gritty reboot but I'd watch it!

RTÉ News @rtenews 4m
Taoiseach calls protestors at today's #1916 commemoration "disgraceful".

Mark Harrison @MarkMyWords 4m
@HMcKee Wasn't "cheating". Don't go there! Yeah, I was out with Lisa. Just didn't mention because it was NBD.

Andrew Kelly @AK_87 4m
@HamSandwichTrismegistus They'd say "You Maniacs! You blew it up! Damn you! God damn you all to hell!" #IrelandOfTheApes

Emma @WheatbixLadyFriend 4m
Point Break. Totally worth watching one and a half times (with an interlude between for Red Dawn).

Gareth Murphy @PapaMurph 4m
Hilarious Skype this afternoon w a UK colleague about Irish Misery Fiction. Oh how we laughed at all the #FuneralsInTheRain

Relive1916Rising @Relive1916Rising 4m
The president of the courts martial is Charles Blackader.

As Above, So Below @HamSandwichTrismegistus 4m
By a quirk of physics, we could use that to watch #1916 in real-time. But could they use it to see us? Wonder what they'd say? (2/2)

Adam Baxter @OccasionalScribbler 5m
@ScottyBoomBoom @Relive1916Rising Social media is, at least of ppl & for ppl. Unlike all today's VIP events. I reckon he'd be okay w it.

Hayley McKee @HMcKee 6m
@MarkMyWords Also do not EVER tell me I'm overreacting.

RTÉ News @rtenews 6m
More fall-out from the Banking Inquiry is expected later this week.

Wil Reynolds @WmRe 7m
Say it now like a disapproving Irish mammy: "Ah, sure will you look at the *state* of the nation!"

Hayley McKee @HMcKee 7m
@MarkMyWords Are you seriously ******* cheating on me and expecting to get away with it? In the 21st century?!

As Above, So Below @HamSandwichTrismegistus 7m
Imagine an object 50 light years away so dense that it literally bends light around it in a u-shape (1/2)

Scott Dawson @ScottyBoomBoom 7m
@Relive1916Rising This is a weird way to be celebrating Pádraig Pearse; picture trying to explain Twitter to him!

Sheela na Gag @Sheela_na_Gag 8m
Raging Bull McCabe #IrishUpAMovie

Mark Harrison @MarkMyWords 8m
@HMcKee You're overreacting!

Maggie Maybe @MM2001 9m
What's the opposite of serendipitous...? Stupidipitous?! Yeah, that.

Mark Harrison @MarkMyWords 10m
@HMcKee We're just friends. You know that. You've met her. Just friends and we went to a party together. I don't see the issue!

Relive1916Rising @Relive1916Rising 10m
90 people are sentenced to death in a series of courts martial beginning on 2 May.

Laura @FAY-leh299 11m
Got called Scrooge today… but I fail to see what's not awesome about a comparison w a wealthy, time-travelling *ghostbuster*!

Jake Collins @FootballAssoicationOfJake 15m
@Relive1916Rising Though I suppose that _is_ the truest commemoration of the country which came out of the whole thing, isn't it?

Kathryn @BewareOfTheKat 15m
@Relive1916Rising So pretty much like all the tribunals we've had since then, yeah?

Hayley McKee @HMcKee 16m
@MarkMyWords Jokes now?! Are you kidding me?!

Relive1916Rising @Relive1916Rising 16m
A total of 3,430 men and 79 women are arrested. However most of these will subsequently be released.

Gareth Murphy @PapaMurph 17m
Cat, pigeons; talk amongst yourselves...

Rachel @PrincessBase 19m
Been reading all day. Should probably go out into the world at some point. Might take book with me.

Hayley McKee @HMcKee 21m
@MarkMyWords ?!

Gareth Murphy @PapaMurph 21m
@OldLefty Exactly! I'm sure Dublin's homeless all got a great kick out it. Oh, wait, most of the O'Connell St. events were invite only.

As Above, So Below @HamSandwichTrismegistus 22m
@AdmiralAunty It's not like it's not on the radio here at least once every week!

Relive1916Rising @Relive1916Rising 23m
General Maxwell orders arrest of "all dangerous Sinn Feiners" including any and all "who have taken an active part in the movement".

Jimmy B @OldLefty 23m
Watched the parade on telly. What an absolute and *utter* waste of money. Pantomime from the ppl who brought you Irish Water.

Ciara @CPlusPlus 25m
Napoleon Semtex #IrishUpAMovie

Relive1916Rising @Relive1916Rising 26m
General Maxwell is installed as temporary military governor of Ireland.

Mark Harrison @MarkMyWords 26m
@HMcKee Maybe we got a little carried away during the celebrations, sure. I mean, they do call it a #Rising, right?

Adam Baxter @OccasionalScribbler 28m
It occurs to me that I am, in many ways, a structure junkie when it comes to writing of any kind (fiction, comicbooks, even academic work).

Relive1916Rising @Relive1916Rising 28m
General John Maxwell arrives in Dublin just in time for the surrender. He assumes command of British forces from Lowe.

Hayley McKee @HMcKee 29m
@MarkMyWords Because you were too busy STICKING YOUR TONGUE DOWN HER THROAT?! WTF?!

Katie Karen @oneillkatie 33m
There was some ambiguity, yeah, but I think my father just compared the inside of a mouldy bag of potatoes to a war grave. Um…?

Relive1916Rising @Relive1916Rising 34m
Pearse himself surrenders unconditionally to Brigadier-General Lowe.

Mark Harrison @MarkMyWords 36m
@HMcKee I'm NOT lying. Just went out with my friend Lisa. Didn't get a chance to mention it to you.

Relive1916Rising @Relive1916Rising 37m
A nurse named Elizabeth O'Farrell conveys Pearse's surrender order to the other Rebel garrisons. #WomenInHistory

Hayley McKee @HMcKee 40m
@MarkMyWords Why are you lying to me, Mark?

Relive1916Rising @Relive1916Rising 42m
Pearse reluctantly issues an order for all companies to surrender.

Keenan Dean @K_F_D 45m
Why on earth is #Rising trending?

Relive1916Rising @Relive1916Rising 46m
Surrounded and outnumbered, this new position cannot be escaped from without further loss of civilian life.

Trish29er @AdmiralAunty 49m
I tell ya, you get some strange looks on Irish roads when doing perfectly reasonable things like singing along to "Gangsta's Paradise"…

Relive1916Rising @Relive1916Rising 51m
The Rebels tunnel through the walls of the GPO and take up a new position at 16 Moore Street.

Suzie @Genuineheadcase 52m
Lunch brought stories of posh weddings. Mystified me; why would one need anything more elaborate than a ship's captain and a Springsteen CD?

Relive1916Rising @Relive1916Rising 55m
Fire from shelling spreads to the GPO, forcing the Rebels to abandon their headquarters.

Hayley McKee @HMcKee 56m
@MarkMyWords You and some girl! Is she the "stuff" you had to _do_ today?!

Relive1916Rising @Relive1916Rising 57m
James Connolly is incapacitated by a bullet wound to the ankle. He passes command to Pearse.

Trish29er @AdmiralAunty 57m
Reckon I won Driving-in-Rural-Ireland Bingo: Caught behind a tractor, a bicycle race, & (my fav) some kind of famine commemoration walk :-)

Relive1916Rising @Relive1916Rising 59m
The O'Rahilly is killed during a sortie from the GPO.

A. Annllov @SjuDənɪm 1h
Quite aside from anything else, I actually like what I do… and that, perhaps, is the misfortune of it!

Relive1916Rising @Relive1916Rising 1h
British troops take the Rebel position at Mount Street Bridge on the Grand Canal.

As Above, So Below @HamSandwichTrismegistus 1h
@Relive1916Rising A hundred years later & oppressive men are *still* trying to silence Sheehy-Skeffingtons @nuigalway!

Mark Harrison @MarkMyWords 1h
@HMcKee I dunno what you're talking about.

Gareth Murphy @PapaMurph 1h
@SjuDənɪm @OccasionalScribbler Well good luck to them with *that* approach!

Relive1916Rising @Relive1916Rising 1h
British troops break into houses along the street & shoot or bayonet 15 male civilians whom they accused of being Rebels (2/2)

Relive1916Rising @Relive1916Rising 1h
British forces attempt to take Rebel barricade on North King St. They advance only 140m at a cost of 11 dead, 28 wounded. (1/2)

Jessica @JessintheWest 1h
The quest to discover how much garlic is too much garlic continues...

Relive1916Rising @Relive1916Rising 1h
An officer named Bowen Colthurst summarily executes 6 civilians, including pacifist nationalist activist Francis Sheehy-Skeffington.

A. Annllov @SjuDənɪm 1h
@PappaMurph @OccasionalScribbler ...They were concerned that his use of "teacher" as a derogatory term would harm his "future as a writer".

Hayley McKee @HMcKee 1h
@MarkMyWords Um, WHY is there is a picture of you over on Facebook macking on some girl at a 1916 party AN HOUR AGO?!

A. Annllov @SjuDənɪm 1h
@PappaMurph @OccasionalScribbler Apparently his agent had to tell him to stop discussing lit critics in such "mealy-mouthy" fashion...

Relive1916Rising @Relive1916Rising 1h
Cathal Brugha distinguishes himself during vicious fighting in and around the South Dublin Union complex. He is wounded in action.

Sean @SeeSeanRun 1h
Honestly unsure what this #Rising commemoration is trying to be. Seems halfway between a Pride Parade & Victory Day in Moscow.

Met Éireann @MetEireann 2h
Light patchy rain expected this afternoon, particularly along costal parts.

Roy McAuley @Suppercollider 2h
Iodine, Rhenium, Lanthanum, Neodymium... The elemental composition of Ireland :-)

Gareth Murphy @PapaMurph 2h
@HamSandwichTrismegistus @Relive1916Rising And between that she was a glorified ferry for the Black & Tans. Weird that we ended up with her.

Relive1916Rising @Relive1916Rising 2h
Rebels at the South Dublin Union (St. James's Hospital) and Marrowbone Lane continue to inflict heavy losses on British troops.

A. Annllov @SjuDənɪm 2h
@PappaMurph @OccasionalScribbler Oh I could never identify the Twiteris Personae. In Writing. #MythOfAnonymity…!

BalbrigganBrownGirl @DaughterOfTheBrehon 2h
If they ever discover a nebula which looks like Muhammad Ali, I hope they name it Gaseous Clay…

Relive1916Rising @Relive1916Rising 2h
This fighting on Mount St. inflicts up to two thirds of British casualties for the entire #Rising at a cost of just four dead Rebels.

Relive1916Rising @Relive1916Rising 2h
Seventeen Volunteers on Mount St. severely disrupt the British advance, killing or wounding 240 Sherwood Foresters.

Anna Dawson @DuskToDawson 2h
The Godfather Slips You a Tenner #IrishUpAMovie

Gareth Murphy @PapaMurph 2h
@OccasionalScribbler @SjuDənɪm Why do I think I know *exactly* who you're talking about…? ;-)

Relive1916Rising @Relive1916Rising 2h
General Lowe orders repeated frontal assaults on the Mount Street position despite alternative routes across the canal.

Adam Baxter @OccasionalScribbler 2h
@SjuDənɪm We don't take criticism that well, do we? :-) Postcolonial mind-set, maybe? #KeepingItRelevant #Rising

Hayley McKee @HMcKee 2h
Hmmmmm… What social media *haven't* I checked today? :-)

Relive1916Rising @Relive1916Rising 3h
Troops from the Sherwood Foresters arrive in Kingstown and heavy fighting occurs as they attempt to cross the Grand Canal.

A. Annllov @SjuDənɪm 3h
@OccasionalScribbler Did that review of mine send out certain men the English… praised? ;-)

Trish29er @AdmiralAunty 3h
If anyone ever makes a Midsomer Murders-style show set in Ireland, Adare is pretty much the perfect place for it!

Hayley McKee @HMcKee 3h
Such a BORING day. Town closed. No one around. Nothing on TV but auld fellas blowing hot air.

Adam Baxter @OccasionalScribbler 3h
@SjuDənɪm Sounds like someone who'd be moaning about closed post offices a hundred years ago!

Relive1916Rising @Relive1916Rising 3h
British troops begin pouring into Dublin as the Rebels fail to capture the city's train stations or ports.

As Above, So Below @HamSandwichTrismegistus 3h
@Relive1916Rising Later she was one of the first Free State navy ships, renamed Muirchú, the "Hound of the Sea"!

Hayley McKee @HMcKee 3h
@MarkMyWords You'd better :-)

Declan Hegarty @DeclanHegerty 3h
Just bought Disprin and batteries… Pretty sure the girl in the shop suspects I'm trying to make meth but don't know how.

A. Annllov @SjuDənɪm 3h
@OccasionalScribbler …Crucial difference there: book-burning is what Nazis do; shooting-something-into-the-sun is what you do with garbage.

Mark Harrison @MarkMyWords 3h
BRB…

Relive1916Rising @Relive1916Rising 3h
Rebel position are surrounded and British bombardment continues with the Helga's guns joined by artillery at Trinity College.

A. Annllov @SjuDənɪm 3h
@OccasionalScribbler Claims I called for his book to be burnt when, actually, I said it should be shot into Sun…

Lazarus @SecondTimesTheCharm 3h
She's an engineer. He's a geologist. Oh, and their friends are Marines. Together they fight... corrupt asteroid mining practices #SFFpitch

Relive1916Rising @Relive1916Rising 3h
The gunship Helga arrives from Kingstown (Dún Laoghaire) to support British forces. She shells Liberty Hall with her 12-pound guns.

A. Annllov @SjuDənɪm 4h
@OccasionalScribbler Yeah, I gave him his one bad review & dude *cannot* get over it. Also can't hide his identity v well!

Neutron Star Comics @NeutronStar_ 4h
Support the books you love!

Hayley McKee @HMcKee 4h
@MarkMyWords Look at you being all mysterious :-) Is cool, hun, no worries xx

Adam Baxter @OccasionalScribbler 4h
@SjuDənɪm Oh yeah…? :-)

Trev @Boogiethnach 4h
Once Upon a Time in the Whest #IrishUpAMovie

Relive1916Rising @Relive1916Rising 4h
Citizen Army forces under Michael Mallin thus retreat from the Green into Royal College of Surgeons. (2/2)

A. Annllov @SjuDənɪm 4h
@OccasionalScribbler Remind me to tell you the story of the Great Irish Novelist (TM) who's been trolling me for two years…

Pop-up Museums Dublin @PopMuse 4h
Take on the roles of Pearse and Connolly in our #1916 #Rising simulator!

Adam Baxter @OccasionalScribbler 4h
@SjuDənɪm Something you want to get off your chest there, buddy?

Jo O'Neill @Joeill 4h
Das Welly #IrishUpAMovie

Relive1916Rising @Relive1916Rising 4h
British snipers & machine guns at the Shelbourne Hotel make rebel positions in St Stephen's Green untenable. (1/2)

A. Annllov @SjuDənɪm 4h
I tell you, no one died for Ireland so we couldn't critique our own stories w a bit of honesty #1916 #Rising.

Mark Harrison @MarkMyWords 4h
@HMcKee I'd love to, sweetie, but I've got some stuff to do today.

Adam Baxter @OccasionalScribbler 4h
@Relive1916Rising Deadly photo of the home-made armoured cars. #Steampunk #WritingPrompt

A. Annllov @SjuDənɪm 4h
Have we reached peak self-congratulatory bullsh*t yet? The levels are certainly #Rising!

Relive1916Rising @Relive1916Rising 4h
British forces take back City Hall from the rebel unit that had attacked Dublin Castle.

Doc Riona @RedLionRoebuck 4h
Amongst Women Fighting Gender Discrimination #AcademicNovel

Relive1916Rising @Relive1916Rising 4h
British forces hastily improvise armoured trucks from the smokeboxes of steam locomotives at Inchicore railway works.

Relive1916Rising @Relive1916Rising 5h
Lowe's troops secure approaches to Dublin Castle, but initially believe Rebel headquarters to be Liberty Hall.

Met Éireann @MetEireann 5h
Changeable conditions likely for the rest of the afternoon.

Relive1916Rising @Relive1916Rising 5h
Lord Wimborne, the Lord Lieutenant of Ireland, declares martial law in Dublin and hands over civil power to Lowe.

Hayley McKee @HMcKee 5h
@MarkMyWords Such a non-day of a day! You wanna come over? :-)

Relive1916Rising @Relive1916Rising 5h
Brigadier-General William Lowe arrives in Dublin from British Army headquarters in the Curragh.

A. Annllov @SjuDənɪm 5h
Paddy Clarke BA MA PhD #AcademicNovel

Dan Whelan @DWIreland 5h
@Relive1916Rising I wonder did anyone there #LoveUlster?

Chris Kelleher @PigAndPoultry 5h
@Relive1916Rising "The right of the people of Ireland to the ownership of Ireland…" <Smashes window with dustbin> <Takes sneakers>

Fionnula @EverywomansTheatre 5h
L'airgead #IrishUpAMovie

Relive1916Rising @Relive1916Rising 5h
Looting breaks out in the city centre as a result of the police withdrawal, especially on and around O'Connell Street.

Relive1916Rising @Relive1916Rising 5h
After three deaths, the Commissioner of the Dublin Metropolitan Police pulls his men off the streets.

Aine Butler @GoOnGoOnGoOnGoOn 5h
Does anyone *really* want to @Relive1916Rising? What's so wonderful about people shooting each other?

Ted Brothers @Tbrothers1985 5h
Would have been ace to have been in Dublin for #Rising pints!

Rose Donellan @CiderWench 5h
Dr. Acula #AcademicNovel

Chris Kelleher @PigAndPoultry 5h
@Relive1916Rising SECURE THE MIKADO!

Relive1916Rising @Relive1916Rising 5h
The British military is caught totally unprepared by the rebellion and their response is initially un-coordinated.

Roy McAuley @Suppercollider 5h
Finally feels like Spring... By which I mean I feel a sense of possibility analogous to the potential energy of coiled medium carbon steel.

Relive 1916 Rising @Relive1916Rising 6h
There are 1,269 British troops in the city of Dublin.

Hayley McKee @HMcKee 6h
I'm the luckiest girl in the world to have @MarkMyWords in my life :-) #PDA

Relive1916Rising @Relive1916Rising 6h
Volunteer & Citizen Army forces capture the Four Courts & Jacob's Biscuit Factory.

As Above, So Below @HamSandwichTrismegistus 6h
@Relive1916Rising That guarantee of "religious & civil liberty, equal rights, & equal opportunities" sure fell by the wayside for a bit!

Relive1916Rising @Relive1916Rising 6h
The Proclamation calls for universal suffrage, and promises to cherish "all the children of the nation equally".

SarahNEY @TheTerribleTierney 6h
Had a dream that I went to find a book on my desk only to discover someone had moved things around on the shelves IN MY MIND! :-(

Relive1916Rising @Relive1916Rising 6h
The Proclamation calls for "the right of the people of Ireland to the ownership of Ireland" and establishment of a republic.

Mark Harrison @MarkMyWords 6h
@HMcKee Right back at you, sweetie.

Relive1916Rising @Relive1916Rising 6h
After securing their headquarters, Pádraig Pearse reads the Proclamation of the Republic on the steps of the GPO.

Adam Baxter @OccasionalScribbler 6h
Is social media our new social *realism*? I genuinely wonder. #MorningThoughts

Relive1916Rising @Relive1916Rising 6h
The flag of the Irish Republic replaces the British Union Jack on the flagpole above the GPO.

Hayley McKee @HMcKee 6h
@MarkMyWords I love you, hun, you know that? :-)

Met Éireann @MetEireann 7h
A new day and the sun is coming out. #Rising, if you will.

Loading Tweets seems to be taking a while.
Twitter may be over capacity or experiencing a momentary hiccup.
Try again or visit Twitter Status for more information.

Hard Up For Heroes

Jimmy Murphy

Growing up in the early 1970s there was always a number of questions any budding new members of our gang were asked: what football team do you support, who is your favourite band and would you die for Ireland? For me it was always Man United, Gary Glitter and yes, always yes. Forgoing old age and dying for Ireland was something I was always aware of. On Sunday afternoons my da would play the same array of ballad songs on his return from the pub across the road with the other men from the flats. As he stacked the same ten or so discs in the battered radiogram his mother had passed on to him, and sat with his dinner on his lap, I always felt left out. For while my other pals were watching highlights from Saturday's big game on *The Big Match* or the Sunday matinee on some other channel, my afternoons were taken up with the same players appearing every week: 'Kelly, the boy from Kilane', 'Kevin Barry', 'James Connolly' and 'Sean South from Garryowen'. Their anthems usually belted out along the balcony, tormenting the neighbours, for a good hour or so with the session always finishing off with 'Up Went Nelson' at full blast, after which my da would retire to bed to sleep off his drunkenness, leaving us all back sitting in front of the telly, just in time for *The Golden Ball* show. So I guess it was no surprise that I grew up thinking that all young lads eventually died fighting for Ireland, the when and where was just a matter of time, and I remember thinking that I'd better get on with enjoying my youth before the knock on the door and the order came to lay down my life.

Dying wasn't something that could happen to kids. You had a sense of it in the air around your nana and grandad, who were ancient anyway, and sure when your ma and da's time came you'd be an old man yourself, and that was a million years away, so there was nothing to fear or be scared of. But then it actually did happen. Someone I knew died, and far from being old and grey it was someone just a few months older than me. He was a school pal and at fourteen he was killed by a bread van as he cycled from his home in Ballyfermot to the pub across from our flats in Islandbridge where he worked weekends as a lounge boy. All I remember of it was the sadness, thinking of all the things I would get to do that had been taken away from him. As we stood around his coffin in the local funeral parlour, the only light coming from two flickering candles that stood either side of a book of condolences by the door, I stared at the bruised face, its mouth half-open, its nostrils plugged with cotton wool, and I remember thinking that maybe all those songs were wrong and dying for Ireland wasn't such a great thing after all for a young lad. So if the knock came to the door I might have to reconsider.

It was five years later before I was to experience death again. This time it wasn't a pal, just a young man I'd met some years earlier at a march in O'Connell Street. It was his beard that caught my eye, one of those half-grown ones, a bit like Che Guevara's, which was who I thought he looked a little like too when he held out his hand for me to shake. I didn't remember his name but when a black-and-white photograph of a bearded, smiling face flashed across the UTV news one evening I was certain it was the man I'd carried a banner with three years earlier. What had stuck in my mind about him was his friendliness, and his smile that put me at ease, as he showed me how to shoulder the huge banner I was struggling with as we made our way along O'Connell Street. It was the first and last time I carried a banner. I remember thinking that whoever made it was good at their job and had obviously trod this path themselves for across the large painted cloth half a dozen small round holes had been cut in it to let the wind pass through.

As the years moved on, my da added more songs to his repertoire. But apart from those ballads I never knew him to be political in any way at all. Come election time I couldn't have told you who he was going to vote for or if he even bothered to. What I do remember though, is him going on about Stickies and Provos when he'd come home drunk on Sunday nights. It was all a babble to me and I could never make out whose side he was actually on as he'd veer from one to the other over the course of his outburst—and even on some occasions tearfully proclaim that they were both right. But whoever's side he was on, it would always puzzle me why he could never see the contradiction of arriving home with *An Phoblact* in one pocket and *The News of the World* in the other.

The first time my da actually got up off his backside and did something political, it came as a bit of a shock. It was February of 1973 and my grandfather, in his house in Ballyfermot, noticed something odd one morning as he was lighting the fire. How it had passed him by some days earlier was bizarre because watching my grandfather read the newspaper was like watching paint dry, only slower. He would read every inch of it, going through the death columns like a fly fisherman, casting his squinted eyes closely over every name to see if any more of his old stock had passed on, smiling quietly to himself if he discovered that he'd outlived an old foe.

That Tuesday's *Irish Press* had covered the incredible news that the British Embassy on Merrion Square had been burnt down. A few days later, and my grandfather was using his stock of old newspapers to light the fire. It was a ritual he practised daily. He'd sit at the dining table and twist the pages into about a dozen short, tight rolls, place a bundle of them in the grate under some sticks chopped from a log with a small hatchet, arrange a few small lumps of coal on top and then light a corner of the rolls with a match to get the whole thing going. That done, he would kneel in front of the small flames holding a page across the mouth of the fire to get a bit of suction up the chimney. Usually all he had to do was hold the page for roughly half a minute and then stand back proudly and call for my granny to look at the inferno he had once again created. But this time as he watched the flames growing behind the paper he saw something strange. At first he thought he was seeing things. It was a photo of the police arresting a man outside the embassy. A Garda had his arm tight around the man's neck, and the man was grimacing as he was being dragged backwards through the crowd. The fire started to take off and the page was turning brown from scorching, and it was about to burst into flames when my granda roared, 'Rosie! Rosie, quick!' He laid the page out across the table, and poined to the photo. It was my da. Granny and granda looked to each other. Suddenly there was a Republican hero in the family.

The photo was cut out, covered in Sellotape to protect it and shown the length and breadth of the street and to every neighbour who passed the gate whether they wished to see it or not. Even the postman was called in to have a look. It wasn't long before news of the photo made its way to our flats and soon it bestowed on my father a cult status among some of the other fathers there. Soon the usual, 'There y'are Tommy', was followed with a discreet nod and a wink which my da, delighted with himself, would return with a stern look and then pass on his way with a mile-wide smile on his face. It wasn't long either until word had spread to my own circle and some of the lads began to ask me if it was true that my da was in the IRA. I, of course, lied and said yes, but it was a secret and I wasn't allowed talk about it, which seemed to work. But, as with a lot of what happened in my family back then, drink was involved. And far from being a hero arrested for petrol bombing the embassy, it turned out that my da had just turned up to watch the action with a few pints on him, and full of Dutch courage decided to make his way through the crowd for a better view at the front. When he got to the front, he leaned over a Garda's shoulder. The Garda, thinking he was being attacked, turned and wrestled my da to the ground and called for help. Soon my da found himself in a headlock, thrown into a Black Maria and on page five of the following morning's *Irish Press*. The police, he said, didn't charge him because some of the crowd sat in the street in front of the wagon and refused to move until he was let loose. And when he was, they carried him shoulder high as if he himself had thrown all the petrol bombs and burned the embassy down single-handedly.

As the seventies rolled on and my da continued to blast out the same old songs, it appeared that too many young heroes were dying for songs to be written about them, never mind sung. Me, I was more interested in Gary Glitter and Marc Boland and my bedroom wall began to be covered in photos of them, usually torn from my sister's *Jackie* magazine. But in between episodes of *Magpie* and *Blue Peter*, the IRA were in the news too, and in 1976 a new hero made himself known to me. Frank Stagg, an IRA man from Mayo was on hunger strike in England for political status and was close to death. Leaflets and posters were pasted around the city and one day on my way home from school I took one from a lamppost and stuck it up between Glitter and Boland. It stayed there for the duration of the hunger strike and a few weeks after he died. Then I eventually took it down after I had a nightmare that he was in my bedroom staring at me.

When I was fifteen, my da started to take me on his Sunday morning drinking sessions to The Pine Tree in Ballyfermot. Here, every week, a tall man, bald, and with glasses would go round the tables selling *The Irish News*. My da told me he was Tomás Mac Giolla, who was head of Official Sinn Féin, the Stickies. About an hour later another man would arrive, also selling a newspaper, which my da also bought, *An Phoblacht*. My da explained they were both from a political party which had split in 1969. One was now the Official IRA and the other the Provisional IRA. My da told me he leaned more to the Officials, or Stickies side, because he was against violence.

It was around this time that five men from a new political party were arrested for robbing a train. They were innocent but an infamous police unit, the Heavy Gang, had beaten false confessions out of them so they were sent to jail. My father, in the outrage that followed, decided it was finally time to act so he joined this new political party, the Irish Republican Socialist Party, and got involved leafleting and selling their weekly newspaper, *The Starry Plough*. Protests were staged around the city and suddenly my Saturdays were taken up with me being brought into the centre of Dublin, given a placard, and put to picketing, of all places, the Mansion House. It seemed every week there was a protest and I would always end up walking around in circles, carrying a placard alongside a small woman in a duffle coat called Mary.

In 1978, I forget for what, a large march was planned from the GPO to the Dáil. A regular face on protests by now, I was tasked with carrying one part of a huge banner that would lead the march along with another man. He was younger than most men I encountered back then, and along with a beard he had a northern accent. He winked and smiled at me then counted to three as we took a pole each and hoisted the banner high against our shoulders. But despite the holes being placed in the material to let the wind through, it was a struggle marching up O'Connell Street and over the bridge.

What else we did that day, spoke about, I have no memory. What I did remember was his face three years later when news of his death broke across the TV; his name was Patsy O'Hara and he had died at the age of twenty-three after sixty-one days on hunger strike. From all the songs I'd heard sung, stories and history books I'd read, I'd finally met someone who had actually died for Ireland. I called my da in and we both sat there in the silence of it all, not knowing what to say to each other. When the report finished I went up to my room wondering if the men who wrote songs about dying for Ireland had ever gone on afterwards and done it themselves.

Nine other men would join Patsy O'Hara and go on to die on hunger strike that year, and before it ended my granda would pass away too, and his fire-lighting feats passed on to my granny. Within a year my da eventually drifted away from his party and returned to coming home drunk with *The News of the World* in one pocket, *An Phoblact* in the other. The Sallins Five were eventually released too, and a blind eye turned to the violent tactics of the Heavy Gang. My own revolutionary dreams had started to fade too, as girls and writing plays started to take up all my interest. Years later I read that the woman in the duffle coat was called Mary Reid, and she had died too, and in very mysterious circumstances, her body found washed up on the Inishowen Peninsula in 2003. Looking back now there aren't any ballads about any of them, or at least none that I've come by. Who knows, maybe some songs are just best left unsung?

Martial Law

Mary Purcell, my grandmother, was born in April 1916,
week of the Easter Rising.
On the same road as she was being delivered, a two-year-old
child ran from the neighbour's house,
for what? One last gulp of fresh air before her mother tucked her up?
She did not know what martial law was.
Her mother could not rewind the film of horror,
could not explain to her dying child, on the roadside, why she was shot
for skipping outside the house after dark.
In every waking hour thereafter, could she not hear her child,
asking what she did wrong, with the little words she had learned
in her little life. She did not die. She was shot down;
gutted like fish in market;
erased from being.
Whose job was it to peel her body off the pavement?
Did they have to peel the mother from her fading figure first?
Nobody asks the woman about the child she once had,
who turned into a sacrificial lamb on the doorstep of Easter.
People, religiously breaking their knees, bending to altars,
where despite all utterance, nothing gives.
But the whole land keeps praying for peace. The Earth sighs a breath
that sounds like a whole epoch shifting onto its other side in its sleep.
My grandmother, Mary Purcell, takes her first breaths of air, a new air;
for Ireland was shifting in the days to come, did she know this—
bare and bawling as she was?

Aisling Fahey

Recovering History

i

My bones know a history
that wasn't taught in my East London state secondary school.

Lately, it has been pulsing,
frantic in its desire for discovery. This history I unknowingly

locked away and lost the key to.
It waits for me to unpick it. *Listen close*, it says, *hear the rubble of a man*

who could have nearly been your grandfather.

ii

Your voice is a site of contrition,
a stamp of ownership. Whenever you speak, you say

England took our land, then our children, countless children,
and would not give them back.

And their children talk with the tongue of a traitor,
a whole empire in their speech.

What do they know of car bombs? Enemy lines
where there should never have been a border?

I come back, a pilgrim for the land I could have been reared on.
Desperate for it to feed me what I need to make sense of myself.

iii

There are things I think I know but cannot name,
more feelings, a shift in air density and heart rate

when somebody makes an off the cuff joke
about how the Irish don't know how to stop drinking

but they know how to mourn, and I nod my head,
offer half a chuckle it pains me to provide.

There are bottles buried at the bottom of the garden.
I know who put them there. I'll never tell.

iv

Can you see the land in my teeth, the country in my name?
I think of it like a flag in a desert, hope the wind will take pity,

fly it like a kite back home.

What come you here with a voice not of your own?
The Irish blood in my freckled face rises to the top.

I blush for what I am not but was meant to be.

If only I wrote these poems down, printed them with my name
in bold, next to a photo of my freckled self,

taken at the height of summer.

Would you call me daughter and mean it?
I think you know I am yours.

I always apologise when somebody else bumps into me on the street.

Aisling Fahey

Making Fire

Joan Win Brennan

This morning I kissed Jasmine goodbye as though it were a normal day, as though it were not the last time. Perhaps after all I held her a little too long, for she squirmed away from me, embarrassed. I stood and watched her run to meet her friends, her small pink rucksack bobbing on her back, the sheer beauty of her limbs a blow to my heart. Later this afternoon she will play basketball, lead her team in the home match wearing the kit I had no need to remind her to pack. She is a capable girl, has inner resources on which to draw. I think she is a survivor.

As arranged, I am the first to arrive. Beneath me the city bathes in autumnal sunshine but behind the sealed windows of the hotel room the air is cool. My bird's-eye view from the fourteenth floor—there is no thirteenth—warps my perception, lends the streets a swoony unfamiliar aspect. Sunlight dazzles the windows of the multi-storey opposite, bounces off the slowly moving traffic; my gaze can find no settled point. A movement at the far corner of my vision draws my attention. In the heart of this city of concrete and glass, among the international banks and coffee chains below, a municipal park harbours a playground where children craft a random choreography of play. Anxious, I strain to distinguish a face, to differentiate one child from another, but the gulf between us is too great. Rendered flat and abstract by distance, by silence, the children seem scarcely human.

A vertiginous shift of blood in the head unmoors me, sets my heart whumping; my limbs are beset by a nervy weightlessness. I remove my shoes in order to feel the deep pile beneath my feet as I cross the anonymous room, skirt the blank white bed where I shall not sleep. Aiming the remote, I flick through talk shows and daytime soaps; the manufactured laughter sets my teeth on edge. I come to rest on a man setting up camp in rocky terrain. He is going to demonstrate how to make fire with flint and steel. The affable heavy-limbed man is a regular on television, always attired in some version of the colour green. Today he is wearing khaki shorts and walking boots, with thick olive-coloured socks. He looks like a giant boy-scout.

With the wood shavings he has collected, the man starts to assemble the makings of a fire, crouching on beefy knees. Now we viewers must ignore the presence of the camera, and subscribe to the fiction that he has no matches or lighter at his disposal. Already he has told us about the importance of the flint which must be very sharp. I file away this information for future use; then remember that I have no more need of it.

From his rucksack the man extracts an implement called a steel, which must be strong enough to resist the pressure of the flint. Suppose, I wonder, finding yourself alone and exposed, you do not happen to have a steel in your rucksack, or indeed a rucksack—what then? My mind dwells distractedly on images of plane wrecks on frozen wastes; debris strewn across the snow, down bleak mountainsides. On stranded passengers forced in extremis to eat human flesh.

I am standing vacant in the middle of the hotel room, still in my coat. This is not good. Stashing my coat in the wardrobe, I heave my rucksack carefully onto the special stand reserved for luggage, stare at it for an instant, feel my stomach lurch. I inspect the fridge, study the mini-bar, but choose to forego the drink that would steady my nerves. I have not touched alcohol for over a year.

The man on the television is talking about the char cloth, which will be used to start the fire. In order to make such cloth you must pack a small airtight tin (a tinder box!) with small pieces of linen, drill a hole in the top and place it on hot coals for twenty minutes or more. Once it has cooled completely, it must be left for several hours before opening, otherwise it will combust.

Jasmine at this very moment may be opening her lunchbox, peering inside to assess the contents. I hope she will notice with what care I have packed her favourite items: pita bread and humus, paper-thin slices of mild cheddar, green olives, a miniature packet of raisins, the crisp mini-apple for her teeth. She is a healthy girl, will grow up tall and strong in a land where such things are the norm. I give thanks for this, but cannot close my eyes, as others do, to those less fortunate. To see clearly is a moral duty.

Drawn back to the television, I see the man in green has removed the char cloth from his tin and holds the blackened pieces in his palm for our perusal. I am aware of a niggling doubt regarding this cloth, which resides in the problem of how one is to start a fire in the wild with this essential item, when one lacks the benefit of fire to prepare it. Perhaps the man travels always with a ready-to-hand supply in that bulky green rucksack he carries, along with his steel.

Last night, before packing my own weighty rucksack, I performed a final dress rehearsal: tried on the loaded vest, checked the connecting wires, the cylinders, the red detonator; went over in my mind the sequence of events. My heart flips into overdrive, I hear my own accelerated breathing. I force myself to sit up straight and take a few moments to collect myself, return my gaze to the television, concentrate hard on the man at his task.

It occurs to me that, in the event of a disaster, the ability to rub two sticks together might prove a more expedient method for making fire. I do not speak from ignorance. I have read and memorised the ins and outs of catastrophes that may conspire to overtake me, have rehearsed escape procedures, such as: play dead if a bear attacks; climb a tree in the presence of lions; run at speed from a swarm of bees. I am aware of the necessity for calmness after a snake bite; have memorised the way to condense water in the desert with a plastic bag and a stone; learned to avoid tall trees in a storm; in the event of a shipwreck, to float on my back in open sea. So many hours I wasted on such things.

This man knows his way around a wilderness or two. I have great faith in his abilities; he is a resourceful man, an expert in survival. He is a man who, it turns out, could recklessly dispense with all need of char cloth and simply make fire with tinder, should he decide to do so, though with difficulty. This reassures me somewhat.

Nevertheless, today, in the wilderness, he makes use of this material, along with a small quantity of dry grass, which luckily grows abundantly close by. With a good handful, the man proceeds to form a nest, on top of which he lays a small piece of the blackened cloth. Now he must strike the flint so that the minute sliver of metal thus generated will burn and fall on the charred linen.

When I watched the video footage of a long-range missile strike, there was no sound as the explosion occurred. Viewing the event from an aerial perspective, I experienced a troubling sense of detachment—it could have been a video game. The seconds ticked by in one corner of the screen so I knew the precise moment when the unmanned drone struck. The only sounds accompanying the footage were the detached male voices of the unseen pilots safe on the ground, perhaps thousands of miles away, who were tracking the action in real time. They could be heard requesting permission to fire; they spoke of targets, of individuals, of engagement; not of killing. After their day's work, they go home to their children.

Tonight Jasmine will sleep in her father's house. He is a good man; I could not wish a better father for my child, and it pains me to deceive him. It is only that he could not follow where I led and I must of necessity leave him behind. At eight o'clock this evening he will stretch out on the bunk-bed with my daughter and she will choose the tattered, well-loved book and hear again the story of Pippi, the little girl who can take care of herself. He will read to her until her eyes begin to close, her breathing slows and, though he tries to fend off sleep, his own eyelids start to droop. I bless them both and hope that one day they will understand.

A moment passes, or several, I cannot tell.

Now the survival expert is kneeling among scrubby weeds. His muscled arms bulge as he holds the flint over the char cloth and strikes downward several times with the steel. Anxiously, I eye the screen; this is surely taking longer than it should. The man explains that it is best to make fire in a good wind, but that today there is no wind. I absorb this information, study the leaves of the trees for movement.

When the drone lets loose its firepower there is no going back; it is a matter of seconds before the target is hit. Alone in the hotel room I replay the internet footage in my head. From an elevated distance I see in grainy monochrome the isolated village coming into view; the zoning in on micro-figures moving across the landscape. The strange silence at the scene. The quiet almost gentle puff of smoke as the missile explodes, the plume rising into the air and spreading, the toy houses collapsing into dust. It is a clean way to kill, the enemy annihilated at the press of a button, and accomplished without military casualties—the ultimate escape procedure. It is called precision bombing.

Only later when the film crew arrives is the 'collateral damage' exposed; only then do we see the dead children. The flak-jacketed journalist is there to interview the bereaved, the maimed, addressing them in English as convention demands, though they answer in a foreign tongue. And, all the while, the camera tracks slowly among the demented mothers, the old men dumb with grief; zooms in for a close-up of the bodies wrapped in white linen, lying in rows like miniature mummies.

Without taking my eyes from the television, I sit on the end of the bed and watch the camera slowly closing in on the survival expert's hands. Am held in suspension as he continues to strike the flint against the steel, generating plenty of sparks, he assures us, but as yet no fire. Until at last a spark catches and a thin wisp of smoke begins to rise. His large red hands are surprisingly dexterous as he folds the nest of kindling carefully around the smouldering cloth. Steady, as mine must be.

The man in green now has my full attention. Cradling the kindling in his hands, he holds the bundle aloft and proceeds to blow gently upon it. Against the smoke his eyes squint, but mine are fixed intently upon him; I hardly dare to breathe. It is a matter of seconds before I see a flame begin to lick the kindling. Now the man must lay the bundle carefully among the wood shavings. In an instant, they are aflame. He adds more twigs, leans back on his heels and allows himself a discreet smile of muted triumph. The tension leaves my shoulders and I release my withheld breath. I switch off the television and wait calmly for the others to arrive.

The Long Road

Matter is mostly illusion,

the Promised Land,
a cold mist.

I still feel the bruise and the ache
from passing through
the solid block—

mouthfuls of broken promises,
shattered baby teeth.

Was it reeds or rushes kept him afloat?
Red Sea, river of blood...

Each of my highest thoughts,
airborne, attached itself to a fine wisp
of down and went forth—

now and again,
I had a pair of goggles
to adjust.

Finally, everyone wants
a safe, well-built house:

a rubble foundation isn't enough.

And yet, I was a weed flower
in the cottage garden.

Otherwise, I vanished indoors,
rummaged in my chest of drawers

until I read what God thought.

Now, through the back of my head,

I view a long acre,
a tramp's heartbreak

and out front

the fruit in my basket
you say you want to weigh up.

Patrick Maddock

Éamon de Valera

Ave, Dev.

A real male—
lead, ram.

Rev, lad.
Olé!

Lover,
dream a leader

lead a demon—
meld or mar.

Dole a meal,
name a deal,
Lean Man.

Rave, rend, damn!

Roam alone
Aloe Vera
on a lemon lane.

No love
no doe a deer
mole-vole.

Moan an ode,
a drama—
or: revel
ever-land-node.

Reel an eel—
no elver,

nor Leon
(evade a Red).

Reveal—delve,
moral rod.
Do, dove.

Name a daemon:
Roma Nova.

Me, Adam
an Eve dome

an era, an aeon
never-end-man...

Amon Ra.
(Leer, Mona.)

Vale, Dev.

Patrick Maddock

It Could Be You

Lia Mills

I

A woman sitting at her window was shot dead in broad daylight. She was reading.

Sitting at a window with a book would be like, say, spreading a towel on hot sand so you can lie down and ask the sun to coax the damp of a northern climate from your bones. You don't expect a gunman.

You could be standing in line at a bank with the news on continuous feed. You're bored out of your mind, following the running heads about a foreign war, a city falling, families displaced. You look away from a burning car, bodies on the ground. It's lunchtime and the queue is long. Your feet hurt. You're hoping the money's in because there's bills to pay—there's always bills—and you're behind with the rent and the kids need a decent meal not just pasta, dear god you're sick of pasta. It's close in here, someone in the queue has BO; you're sweaty under your hair, maybe it smells funky too and—something loud happens, glass breaking, a shouty voice *Everybody out! Get out!* At first you don't get it but piece by piece you make sense of it: that man there jumped the counter; the teller who was there before went down under him the way they do in rugby; people in ugly clothes wave guns and sticks and break things; over there people are being herded into a back office; there's arguing, shouts. More glass breaks. People edge towards the door. Someone grips your arm. Your heart skips but it's only the woman who was behind you in the queue, saying *Come on!* and you do. The pair of you shove through the crowd swarming the door as though you've always known what elbows are really for. Outside you breathe deep, gaspy breaths your ribs are sore from holding onto and look back, where some skinny kid is hanging a flag you've never seen before from a window.

II

The first fatalities were policemen, after which the law crept away and hid for the duration.The cavalry arrived. Their horses were shot from under them.

A band of older reservists who had been sports stars in their youth were on their way back to barracks from manoeuvres in the mountains. The real war was off on the continent. The words *Georgius Rex* were stitched into their tunics, so they were inevitably known in Dublinese as the Gorgeous Wrecks. It's a long walk from the mountains but they were nearly there. I'd say their feet were sore, their minds fixed on whatever brew waited for them in the barracks. They carried guns but no ammunition. You could say that they were armed. You could say they were unarmed. The true thing is that they were shot, on a sunny spring day on the streets of their own city. Some of them were killed.

The gunmen cut off the phones. They cut off the gas. They turned dogs and cats loose from the pound so they wouldn't starve. They smashed windows and furniture and blocked the streets. They dug themselves in among the citizens—into businesses and homes in the heart of the city—and waited for the soldiers to come for them. They took hostages. They hijacked cars and vans and bicycles. If citizens resisted, they were shot. The trams and trains stopped running.

The soldiers came. At first, before they got properly into the swing of things, both sides would cease fire long enough to yell at the citizens to let them at it, to go home, out of harm's way. But they were slow to cop on, those people. They didn't get it, what was going on. They couldn't believe what their eyes and ears were telling them, that they could be gunned down on the same streets where they lived and worked and shopped, where their children went to school, where they leaned on sills to gossip with the neighbours. Citizens were shot. Scores of them.

Hundreds of them, actually, by the time it was over.

They say a blind man, feeling his way across an empty road with a white stick, was shot by a sniper and lay there moaning, hurt, helpless. They say the St John's Ambulance man who went out in the open to help him to safety was shot dead. That the sniper shot the blind man again to finish him off.

More soldiers came. The gunmen killed them. Gunmen were killed.

The city turned on itself, let rip. In an orgy of destruction, it laid waste to its own impoverished, ravenous self. The stables caught fire. More windows were broken. Holes were knocked in walls. There was looting, there was chaos. A man who tried to stop it was lifted by the soldiers, who used him as a hostage while they drove around. A human shield. Then they shot him. They shot journalists. They made a boy kneel in the street and then they shot him.

More soldiers came. There will always be more soldiers. There was a curfew, there were roadblocks. People went hungry. There were bombs. A woman sat by a window reading. She was shot. All the windows broke. The hospitals were full. The gunmen were in a hospital. The soldiers came. There was shooting. A nurse was killed while soldiers and gunmen killed each other. The soldiers burst into homes, took men outside and shot them. The soldiers took hostages. They shot them. There were bodies on the streets and not enough coffins to bury them. The nights were fiery.

Inside the city, people tried to help. They went out in cars to carry the injured to hospitals. They took bleeding strangers into their homes. They brought food and sheets and towels to emergency clinics set up in living rooms and kitchens. The ambulance drivers drove through flames. The firemen. The doctors and the nurses. Two girls went out under fire to carry cups of water to dying men. A man went out onto the steps of his house to see what he could do. Hours before, there'd been a bloodbath there. He'd helped to carry injured men and boys in uniform to safety. They shot him there. They killed him.

On the Thursday, Dublin began to burn in earnest. The soldiers made the firemen stand down so the buildings would blaze away to nothing and they'd have a clear line of sight to their targets. Glass melted and ran down the walls. People stood on hills outside their city and watched it burn.

The gunmen surrendered.

The citizens were: shocked, traumatised, elated, glad it was over. Some of them were ruined. Many were bereaved. They were hostile, angry, sympathetic, proud. There was a lot to feel and not much information. They didn't know what we know. We don't know everything. We never will.

The gunmen were rounded up for gaol. The general ordered their leaders to be shot. The soldiers shot them—Connolly so badly wounded they had to tie him to a chair. To shoot him.

That's where our national creation myth began. And just to make sure that it would grow into an unstoppable motivating force, more than three thousand men and women were rounded up to be interned in English and Irish jails.[1] By the time they came home they were heroes.

You know the rest.

III

Pearse said he would surrender, not because they'd been burned out of the GPO and were tracking back through burning streets that led to the massed and waiting arms of the British army, but to spare the citizens of Dublin. You'd have to wonder, did he look out the windows at all in the previous week? Did he listen?

- 485 people were killed in Dublin that week, more citizens than rebels and British Army put together. Almost one in five of those were under 19 years old.[2]

• 100,000 people—one third of the population of the city—had to go on relief because they'd lost everything in the fires.[3]
• £2,500,000 sterling worth of damage was done—including the destruction of 179 buildings in the centre of Dublin and the ruin of businesses that never managed to reopen.[4]

Most of it happened in an area of roughly four square miles.

Meanwhile, the war in Europe continued. In just one battle, on just one day of that week—Thursday, while the fires in Dublin took hold in earnest and the firemen were held back—the 16th Irish Division of the British army were subjected to a gas attack at Hulluch (France). There were 1980 casualties: 570 killed outright and many more to die later, their lungs in tatters.

They say the German soldiers held up placards to let the Irish soldiers know what was happening at home.

These facts were not exactly hidden but it's safe to say they were obscured. Yes, I think it's safe to say that. The story we were told had different starting points, all leading to the moment when a gallant band of patriotic men and women set out to wrest their country back from the ancient enemy. The eight hundred years. The few against the many. The sacrifice. The story we were told was heavy on the sacrifice, how close it came to martyrdom. No, wait, it was a kind of martyrdom. A noble thing, to die for faith or country—and, sure, in Ireland didn't they amount to the same thing. Never mind if that's what millions of others were doing on the continent and elsewhere, all for the sake of one ism or another.

IV

It's hard to think about 485 people dead in the space of a week, even though we see it on our screens so often now. It means more when you look at them singly. The man on his doorstep. The blind man with his stick. The ambulance man who went to help him. The woman sitting at her window. I'd say she was minding her own business, but since she was reading at the time there's no knowing what business she was actually about.

Reading was how we got off the island and into the light of broader, more supple ways of thinking when I was a teenager. It seemed to be the case that writers who questioned or undermined our most sacred assumptions about ourselves had to shut up or get out.

Spare a thought for the administration that allowed inflammatory language to run unchecked in print and on the streets. Look where it got them. Our own crowd were less tolerant, later. In the interests of controlling our sense of who we are and what we might become, they were enthusiastic in the redaction and censorship of books and films. If a book was seen as anti-Catholic, anti-Irish, or anti- the Irish Catholic values we were all supposed to share, it didn't stand a chance. Books were burned, denounced from the pulpit and outright banned. Anyone who didn't like all this could leave, weren't we better off without them.

I first read Edna O'Brien's *A Pagan Place* when I was fifteen. It blew my mind wide open. Soon afterwards I read John McGahern's *The Dark*. They were both banned, which was partly why I read them in the first place. I hid them inside false covers and read them in plain view, at school. Between them they set off seismic tremors in my mind. Truth was possible, in fiction—even in Irish fiction. Fiction could be real. For the first time I was almost as interested in the writers as in their books. I wanted to know who they were, how they'd found the courage to do it, what price they'd had to pay. Where were they now? Elsewhere, of course. That's what happened if you put your truth on paper—you went into exile.

John McGahern changed everything when he came back. He published another novel and he stayed. If you're looking for examples of courage and radical turning points, that's as good as any and better than most.

You'll say this was back in the last century and it was. You'll say the times were different and they were. But this is still true: reading matters. Reading changes minds.

V

You grow up with a deep unchanging physical love of this country, a fierce attachment to certain places, the curved blue shoulder of mountains reaching an arm around a city, the long tongue of the sea moving in the mouth of a bay, its many voices; stony ground and scarlet setting suns, mirrored lakes and empty beaches; the sensation of cool moss on the bared sole of a tired foot, the human scale of its cities, the crooked rooflines of a street. You share its sense of humour, its fluency, its spite. It hurts to leave these things as so many of us must, for reasons to do with the State, which is not quite the same thing as the Nation and certainly not the same as the country. A State is less easy to love.

When my family and I came back after ten years in America, I spent several years studying and teaching women's writing and cultural history of the period leading up to the Rising. See how interesting that is, as though the school curriculum's influence was so deeply etched in my mind that I still, as an adult, thought that history stops—and begins again (but differently)—where the Rising starts. In my time we did a little leapfrog over the first world war and skidded past our own War of Independence and Civil War. We don't know everything about those, either.

I knew—and loved—the story of the Rising. It has all the elements of great fiction: characters larger than life, a strong plot, romance, betrayal, hopeless odds, the surprise twist at the end that changes everything. New life in the ruins of the old world. I knew the stirring speeches that led up to it, the alliances and disagreements, the very real civic groundwork that so many ordinary men and women did to improve the difficult lives many Irish people lived under the British administration, the efforts to awaken/restore a sense of national pride. I knew what the public figures did and said and wrote. I had admiration for some and affection for others and knew right well that most of them would disapprove of me. But in all that time I managed never to look at the numbers. I'd never seen the photographs of O'Connell Street in ruins. I must have seen them, in the sense that my eye may have glanced at them, but they left as little impression as the microwave energy that passes through all of us right this very minute—my minute writing this and yours, reading it. It's not as though those facts are hidden. They were easy enough to find and that was a shock too. How close to the surface they are and how unseen. Our representatives still talk about the sixteen men who were executed, as though theirs were the only lives that were lost. They talk about what those men would want. As if they'd been elected. They talk as if they knew them, as if they own them, as if they, the representatives, are the ones those men would choose as their successors. As if they are worthy to succeed them.

These days we have what can feel like a numbing habit of referendums. Look at the recent list: on Judicial salaries and on giving additional powers to Oireachtas committees (October 2011); on the European Fiscal Treaty (May 2012); on Children's Rights (November 2012); on Abolition of the Seanad and establishment of a Court of Appeal (October 2013)—and many more on the horizon. We only get to have a say in shaping our Constitution thanks to the battles the 1916 leaders fought, but during this increasingly tedious serious of campaigns the seditious thought that they had no mandate for their action crept into my mind. That if we woke up one morning now, in the twenty-first century, to find the city taken over by armed men whose intentions were unclear, our feelings would not in any way relate to the gratitude and reverence we're supposed to feel for the signatories of the Proclamation, the almost incantatory sound of their names. The recent marriage referendum was a different thing entirely. That amendment was passed on a wave of joy and hope like nothing I've seen on this island, ever. It was a real and utterly bloodless revolution, and the change was born of stories told with great courage and belief in people's ability to hear and understand them.

VI

In December 1915 Padraig Pearse wrote of the war in Europe: 'The last sixteen months have been the most glorious in the history of Europe. Heroism has come back to the earth... The old heart of the earth needed to be warmed with the red wine of the battlefields.'[5] It sounds mad, now, knowing what we know about that war but he wasn't, by any means, the only one to deliver this kind of rhetoric across Europe at the time.

Take Tom Kettle, for example: constitutional nationalist, parliamentarian, poet and economics professor at UCD. When the German army invaded Belgium in August 1914 Tom Kettle happened to be there, buying guns for the (National) Volunteers. He stayed on for a couple of months as war correspondent for the *Daily News*. In one of his dispatches he wrote: 'War is hell, but it is only a hell of suffering, not of dishonour, and through it, over its flaming coals, Justice must walk, were it on bare feet.' Kettle was a Redmondite. Back in Ireland, he joined the British army and became quite the poster-boy, urging Irishmen to enlist. Redmondites believed that the contribution of Irishmen would support the case for Home Rule once the war was over.

Rhetoric is one thing. The reality was different. 'It is a grim and awful job,' Kettle wrote to his wife Mary from the battlefield. 'No man can feel up to it.' His poem for their daughter Betty shows a shift in his awareness of how conflicts are manipulated.

> ... they'll give you rhyme
> And reason: some will call the thing sublime,
> And some decry it in a knowing tone.
> So here, while the mad guns curse overhead,
> And tired men sigh with mud for couch and floor,
> Know that we fools, now with the foolish dead,
> Died not for flag, nor King, nor Emperor—[6]

The poem acknowledges something else again: 'You'll ask why I abandoned you... to dice with death.'

Many of the executed leaders were fathers. Many of the soldiers who were killed during Easter Week were fathers too. Others were only boys. The citizens who died ticked all the relationship and gender boxes: fathers, mothers, siblings, children, friends. 485 fatalities. That's a lot of futures stolen and families destroyed. A lot of lives ruptured and thrown off course. A lot, they might say today, of collateral damage.

'Collateral damage' is the kind of phrase we have to resist. Language matters. If you want to desensitise people, first you drain words of meaning, attach antiseptic labels to actions, restrict the options for understanding or sympathy with the thing-to-be-destroyed, whatever or whoever that is. On the other hand, if you want to incite people to hatred, words will do it. Language gets under your skin. The way music can interfere with the rhythm of your walk, language can either disorder or ignite your thinking, it sets the neurons firing differently. There are medical tests that require you not to read because it causes demonstrable changes in your brain. The words we use matter—they have destructive as well as creative potential. Reading changes minds.

So does experience. Exposure to the reality of war changed Kettle's ideas. In a letter to a friend from the battlefield, he wrote: 'If I live, I mean to spend the rest of my life working for perpetual peace.' He was killed at the Somme on September 9th 1916, four months after the executions in the stonebreakers' yard of Kilmainham Gaol. He was 36 years old. He left a wife—Mary (Sheehy)—and daughter, Betty (3).

Tom Kettle was a friend and colleague of Tom MacDonagh, poet and lecturer at UCD, who was executed as a signatory of the Proclamation. MacDonagh was killed by a firing squad on May 3rd 1916. He was 38 years old. He left a wife—Muriel (Gifford) who drowned a year later—and two small children, Donagh (4) and Barbara (1).

Our own poet/soldier Francis Ledwidge wrote a haunting lament for MacDonagh, still popular today: 'He shall not hear the bittern cry/In the wild sky…'[7] Three months later, Ledwidge was dead too. He was killed at Passchendaele on July 31st, 1916, three weeks short of his thirtieth birthday.

Any discussion of the intricate mesh of connection between these figures—or of the key events of the Rising—and in the context of writing and war, has to include Frank Sheehy-Skeffington.[8] Writer, journalist, activist (feminist and pacifist) he campaigned against conscription in the early days of the war and was jailed for it. Previously he and his wife Hanna, a teacher and writer, had campaigned for women's right to a university education and for women's suffrage. (Hanna was the founder of the Irish Women's Franchise League and a founding member of the Irish Women Workers' Union. Along with Louie Bennett, she was a delegate to the International Women's Peace Congress in the Hague in 1915 but they were prevented from travelling by the British administration). Frank was the man who tried to stop the looting in Dublin and was lifted by soldiers, used as a human shield and later killed in Portobello Barracks. His friends in college included James Joyce and Tom Kettle—who was also his brother-in-law; Kettle's wife Mary was Hanna Sheehy-Skeffington's sister. Kettle and MacDonagh had both been members, with Frank, of the Citizens' Peace Committee formed in response to the Dublin Lock-out in 1913. A close friend of James Connolly and initially a member of Connolly's Citizen Army, Frank Sheehy-Skeffington resigned when its policy shifted towards militarism. He was shot by a firing squad in Portobello Barracks on April 26th 1916, aged 37. He left his wife, Hanna, and their son Owen (7).[9]

Poets had plenty of stirring, lyrical things to say about the war, at first. Before reality struck. 'They shall not grow old, as we who are left grow old' wrote Laurence Binyon in 1914. Binyon survived that war and lived to see the next. He died in 1943, aged 74.

Rupert Brooke, of 'for ever England' fame, wrote, 'War knows no power. Safe shall be my going,/ Secretly armed against all death's endeavour.' Later, but not much later, he wrote: 'We have taught the world to die.' Brooke, who actually saw little action in the war, died of sepsis (from a small cut) on a French hospital ship in the Aegean on April 23rd, 1915.[10] He was 38 years old.

Charles Sorley, a Scottish soldier/poet, said of most early war poetry, 'it is a living lie.' He wrote:

> When you see millions of the mouthless dead
> Across your dreams in pale battalions go,
> Say not soft things as other men have said…

Sorley was killed at Loos, near Hulluch, on October 13th 1915. He was twenty years old.

VII

Pearse's words can still interfere with a reader's pulse rate. *Naked I saw thee… Beware the risen people… While Ireland holds these graves, Ireland unfree shall never be at peace...* You could forget which century you're in until you lift your head from the page. Not everything he wrote was quite so inspiring. In 'The Murder Machine', an article published in January 1916 in a pamphlet of the same name,[11] he referred to Irish people who didn't reject their education in the British system—in other words, Irish people who disagreed with his worldview—as 'Things', masquerading as men and women. 'Men and women, however depraved, have kindly human allegiances. But these Things have no allegiance. Like other Things, they are for sale.' Ireland, he said, was a nation of slaves.

Before his oration at the grave of O'Donovan Rossa, not many people would have known who Pearse was. He was a teacher, a poet and something of an ideologue, judging by his more inflammatory writing. He had a fondness, even a longing, for his personal notion of death and the glory that would follow.

Unpick the rhetoric and this much is still true: Connolly, Pearse and the others acted for what they believed to be the common good, as the Proclamation says. We are what we are now because of them. We'll never know what else we might have become. It's thanks to them that we ask different questions now, free of the stale old ruts of hatred, resentment, suppression and mistrust. They did, after all, pay with their lives. They did it for the future, for us—for those of us, that is, who stayed when the inconvenient dissenters left, all those who couldn't do business in the climate that followed all our wars, those who couldn't live in a Catholic hegemony, those who were driven off the land. Not to mention all those who have been hidden, interred uncoffined in dark and unmarked graves in that same land since.

Taken selectively and in the context of our history, Pearse's words seem thrilling and magnificent. We still teach them to our children. But what else do we teach them? Of all the black-hole silences of Easter week (never mind the truths, the lies) the blackest has to be the silence around the fact that ordinary people did what they could to help other human beings who were bleeding, torn and broken on their streets, calling for help. Some of those citizens paid for their humanity with their lives. We are only beginning to admit to this, or to the extent of the casualties. It's as though acts of humanity were considered shameful—or dangerous—in the light of patriotism. The habit that stuck was one of secret societies, covert violent action—often against civilian targets—and reprisals. We think our wars are over, but are they? If Europe disintegrates. If protectionism gains a foothold. If fascism returns. If Islamic State has its way. If. You think that can't happen? One hundred years ago, they didn't expect the gunmen either.

When my generation were taught about the Rising such outrageous acts as bringing a cup of water to a dying teenager in a British soldiers's uniform were unmentionable. Giving comfort to a dying boy in uniform could still cost a woman her life in the 1970s, although we like to think it wouldn't happen now.[12] The Rising, as it was told to us, was all about the rights and the wrongs of it, success and failure, the winning and the losing and which side, freedom gained and lost, gallantry, martyrdom. I'd have liked my younger self to know the full story, to know that other options are open to us in choosing the kinds of people we want to be. I'd like my kids to know that you can give your life *to* something you care about instead of *for* it.

What a difference a single word can make.

VIII

As the commemorations loom, the rhetoric returns. The egos haven't gone away, you know. I'm only saying. And even now there's people reading this who'll say who is she anyway, and what kind of name is that, Mills? It's an English name, they'll say. Never mind that that particular line of family is rooted in inner city Dublin at least as far back as 1815—which is as far as we've been able to go, the records having been destroyed in one skirmish or another. Never mind that all the women's names, the names that get lost in time, are as Irish as you'd like: Dunne, Kelly, Kavanagh, Hart. There's a Scottish-sounding Jameson and one intriguing Edge.

This is how they try to keep you quiet. They say you're not Irish enough or you're too Irish, you're not Catholic enough[13] or too Catholic, too feminist, not feminist enough, too middle class, too inward-looking/backward-looking/ outward-looking, too pacy or too slow, too familiar or too strange, too fond of black polo-neck sweaters.

What they say shouldn't matter to you while you're rooting around with your pen. Nothing should be further from your mind as you grapple with a sentence, where a single inaccurate word or misplaced comma can change your meaning. This is the real work, to be conscious of language and how it's used, to consider how you use it yourself as you explore what it means to be human in your time. The business of exploring what it means to be human might seem elegiac, if not downright nostalgic, with cyborgs and posthumanism on the horizon—if not already here—but it matters. You are, after all, human. You're not enough, you never will be, but that dissatisfaction is the very thing that keeps you going. Beckett said it: try again.

Go back to the beginning. A tantalisingly lovely spring day, a public holiday. A woman worries about someone far away—a lover or a daughter, working in one of the world's torrid troublespots where mass-murder, kidnapping and mayhem have become the norm. She wishes they were home, safe. She goes to a chair beside the window for the light, for air. She picks up a book and opens it.

1. O'Connell, Joseph E. A. Jnr *Dublin in Rebellion: A Directory 1913-1923* (Lilliput Press, 2006)
2. Glasnevin Trust 1916 Necrology www.glasnevintrust.ie (accessed 04/08/2015)
3. Caulfield, Max *The Easter Rebellion* (Gill and Macmillan, 1995)
4. ibid.
5. 'Peace and the Gael', December 1915
6. 'To My Daughter Betty, The Gift of God'
7. Possibly a reference to MacDonagh's own poem 'The Yellow Bittern': 'A bittern calls from a wineless place…'
8. The surname Sheehy-Skeffington was the combination of Frank's name, Skeffington, with Hanna's, Sheehy.
9. Frank Sheehy-Skeffington was the person Connolly trusted to preserve his ideas and ideals. He wanted Frank to be executor of his papers and had to be told, within hours of his own execution, that Frank had been executed before him.
10. The second Battle of Ypres began on April 22nd that year; the landings at Gallipoli began on April 25th leading to a sustained battle. More than a hundred men from the Dublin regiments were killed in those two conflicts. The Rising in Dublin began on April 24th 1916, close to the first anniversary of the bereavement of many of its people.
11. This was based on an earlier article in *The Irish Review* (1913)
12. Jean McConville, a widow with ten children, was 'disappeared' by the IRA in 1972 from her home in Belfast. Her body was found on a beach in County Louth in 2003.
13. Critics question this statement, but at the time of going to print, a child can still be denied a place in a primary school on the basis of his or her religion.

Walking Through Truth Land

Desmond Hogan

'No foot, no horse.'

A man with a face like a sea otter's speaking to a man with a ferocious red prophet's beard, like Ronnie Drew of The Dubliners.

A man like a grizzly bear with white flour thrown on his head makes an analogy.

'If you want to buy a bull, you judge him by the size of the balls.'

A passerby with head like a bullet with tomato-coloured cheeks, takes up the point.

'I'm allergic to oranges. My balls are as big as them.'

He's referring to the orange in the grizzly bear's hand.

'The foal touches the bag and milk just comes pouring,' attests the sea otter who is wearing a Bronte tweed flat cap.

'We'll split a hundred in Christ's name,' suggests Ronnie Drew.

'The truth is the truth is the truth!' cries out a man with a crutch, habit brown ankle socks, who joins them.

'We're looking for sexy underwear,' a youth in pink singlet with carp face, like a carp with a shaven head, towing a girl with black pudding stand up hairstyle, tells a Romanian woman in a Scheherazade dress—top red to breasts, then gold, blue and red pattern down its middle, oriental blue skirt with gold hemline.

The Romanian woman is selling dimensional pictures which shift image as you move yourself—Christ pointing to his heart which can become the Virgin

Mary—a Photoplay cover girl (Mollie Ann Bourne, Mamie Van Doren)—who looks as if she's had a ghetto nervous breakdown.

Reading glasses. Hairpieces. Fretwork, many coloured, collapsible planet playthings for children.

One Direction posters and transparent (other than logo) plastic shopping bags—the boys romping or showing their bird, rose, anchor, brigantine tattoos.

Ann Breen CDs with a sepia, photocopied cover of Ann Breen with clasp earrings, large American-style teeth.

On one side of the stall furniture with sex shop fuchsine upholstery.

On the other a cuisine which promises foot long German sausages and chimney cakes.

Over all this—including framed pictures which give an illusion of depth (cross on right side, Ascension left, Flight into Egypt top, Crown of Thorns bottom, thumbnail Last Supper, Stable at Bethlehem, view of Jerusalem in corner niches)—Seamus Moore belts out: 'The old red flannel drawers that Maggie wore. They were tattered, they were torn.'

Paddy was a pye-dog wandering the road past the priory. A woman with two stub teeth, one on each side, wearing a raincoat she bought in Killarney for the first time, holds him on a leash.

'It's a holy place. But it's gorgeous,' she says about the priory.

It's like walking through a meadow of water forget-me-nots in the land given in frankalmoign—no obligation except praying—to the monks. It's like walking through the colour of someone's eyes you once knew. You keep expecting someone to say Hello but no one says Hello, and you think no one is going to say Hello, until a boy with octopus roach, in a T-shirt with The Jetsons in an aerocar, who couldn't be more than thirteen, near the fourteenth-century bridge, says, 'I'm twenty-seven. Say a poem.'

Baldy Cock Bracken bombed Bucko Bracken the other night. Drugs. Bucko makes his own false teeth. Baldy Cock swapped his trotting horse for two Jersey cows. There are millions of horses in South Hill. Fifteen boys got fifteen horses in O'Malley Park, put on balaclavas and smashed security cameras. Roane got a Clay tattoo on the small of her back. That was her husband's name. But he said it was another Clay. The one they met at a swingers' night at a sauna called Eye Candy. She went to a wedding and stayed all night. He cut the tattoo from the small of her back. He said he should have cut her eyes out and left them beside her.

I have an audience now of South Hill boys like weasel kits, one in a T-shirt with shark's face and wide open mouth, another in a T-shirt with nine posing ferrets, two of them French kissing, another in white T-shirt with Daffy Duck against a sepia lake with lots of mallards on it, another in T-shirt with headless gorilla, another in black T-shirt with spider's web on it, another in black T-shirt with fire brigade on it, another in white T-shirt with two grey pitbull dogs with flews, pink tongues showing and underneath Bow Wow Wow.

There's also a man in clove and cinnamon pinstripe suit, fly three quarters the way down, with his sister's rose quartz wedding ring and a nineteenth-century watch from Amsterdam.

'He could be gay. He could be a child molester. We'll see him on BBC Three,' cautions a man with a head like a donkey's head with bald pate, donkey's grin among a group of youths with hair like saffron as a condiment sprinkled from the heavens, all in grey track suits which made them look as if they are wearing cement.

I recite W.B. Yeats's 'In Memory of Eva Gore-Booth and Con Markiewicz' and have to recite the part which demands a raised rhetorical voice for them on demand five times, each time earning a cheer as for a triumphant soccer conclusion and when I'm finished there's a mood swing—a revenge for the poem, a punishment for the light of evening at Lissadell, withdrawn pardon for the one condemned to death, execution on hindsight.

Three of the boys produce plastic pistols brought back from Lanzarote and start shooting at me with concentrated plastic pellets.

I hide behind a Range Rover with a trailer attached but a boy in a purple T-shirt with green dinosaur's death's head, sunglasses on the dinosaur's brow, eyes a historical blue—blue that used blot into the copybook once and he passes it on to my copybook (lessons about the sacrifice of life in 1916 and the kneeling in the dust expected for this at a school where women queued outside the classroom on Fridays with Vincent de Paul vouchers)—shoots a pellet from behind the trailer which hits me under the eye.

I take refuge among the amusements in a burdock field of derelict sheds—the dodgems spin around to Ed Sheeran singing Rihanna's 'We Found Love'; there are Victorian galloping horses, fuchsine in their cheeks, a train with carriages marked York, Normanton, Sheffield, and a Jungle Adventure aerocastle with crimson bonobo (pygmy chimpanzee) and green tiger on it—but the youths in trackie suits like cement are on the premises.

'What is this poetry about?

Poetry isn't wanted here.'

I feel like the duck in Hook the Duck (anyone can be a winner).

I try to make a getaway from the town, heading in the direction of the priory, where you could still see the string-course built to prevent assault by weasels and martens, when a youth with urban fox hair, locks, rodeo-denim blue eyes, in T-shirt with a tomcat's face and the words *Part Animal*, stops me.

'Say that poem for me.'

I have to recite 'In Memory of Eva Gore-Booth and Con Markiewicz' to an audience of grey guinea fowl with white dots, khaki ducks, chiltern ducks, Welsh harlequin ducks, red mottled leghorn chickens, white leghorn chickens in cages beside us, while One Direction sing 'Story of My Life', and a youth with hair the colour of a tribe of apricots spiels his product—house cleaners.

I'd met him before on a Dublin street.

'Are you looking for a hostel?' he asked me.

Shanno Sugruf was his name, he said.

'I'll never set foot in Cork again.

Never or never is a long time.

I'm not going back to Cork. I'm not going back there. I'm not going back to Cork.'

A borstal mark tear under right eye means bereavement.

A borstal mark tear under left eye means you've murdered someone.

He had a borstal mark tear under right eye.

To grow up with brothers writhing and wringing around one another like ferrets in a deep basket.

One of those brothers was knifed to death.

His sister who always made the pilgrimage to St Fanachan's Well in Mitchelstown on his feast day, November 25th, in a Zhivago hat and fake mink coat, killed herself the same day.

Turn left at Tesco at the top of the town. Brigown Cemetery is on your right. You turn left at the crossroad to Mulberry. A raised footpath lined by old beech trees. Then you drink water from the well.

St Fanachan had a battle staff, the Cenn Cathach (Head Battler) which he carries in a statue of himself outside Mitchelstown Garda Station (he is sitting or crouching) in which he has the resigned look of one of the Mitchelstown guards.

St Fanachan asked seven tinsmiths to make seven sickles on which he mortified his body for seven years.

Bushes are cut along edges of fields for drainage in these parts and the felled bushes piled in the middle of the fields before being set on fire.

Shanno was not allowed out of Cork Jail for his brother's and sister's funeral but there were fires in the fields in his mind.

'Cork Jail is a shit hole. Pisspots wait until morning. To get water you fill your bottle and come back to the kettle in the cell.

'You get to know a few fellows. You don't say you're this. You're that. You share the munchies. Jelly popping candy shells and Cadbury Creme Eggs and Cadbury Bubblys and Cadbury Golden Biscuit Crunch.'

He showed me a white Portlaoise photo-identity card.

'My family killed people and when I was put in Portlaoise a man from Togher, Gummy Gheeze—the only person there with no teeth—took me under his wing and protected me. Otherwise they'd have stuck a shaft in me because of my family.

When I was fourteen another Traveller boy of fourteen—The Pedlar they called him because him and his brothers would take copper and wire from newly built houses—stuck a bowie knife in my hip, ran it over, dented the hip bone. If I hadn't turned I'd be a dead man. He was aiming at my stomach. That happened on We the People Street.'

Shanno looked like a baby kangaroo with a hip-hop hair style then. He carried half a golf stick as a weapon and later a stanley knife.

Since that happened We the People Street has changed. The youth club paint the galvanized walls for Easter and Christmas.

There are pine trees now, a log hut with tied back green curtains which have salmon trim, wine door with letter box.

There's a discarded black boot high-heel and the pavement is strewn with cupcakes in baking cases.

Nearby Barnardo's Better Futures.

They are knocking houses down. There are metal fences and there is rubble.

A youth with outraged auburn hair, facial bruises that indicate some important nutrition is missing, is doing circles with a sulky in St Vincent's soccer field where a pizza delivery boy was recently dragged in and mangled.

Youth have hanged themselves on goalposts in Knocknaheeny. Maybe they've hanged themselves on this one. But it's not as bad as Tralee, County Kerry.

In a house the colour of an armadillo to the Ascension Church side of St Vincent's soccer field—sixty years old, cross on top of it warding off the threat of industrial waste land owned by Nama above it—with Kashmir white geraniums outside it and a shrine with the Sacred Heart and the Blessed Virgin, both with hearts like blood octopuses, spider leg tentacles around the hearts, she with a wreathe of plastic dianthus, there's a photograph of seven Tralee youths, one kin—his hair and features have the gleamings of the liquid scarlet berry of the strawberry tree—against a goalpost in Oatfield. Five attempted suicide on the goalpost. Four succeeded, including their kin.

A bus with Lionel Richie's face blown up outside it and an Ava's ice-cream van goes by and I continue up the hill.

They had reunions at Gerry Whelan's pub in New Square in Mitchelstown, which was once a barracks, the boys who'd been in Cork Jail together. Shared cigarettes outside the pub, trackie bottoms pulled up like toreador trousers, pompons as big as dumb-bells on woollen caps.

(Shanno lifted a weight bar with car wheels on the end of it in Knocknaheeny. 'I'm like Scarface. All I have is my balls.' When Shanno's pubes were just coming, brick red like the knot's summer breast when he comes in August, those balls were objects to be handled by brothers who boxed in a boxing club in winter, wearing plum tomato coloured boxing gloves, horse iodine all over the place because of all the blood, and a turf fire lighting and they all boxing around the fire. The extra-lean amber August fox, snowy face, ravishing black outlines—pared down truth—who comes to steal the silver birch Japanese cocks and what they called silver fanny hens in the back garden, you learn something from this.)

And outside Gerry Whelan's pub Branchy, one of the boys who'd been in Cork Jail, would crouch like St Fanachan outside the Garda station, ears of his white afghan hat dangling, to receive the kisses of Cocoa, a mongrel terrier, brown as the body's recesses.

Lidl in Mitchelstown is the same as Lidl everywhere else but Cork Jail is different from other jails.

The circus animals are held in quarantine in England so Mary Chipperfield brought her circus to Spain. Her father came to visit her in a chopper.

Being in Cork Jail was like being a circus animal in quarantine in England.

Twenty-three-hour lockdown padded cell in Mountjoy, on suicide watch, wearing nothing but black briefs with yellow lower hem and a pouch with ferret's face with two white eyes, before being sent to the committal prison of Portlaoise. That was after Cork Jail. And what did you think of? Branchy Kennevey who'd been in Cork Jail with him was from Fermoy, his family married into the Travellers at Castletownroche, and he'd told him how in Beechfield Cemetery during the Famine starving dogs—a dog for Shanno would always be his father's dog Mr Wrinkles, Australian shepherd and pit terrier, colour of night and a moon and a hamster, his father would take walking by the wood dock by the Lee—would dig up paupers' graves, the gravediggers not digging deep enough, coffins buried a few inches from the surface; the snuff porn—a man with bloodhound's face sprinkled with pepper, Messiah length hair, in Knocknaheeny videos his ten- and nine-year-old sons having sex and disseminated it and that was called snuff porn—that used happen in the lanes of the military part of town, Little England; about the black boy Jimmy Durham from Sudan, his mother killed on a boat in which she was taking him to Egypt when attacked by Durham Light Infantry, the Infantry taking him, christening him, eventually bringing him as a regimental bandsman to Fermoy where he died not much more than a boy, of pneumonia, his Fermoy grave marked by a white cross.

And about Pob Horken, a Traveller boy from Fermoy, still in Cork Jail, stud in his left ear, mass wafer-white rosary around his neck, sides of his head like a shorn rabbit, altogether with the look of a Vincent's Workshops toy punished by many hands, listening to these stories in a tank top—Montano as Scarface on it with butt of cigar in mouth and the words *Drugs Saved My Life*—with ferret eyes.

Up from Cork with a mobile phone charger and twenty-five euros. Most of it spent on the first night's hostel.

Near Spar on Amiens Street.

'If I have to beg on the streets I will. I did in London.'

And he displayed a souvenir other than Portlaoise Jail identity card—stub of an Aer Lingus Heathrow ticket.

'There was a pile of horses on the commonage by Apple computers. The horses turned up the soil. They took everything. The Turleys don't even have a goat left.'

This hegira from Cork to Dublin would become hostels in Georgian houses like tomatoes Romanian women scavenged at the end of the day on Moore Street or Camden Street, no horses in his dreams in these hostels, only heartbroken zebras grazing.

'Stop shooting me,' he would say to the city where he would queue in Skipper's Lane by St Peter and Paul Church for the food parcels the Capuchins give out and where he would sit in a café with fire brigade red seating, tiled fire brigade red enclosure to fish and chip counter with a woman whose hair was as Canadian snow, around her neck a large roundel medal of Our Lady of Pompeii with Saint Catherine of Alexandria (from whose head milk flowed when she was beheaded, who appeared to Joan of Arc with a crown on her head) before he accompanied her, her hair surf-suds against the Liffey, she trailing her carry on, carrying some of her belongings in plastic bags, to a night refuge where in late summer she eats blackberries—she's picked in the city suburbs—in a yogurt tub for her supper.

Walking through Truth Land.

Looking for accommodation in this city was like cruising through Golgotha and it was on one of those days of looking—I'd seen a picture of Padre Pio stabbed on a hallstand and met a youth in Timberland boots (Shanno was wearing tan Caterpillar boots from Penneys) fleeing unsettled Moscow by that hallstand on a similar search—days of epileptic daffodils.

Becoming homeless suddenly is like having a bomb dropped on your life.

'Not fit for rats to live in,' the Moscow youth said about some mecca for silverfish he'd seen that day.

Looking for a room in this city was like a woman having an abortion.

'Where will I get a one bedroom flat in this murk?' said a woman in Argyle socks, white plimsolls, diamante hairband, bortsch pink jacket, rose mittens with sky blue lines in them sticking out of her jeans pocket, young but with a despairing orangutan's face, as she entwined herself deeper in the youth with highlightings in his jeans, with whom she was sharing a roll-up.

'I've a lot of worries. I'm going to walk into the Liffey. I'll drown,' a man whose legs wobbled like a grasshopper's so he looked like a grasshopper with copper hair, had avowed as he looked at a black guillemot on the Liffey, who had just turned black again after being white for winter, whom he was thinking of joining. Did he know that a dune-coloured rabbit, who likes flat parsley, of a man who'd been homeless for twenty-two years, from out there in Ballyfermot where the Gala Cinema is now Bingo, was flung in the Liffey near this spot and redeemed by his owner? 'Happy as Larry now,' says his owner in a deerstalker hat as the rabbit looks out inquisitively from the zip top of a carry on as the man's pomeranian follows them.

Shanno had seen a black rabbit on his way from Cork to Dublin.

'We're a family of two and we're homeless,' a woman with Toby Jug countenance told me, paraffin purple ribbon at back of her hair in crab smock, striped trackie bottoms, the only feminine thing a delicate leopard spot scarf tied around her neck. Her teenage son beside her demonstrated his pink flushed leg—a shop girl's leg—in blue and suffering plimsolls by pulling up his trackie bottoms. Baby fringe. Adonis luxuriant mouth, facial features.

When they did have a home he was taught boxing at Frank Kerr Memorial Hall Boxing Club in Drimnagh—where opposite Luigi's Fish and Chip Place and Pizzeria two Polish youth were asked to buy drink from an off-licence for underage drinkers, refused, screwdriver driven in one of their heads, the other jumped off a crane from grief—by Michael Carruth, Barcelona Olympic boxing champion, masseur to the Westmeath Football team, from a Protestant North of Ireland family who became Dublin Catholics, great granduncle executed on Republican side in the Civil War.

'My nose has been broken so many times I don't notice,' said Shanno showing me a photograph of Conor 'Notorious' McGregor, mixed martial arts artist—boxing, kickboxing, Brazilian Jiu Jitsu, capoeira—wearing only leather briefs, with the Tricolour draped on his shoulders.

He'd wait in Dublin until he saw Conor McGregor oppose Cole Miller in the UFC fight in mid July.

In Knocknaheeny Shanno would box wearing nothing but faux lion skin briefs and then have a Breast in a Bun meal from Burger Hut.

To beg I am not ashamed. He did it before when he lived with his father, Savage, eyes the colour of gravestones, in Milford Estate, near Surrey Docks. There was a black dealer there called Elephant. 'What do you expect me to do?' Savage had asked Social Welfare, 'Swim back to Knocknaheeny? Swim back to The Glen? Swim back to St Lukes? Swim back to Blackpool Shopping Centre?' Savage died of a heroin overdose. 'If God wants you, he will call you.' Elephant gave up dealing and started a house church in Milford Estate at the same time. 'I was convicted in my soul.'

Del Del his mother, dirt on the street, Shanno said, sex for the crack.

A woman like a Samurai wrestler walked past us, cigarette like rockets in each ear.

Del Del goes begging with a foxy long-haired chihuahua Little Ted, as she leads a blind man, Eyeball Furney, who wears a sombrero.

You'd see them near Heckscher (suppliers to the piano trade since 1883) in

Kentish Town or New Camden Chapel Methodists Church with its two pillars or the yellow and green brick Hope & Anchor pub on Crowndale Road or situating themselves under the George's flag somewhere, she a woman with high forehead, cleft bald spot at the back of head, algal—hanging grooves—in face, like stalactites, often in fudge-pink flared trousers.

She called you Baby until you were six or seven in Knocknaheeny, dressing you in a cinnamon suit like a prince.

Taking the 202 bus to Knocknaheeny is like being in the Armageddon of a courthouse, faces colours of Dracula make-up, blue, purple, red. A gallery of prison tattoos. Perhaps it's like being in Portlaoise Jail.

He wasn't afraid of death Shanno told me. He was afraid of being a vegetable in a wheelchair. Showed me the meat cleaver scar on his forehead.

Four gangs after one gang. They come up from Togher.

'They're *jalous*.'

He and his brothers had a Wembly .22-calibre revolver. 9mm automatic handgun, a Beretta.25, a .38 revolver, a .12 gauge shotgun, a Smith and Weston Full rifle, a 2.2 rifle, a sawnoff biretta rifle.

There'd been shots through the window. He was afraid to go into the back garden where the silver birch Japanese cocks were.

In his mind it was all like when Skigger, a cousin of theirs, roach like a Khepresh, a Pharoah's war crown, was chased by a squad car out the South Ring by-pass tunnel, went up an embankment, was killed.

The story of my life on a Dublin street where a girl in fuchsine jump suit passed—in this city of herring gulls who approach those sleeping out as if they are smoked haddock on sale, of kestrels in belfrys, of guillemots on suicide water (eight and a half thousand people had disappeared in the country in the past year a man with facial growth the colour of Lucozade, in Smartie red jacket on a bus coming into the city had told me, leaning his head back on the seat like an apostle, many left the country, many committed suicide)—like a flamingo on crutches.

Lego, Shanno's oldest brother had died in his sleep aged forty-nine.

'Nine yards in and out,' he'd said about the farm-school he'd been sent to in Cork after being caught shoplifting. Thirteen. Shared a room with a sixteen year old. But then you're spoken for, matched at a very early age with a Traveller girl, married in St Mary's Cathedral, The North Chapel.

'Go in there and say a few prayers for Lego.'

Young, Lego had an Adonis roach with frontal spare rat-tails. Ash Wednesday ash moustache, cigarette periodically put in his mouth not so much to smoke as a habit of show, as saying he welcomed attention.

When he died he was a man with a harelip who looked as if part of his face was chewed away by the dog which leaped off Dracula's ship.

Lego's coffin was borne in a black, gilded edge funeral hearse coach drawn by two cream draught horses, the kind the guards use, but with white plumes, the driver all in black, but not in a top hat, but black homburg hat, the coach covered with teddybears, horseshoe wreathes, bird-cages trussed with flowers, past Key Cabs and Mahony's (minerals, tobacco, newsagents, top-ups), past St Vincent's soccer field where a sulky doing circles was followed by a black greyhound and an indeterminate hound, girls behind in hoop earrings and diamante belts like the gold and silver of Montezuma which Spain seized from Mexico, to St Mary on the Hill Church.

Outside it a woman in Capuchin friar type raingear, was heard to say: 'They eat too much. They drink too much. They smoke too much. They have sex too much and they don't take exercise.'

At the top of the hill, past the flanks of fawn, mauve, grey, terracotta, emerald, bottle green houses, past the industrial waste land owned by Nama, past the reservoir with one skewbald horse, soiled like a turnip just picked from the ground, left after the confiscations, is a shrine with a statue of the Blessed Virgin and the Sacred Heart, two kneeling angels, both with their heads chopped off, an empty Green Giant corn on the cob tin thrown on it, the kind of memorial shrine Lego will have, a halting site nearby, a field with empty gas canisters and lopsided horse boxes between the halting site and the shrine, where a mallard and his wife live, far from water.

Looking down at Cork from here is like looking down at it from space or from Heaven.

Down there in Cork there are some who believe that there are people who live in Knocknaheeny who dognap small domestic dogs—schnauzers, shih tzus, crested Chinese, Lhasa Apsos, Tibetan terriers, Japanese chin dogs, Boston terriers, Mexican hairless dogs, West Highland terriers, French bulldogs—and throw them to wild Rottweilers in Knocknaheeny for bets and then set the Rottweilers on one another.

One woman who dresses in dignified black from head to foot, black cloche hat, except she wears Clube de Ragatas de Flamengo scarlet and black stripe soccer stockings, claims Gisela her Daschund puppy perished in this way.

'I'm a Traveller,' Shanno tells everyone he meets to extricate himself, to save his history and his family history—his family used go to Spilsby in Lincolnshire once from Cork for potato picking, the fasten penny contract for autumn and winter work, Hogmanay more celebrated than Christmas because the bosses were Scottish, Scotland the coldest country in the world it was said and the Cork Traveller women marrying into the Scottish Travellers who were always drinkers and who had their own ways and the Cork women having to adapt to them but now they say there's a new generation—from the colour pink which is the colour of poverty.

A rose-pink blanket with white rabbit heads over a mulatto baby, his white mother holding pink purse with galaxy scintillation, her hair pink-sienna.

Dirty purple, plum, claret anoraks.

Over another baby a power-red blanket with aquamarine owl heads on it.

Amid the reds there's a child's forget-me-not blue eyes in homeless seagull-featured face.

Another small boy with light ginger hair, front tooth missing, dabs of ointment snow over his face, in lemon and orange plimsolls, says, 'I'm ringing my nanny.'

Walking through Truth Land and who did you meet?

A man who stands on Nicholas Street beside Christ Church Square all day, opposite St Audoen's Catholic Church from which Poles steal candles and boil kettles on them, black woollen hat pulled down on his face which greatly resembles that of early Abbey actor Barry Fitzgerald, extra large carry-on beside him, bags, wears a black rain cape which makes him look like a Connaught nun, but when summer comes closer—and the blue geraniums and black mullein planted by a gardener who died suddenly after planting them intermingle in St Audoen's medieval church where Margaret Ball, thrown into a dungeon by her own son for not taking the Oath, is buried—and the date of the Conor McGregor and Cole Miller fight (you did Thai boxing and main boxing yourself) draws nearer, wears true white plimsolls and you can see his tie, white tie, interlocking signal red and black bar patterns.

He takes notes.

'I'm watching the traffic until five.'

'Why don't you sit down?'

'Bring me an armchair.'

*

King Shanno is running wild.

With his hair colour Shanno through Dublin like a cardinal bird let loose in the streets.

Bearberries grow where the Sugruf Traveller king's horses, banshee-white and lavish-haired, graze, and fleabane outside the cemetery where he is buried.

On the Sugruf king's grave, with its blooded marble cross, is a tall Blessed Virgin in white and blue, her teenage son to left side, in azure garments, pointing to his heart, peony-size rose in left hand, his hair curly Titian red of the Sugrufs.

Criminal, convict, prisoner, beggar: but the part of you they didn't get hold of has royal blood, is a king; in such a cosmogony you had ancestors who were kings before Christ healed the ten men who were lepers.

Such cosmogonies help you to walk through Truth Land. They sit beside you when you are a pariah dining at Morelli's, established 1959, or Iskander's kebab house—shawarma specialist (marinated slices of lamb, chicken built up)—or Aussie Outback BBQs.

'Brother.'

The sores on a junkie's face outside Good World Restaurant are as big as lollipops; Tinker's, Traveller's facial features once, auburn colouring still in the hair, the features having become amorphous—they are not adrift from tribe, they have excommunicated themselves from Tribe.

'O the streets of Dublin city can be friendly and so bright
But sometimes seem so lonely for strangers in the night.'

Big Tom blasts from a white Traveller van with bars on top, which looks like an argument, a fight, a stoush, and you wonder are these Royal Kin?

To follow the seal up the Lee to the Swimming Hell Hole as he looks for salmon. You can't eat raw fish. You need other sustenance—Morelli's, established 1959, Iskander's kebab house, Aussie Outback BBQs. To follow the seal down river, as he snortles like a king, disturbing herons who complain like lags, his belly full.

But the river is not his Kingdom. His realms are when he reaches the salt tide, past the salmon pass and the half barrier to one side of the middle bank. This place is not your Kingdom, will never be your Kingdom.

When my father died first to greet me outside the church was Bridie Lawrence, a Traveller woman—thin as an eel, sharp featured as an axe, hair in two separate strands, sockets in her face, in someone's cast off chin up coat—with her fracture of sons who had hair the colour of New England in autumn.

I went almost immediately afterwards to Lissadell Beach below Lissadell House with a friend, a guard from County Kerry. Forget the pain and remember the flowers he liked to say.

It was the tall goldenrod, the autumn hawkbit, the water-forget-me-nots, the Japanese knotweed, the Russian vine, the toadflax that day. Toadflax used be used for dropsy. The hemp agrimony had turned to banks of fluff like mattresses slashed to pieces.

When I was a child my father had taken me to a summer magic lantern performance of *Twelfth Night* in the Greek Temple on the lake in Blackrock Park where the rudbeckias, the coneflowers thrive until late November.

'Not a flower, not a flower, sweet

On my black coffin let there be strewn.'

The barnacle geese had already arrived in Goose Field and sounded like a pack of dogs.

My mother had given me my father's gold stretchy band watch.

'Here, wear this jewel for me…'

I'd left it on the beach with my clothes when I went swimming and a mist and late October darkness came and I couldn't find the watch with my clothes and I searched for an hour or two, in the dark, on my knees, sifting and flaying the sand, until I found it and I held it in my hand and I held his stories of rebellion and civil war, and to forget the pain the water-forget-me-not river.

The Philadelphia Frocks

Both are beautiful, black, dressmaker made, dancing frocks,
knee length; one silk, scattered with ribboned blue flowers,
narrow, tight bodiced, the other spins with pink and white

lily of the valley curling a flarier skirt, taffeta sash.
Long back zips whisper America, confident, generous,
safe and smiling, blown kisses and brave waving

from decks of ships leaving behind a cold island, a colder
Europe. Eight siblings out of nine gone, watching from
the heaving decks mountains they will never see again.

Clooneigh is evening dark and furniture glows, deepens,
glows in the turf warmth. A suitcase lies across a chair;
two young women are going through clothes; a little girl

watches and listens to the ticking, ticking of the clock
above the fire. She loves this clock, the American clock,
sent proudly back seventy years earlier. Later in her life,

someone in England will try to mend it, fail, her last sight
of it will be in silent pieces but that night in the gold light,
glass case gilded with ducks and bulrushes, it speaks

as her mother and her aunt shake dresses into
straightness against themselves. The child thinks these
film stars' frocks, so dark and pretty, unfolding from

their ocean voyage and breathing perfumes she is too young
to name. She feels the distance, the Atlantic
drift of homesickness and loss touch her face and the black

and flowered fabrics open out like weeping; she knows
the journeying girl who wore them often cried herself
to sleep. Over the years hips and midriffs widened.

The frocks stayed slender, reeled to yet another country,
into her life, ready for more dancing, more heartbreaks,
quarrels, perfume, after dark behaviour. She kept them safe,

remembering how long a journey they'd made, still
East Coast beautiful, sad ghost scents of powder compacts,
vanishing cream, patterns knotted and intricate like a family.

In her wardrobe they hang for ever in that first evening,
the fields quiet, the cattle brought in, lights in the window
of the sleeping farm and Philadelphia so far, so far away.

Mary Woodward

Mivarts Hotel, 1847

A London winter at its most indulgent, well worth the cost: smart,
select. His wife and daughter enjoy the Mayfair shops, while

he spends mornings riding, lunches at his club in Regent Street,
is back for tea—just ladies' nonsense, not what he would call a meal:

lettuce hearts, thin bread and butter. Almond biscuits. Iced fancies.
Tea with lemon in china you can see through. And the gossip...

the Archduke and the pretty hat-shop girls, the French Comte's
fat wife's lovers, and the German industrialist with that charming,

witty, young male secretary. He nods knowingly; it's good
to see them so relaxed and happy. Impossible back home

where there are shadows at every turning. They forget it here.
But he cannot: on his desk each afternoon the letters demanding

answers to that eternal, ghastly question—what's to be done about
the tenants? *Even the good ones who always pay their rent cannot,*

despairs his agent, ready for the bailiffs. Eviction is slow; trailing
sick children and half-dead parents, just how far off will they go?

Food has come from America: Indian corn, which takes hours to cook—
if there's enough turf—a hard grain they can't digest, adding to

the cramps and vomit of typhus and dysentery. Yes, shipping off a few
will help. No remedies. No solutions. Till the assassin in the lane.

Mary Woodward

Poblacht na Hero

Iggy McGovern

The first time I saw the mural I thought: You'd only find the like in America!

Let me explain.

This is 1976. I am the fiddle-player and General Manager of The Irish Boomerang. (It's an old joke—the Irish Boomerang doesn't come back, it just sings about coming back!) We are yet another second-rate folk group, trying to make a go of it in the States, topping (and tailing) the bill at The Shamrock Bar in Chicago. The mural in question is the backdrop to the little stage at The Shamrock; it shows Pearse and Connolly in vivid green tunics in front of the GPO in Dublin. They are posting up the Proclamation. Because the poster is curved around one of the pillars, there is not enough room for all of POBLACHT NA hEIREANN. So it is easy to imagine the artist thinking: POBLACHT NA hEIR looks kinda dumb, why don't I just make it POBLACHT NA HERO?

'Is that okay with you, Big Mikey?'

'Yeah, okay, just do it, will ya!'

Big Mikey, part-owner of The Shamrock, Irish-Italian patriot and all-round scum bag, has us over a barrel. A small matter of work visas, not to mention the last known address of Seamus, guitar and vocals. Not that Seamus was ever convicted of anything; legal niceties were not much in vogue in the Belfast of the early seventies. It was just about some milk bottles, according to Seamus. High octane milk and a lighted rag and a pitcher's arm and strike one! It wasn't too long before the snatch squad put him out of harm's way, up in the Kesh doing six O Levels. He was such a model internee that they let him out to attend his granny's funeral. He promptly gave his escort the slip, hopped over the border and caught a plane to join us in the Windy City.

'Us' was myself and Tony, button-squeezebox, recent graduate in History & Politics, keeper of dangerous company. Tony's idea of relaxation was hanging out at a crosstown jazz club, the only white face there, if not in the whole neighbourhood. By any odds he should have been mugged or murdered but the squeezebox was his passport. He had made friends with a black player called Toby. Tony and Toby, the Windy City twins. Indeed, they did look like brothers, or half-brothers at least: the same frame, the same bouncing walk, the same complete lack of common sense. Like that Saturday afternoon when the pair of them landed into The Shamrock, drunk as lords. You could have skated on the permafrost that spread throughout the place as Toby addressed Big Mikey—'Yo, Brother, Ah'll be havin' a point o' gueeeness'—in his best buttermilk brogue. Before Big Mikey could get his considerable frame out from behind the bar, Seamus had managed to hustle them out the door. A few heated words were exchanged, with Seamus having the final say:

'Just remember this, Tony, you can go back home anytime—I can't!'

So, The Irish Boomerang continued to dish up a mix of come-all-ye and rebel songs three nights a week at The Shamrock. We were starting to draw bigger crowds and Big Mikey was softening towards us. We got a pay rise and the promise of more to come if we 'kept our noses clean'. This last comment came with a hard look in Tony's direction. Toby couldn't drink in The Shamrock but he was a frequent visitor to our apartment, even joining in our practice sessions. He was a born musician; he just had to hear a tune once and he could play it straight back to you!

At the beginning of March, Big Mikey called us into his office. This was a big step up; only the Mafia types who co-owned The Shamrock were permitted in this shrine to all things Oirish.

'Siddown, boys, wanna beer? Ya know Saint Paddy's Day is coming up and I've been thinking of doin' something really special. Did ya ever see a movie called *Darby O'Gill And The Little People*? It has that great Irish actor Sean Somebody Or Other in it!'

I could see Tony framing a suitable sarcasm: that would be Sean-as-Irish-as-the-bagpipes-Connery, perhaps? I decided to get in ahead of him:

'Yeah, Mikey, great show! How about those dancing leprechauns, weren't they just fantastic?'

This was my first mistake.

Big Mikey nodded in approval.

'Ya goddit in one! Boys, I want ya dressed up as leprechauns for Saint Paddy's night. See, here, I've already gotten ya the hats!'

From under his Connemara marble desk he produced three elongated pork-pie hats in fluorescent green; on the front of each was a big 'L' (presumably for leprechaun or was it for loser?). We stared in stunned silence at the leaning tower of green. Then Big Mikey said softly: 'I'm making real good progress on those visas, boys.'

Seamus reached over and took the topmost hat and solemnly placed it on his head. Tony and I slowly followed suit. The Irish Boomerang had sold out for The Crock of Gold.

But our humiliation was not quite complete. There were also flimsy shirts of green paper, printed with horseshoes and shamrocks, and knee-length breeches of the same material. The only consolation was that the fabric would not last more than one night. As we crawled out of Big Mikey's office, I'll swear he was laughing; you couldn't blame him.

We spent the next fortnight keeping each other from leaving town. Only for Toby, we would certainly have lost Tony. Even Seamus was prepared to risk losing the all-important visa. The closing argument the evening before went something like this:

'It's only for the one night, right?'

'Right.'

'And everyone will be scuttered, anyway, right?'

'Right.'

'Including us, right?'

'Especially us!'

'So, we'll do it?'

'Yeah, might as well!'

As if to put the Almighty's seal on this bad bargain, the phone rang.

'It's for you, Tony, it's your Ma.'

Another Granny down and Tony's parents have booked him on a flight home the following evening.

'Well, the lengths some people would go to, just to miss the Saint Paddy's night gig!'

'Lucky Leprechaun, what will you do with your other two wishes?'

But beneath all the banter we were thinking that without a squeezebox

The Irish Boomerang was a pretty thin sound. Big Mikey would not be at all pleased. Those visas were once more a fading dream.

'Toby could stand in for me. Couldn't you, Tobe?'

'Yeah, no problem, man!'

Seamus exploded: 'Are you mad in the head? Have you forgotten what happened when you brought Toby into The Shamrock? Big Mikey would rather see an Orange Band up on that stage than a black leprechaun!'

'Of course, he could always wear make-up!'

My big mouth again! Two minutes later, a whiter than white-faced Toby paraded before us. When we added the leprechaun hat and the squeezebox, you could almost convince yourself that it really was Tony.

'But what about his hands?'

'They'll be out of sight on the sides of the squeezebox. We'll keep him out of the main light, anyway.'

Finally, it was decided that we would all wear the face make-up and, for good measure, we would paint shamrocks on our cheeks. Operation Fairy Child had begun.

On Saint Patrick's night Seamus and I slipped into the dressing room at The Shamrock while Toby stayed outside in the van.

'We'll only bring you in at the last minute, Tobe. We don't want any close encounters with Big Mikey.'

Sure enough, Big Mikey's bulk filled the dressing-room doorway. He was in great form, thanks to a few green Martinis.

'Okay, boys? Hey, where's Huck Finn?'

'Tony, is it? Oh, he had to meet someone. He'll be here.'

'He ought to spend more time with his own people.'

'Well, he's certainly doing that tonight, Big Mikey.'

'Good. Okay. So what's with the war-paint?'

'It's an old tradition that the leprechauns had very white faces. I guess they missed that in *Darby O'Gill*.'

'Get outa here! Nice to see ya entering into the spirit of this. Do a good show, boys, I've got some "family" coming in tonight.'

Which was the only thing missing from this farce: the front tables occupied by The Friends of Italian Opera.

And then we were on, to drunken applause and the occasional shout of 'Hey, Bianco!' Toby was in the shadows, stage left, Seamus was centre and I was on the right, Pearse and Connolly were behind us. I was thinking that the

GPO might have been a lot safer than this. But then the gig started and Toby put new life into those tired old tunes and soon everyone was having too good a time to notice any difference.

We were getting down to the last couple of numbers when it all started to go wrong. Elvis was to blame, in a way. After watching a re-run of the Hawaii concert on television Seamus had taken to bringing a white towel on stage. 'For the perspiration,' he would say. But really he hoped young women would fight over it (and him) when he pitched it into the crowd during the last set; the cleaners always found it in a corner the next morning. But the solid phalanx of gold-toothed, gold-chained gorillas at the front tables made him think again and this time he flung the towel into the wings.

In slow-motion action-replay I can still see Toby's arm rise to expertly field the towel and then begin to wipe his face. Just as Seamus is saying 'and on button squeezebox, Mister Tony McNamara,' he steps forward into the full glare of the lights, a poor imitation of a Black and White Minstrel. He makes a low bow, so low that he is practically eye to eye with Big Mikey who grabs him by the green paper shirt, and when he straightens up, his bare chest is revealed in all its ebony glory.

There is a stunned silence which I fill with an inspired if wobbly introduction to 'A Nation Once Again', bringing the audience struggling to their feet. That's how we always end our show. A few rousing choruses of 'A Nation' marches them up to the top of the hill, but you can't leave them there, of course. That's when Seamus will come forward to sing unaccompanied the slow, plaintiff and very rebel 'Only Our Rivers Run Free'. And Toby is already three blocks away and running.

Seamus steps forward. He opens his mouth but it's not 'Only Our Rivers Run Free', it's that great anthem of Civil Rights, 'We Shall Overcome'. They don't get it immediately but when they do, all hell breaks loose.

Seamus will tell you that he saw the bottle coming. But he also says that what he actually saw was a Belfast milk bottle with a burning rag in it and he just could not duck. He went down at the feet of Pearse and Connolly.

POBLACHT NA HERO? Ya goddit in one!

i measc mo dhaoine

for Máirtín Ó Direáin

there is another language we can speak
we have always spoken
learned at school at the same time
we wrote down words on sharp yellow paper
little rectangles for our butter boxes
to take from our ciseán at going-home time

it is the language of fireplaces sunk in walls
fireplaces that sit on Patrick Street
next to newborn babies and mothers
having a smoke in Hello Kitty pyjamas
royal blue boxes of Roses past their sell-by dates
ward sisters with upside-down watches

stuck in walls of partly demolished buildings
twenty feet up, hearths facing outward
brass and steel grates showing their teeth to passers-by
laughing at us
the innards of these buildings
held in so tight, hammered, melted into concrete

they're worth something you know
my mother says as we pass
someone will take those some night
bandits skirting through scaffolding
pulling the hunks of metal from fifty-foot walls
implanted like caves in the souls of new homes

Julie Morrissy

Frank O'Connor's 1920s Cultural Criticism and the Poetic Realist Short Story

Hilary Lennon

In a private letter to his friend Sean Hendrick in 1925, Frank O'Connor wrote with the intention of seeking support 'in a matter of pure necessity' and asked his friend to write to the editor of the *Irish Statesman* under an assumed name. O'Connor and poet Geoffrey Phibbs were attacking the 'literary language of our Dublin friends' and he wanted Hendrick's help to 'dispose of the Irish Literary Renaissance in a suitably undignified manner'. Ironically, in the same letter O'Connor mentioned he was holding on to a copy of *Ulysses* for Hendrick as he was 'afraid to send it through the post'. Though O'Connor was primarily engaged with the cultural debates that were taking place in the pages of the *Irish Statesman*, particularly the issue of re-Gaelicisation and its impact on Ireland's literature, the letter also reveals the aspiring writer's own anxiety of influence concerning his immediate Irish literary predecessors. Caught between his two father-figures—writers Daniel Corkery and George Russell (AE), who had positioned themselves on opposing sides of the re-Gaelicisation debate—and eager to distance his writing from both the romanticism of the Revival and the experimentalism of the modernist movement, O'Connor's epistolary machinations in the 1920s formed part of a concerted effort to carve out his own literary philosophy.

It is commonplace at this stage, of course, to situate O'Connor's notions within a framework of disenchantment with Romantic Ireland and with the ascendant aesthetics of modernism, in conjunction with an implication that in the mid-twentieth-century Irish short story, progression of the form had been replaced by fiction concerned with regionalism and national debate. While this compartmentalisation is in part borne out by O'Connor's œuvre, the result is often a restricted localising of the writer alongside critical declaration that he is best read within an autobiographical context. Instead, what has only been intermittently and cursorily noted of O'Connor's writings is the fact that his creative imagination had also continued to interact with, encompass and build on the achievements of an earlier short-story tradition. This interaction resulted in his work being strongly influenced by international achievements in the form, and O'Connor's subsequent development of, this essay suggests, 'poetic realist' short stories.

Notwithstanding a concentration on poetry throughout this decade (and his original unpublished poetry does contain literary merit), O'Connor tended to believe his greatest success and satisfaction was located in the short-story form. In a 1926 letter to Phibbs, he admitted as much when he wrote that: 'It's only in my stories I'm getting what I want though I slave more at poetry than at anything else'. It is evident from these early short stories—between 1926 and 1929 six uncollected and two collected stories were published in the *Irish Tribune*, the *Dublin Magazine* and the *Irish Statesman*—that O'Connor was already well aware of short-story traditions before he embarked on his own experiments. It is difficult, however, in this period to accurately trace his reading history in the genre as O'Connor was already working as a librarian when he commenced writing short stories and had ready access to books (Boole Library in University College Cork holds his personal library and this contains a vast array of short-story collections, but no chronological record exists of when the writer obtained these books). O'Connor claimed in his autobiography, *An Only Child* (1961), that he had a marked attraction for poetry in his youth and that the majority of his reading had focused on this pursuit. Yet, the autobiography also alludes to the fact that from a young age O'Connor had been regularly reading short fiction in the weekly boys' magazines and in penny publications such as the *Gem* and the *Magnet*. It was an early influence that had provoked intimations of social displacement in the artist as a young boy, which he acknowledged in *Towards An Appreciation of Literature* (Metropolitan, 1945): 'they created standards of behaviour in my mind which could not be fitted in to the life about me'. Discovering his former teacher's first collection of short stories, Corkery's *A Munster Twilight* (1916), also had a considerable impact: 'that settled the hash of the English boys' weeklies. I did not know their authors as I knew Corkery, and henceforth their creations would be less real to me that his, little as I might understand them'. (*An Only Child*) Reading stories that O'Connor could culturally relate to was a stimulus that would remain with him, as he would always seek to depict Irish life in his own writing.

It was Corkery too who first introduced him to nineteenth-century international prose writers after O'Connor had joined Corkery's weekly cultural gathering, the Twenty Club, prior to the outbreak of the Irish Civil War. It was in this select club where O'Connor also met writer Sean O'Faolain, who gave O'Connor his first Turgenev to read. Tellingly, he mentioned in his autobiography that whilst imprisoned in Gormanstown internment camp in 1923, he wrote a prize-winning essay in Irish on Ivan Turgenev (this essay appears not to have survived). In addition, in a 1924 letter to Hendrick, O'Connor directly referred to the fact that he had been reading the nineteenth-century masters of the short story. His subsequent and substantial mid-to-late 1920s cultural criticism repeatedly signalled an admiration for nineteenth-century Russian and French realist short-story writers. (He also started learning Russian and French in this period.) From 1923 onwards, as mentioned in another letter to Hendrick, O'Connor was also reading the short stories that featured in the *Dublin Magazine*. Taken together, his letters, autobiography and literary criticism confirm that O'Connor was already very well-informed about national and international trends in the short story before he first ventured into the form. Locating O'Connor's 'realist' short stories, therefore, specifically within an oppositional stance toward the heroic romanticism of the Revival and the experimentalism of modernism negates the impact of his literary influences.

The nineteenth-century Irish short story also had its source of inspiration for the writer. While George Moore's *The Untilled Field* (1903) has been largely accepted as marking the beginning of the modern Irish short story, a recent study has extensively broadened the field of research into the nineteenth-century tradition. As Heather Ingman contends in *A History of the Irish Short Story* (2009), the characteristics of the modernist short story—'impressionistic, concentrated, resisting narrative closure'—were already present in Irish fin-de-siècle short fiction, notably in writers such as James Stephens, W.B. Yeats and George Egerton. Although the above-mentioned distinguishing features are habitually attributed to the modernist story, these are traits which are also discernible in several O'Connor stories. It suggests the point that the modern development of the form itself leans towards a tempering of the modernist/realist critical boundary. Short story thematic and technical characteristics (such as, for example, fragmentation, disconnections, alienation, anti-heroic modes, spiritual bankruptcy, open-endedness, and character interiority) are features common to both the modernist and modern-realist mode, pointing to central continuities between apparently divergent literary classifications. As a case in point, Joyce's *Dubliners* encompasses both realist and modernist attributes. Connections between Irish literary realism and modernism are further illustrated by the fact that Patrick Kavanagh's epic, *The Great Hunger*, has been hailed as one of the most important contributions to twentieth-century Irish literary realism while simultaneously recognised as strongly stylistically and ideologically influenced by T.S. Eliot's modernist epic, *The Waste Land*.

On a broader scale, the nineteenth-century short story tradition had a perceptible bearing on twentieth-century literary developments. Gregory A. Schirmer's 'Tales From Big House and Cabin: The Nineteenth Century'—published in a 1984 collection of essays edited by James F. Kilroy, *The Irish Short Story: A Critical History*—is one of the very few, albeit short, attempts at a literary history of the nineteenth-century Irish short story. He provides a damning overview: 'the mirror of Irish short fiction… was cracked—marred, at its worse, by annoying didacticism, purple prose, weak characterisation, uncertain narrative line, and a general disregard for aesthetic form'. Despite being published thirty years ago, Schirmer's chapter continues to serve as a useful guide. It does also recognise the artistic achievements, highlighting innovative aspects of nineteenth-century short fiction which anticipate the modern form—the manipulation of narrative voice, careful and economic selection of detail, inner psychological despair, and a self-reflexive irony.

This progression in nineteenth-century short fiction, however, did not take place in a literary vacuum as it resonated with advances being made in continental Europe by the Russian and French masters, by writers such as Turgenev, Chekhov and Maupassant who each played a leading role in the development of the modern short story. Both twentieth-century Irish modernist and realist short-story writers are critically acknowledged, though often perfunctorily, as fundamentally influenced by French and Russian short story literature and yet themselves are oft-times classified as contradictory and opposing categories of the form. On this basis alone, though this essay does not allow for it, an argument could be made that the subject requires further exploration of connections between the two modes.

It was American writer Edgar Allan Poe, of course, who had first articulated a critical definition of the short story in 1842. Poe had stated that the short story imparts a 'unity of effect or impression [which bestows] the deepest effects' on the reader'. Poe's emphasis on the economy of effects was a definition with uncanny accuracy. Slice-of-life episodes and intense compressed arrangement of form and content governed the evolution of the Russian and French short story. Maupassant's technical craftsmanship, single revelatory moment, and economy of narrative force; Chekhov's fragmented, suggestive and sparse episodic style; Turgenev's compacted and evocative method:

all in turn influenced the stylisation of the Irish short story. Moreover, their socio-political concerns—Maupassant's thematic focus on the marginalised in society, Turgenev's exploration of social injustices imposed on Russian serfs, and Chekhov's portrayal of the petite bourgeoisie—reverberated with O'Connor when he sought to convey the condition of life in post-independence Irish society. Nineteenth-century French and Russian realist short stories had dispensed with romantic conceptions of society and were instead attentive to such issues as religious repression, repressed desires, and frustrations with urban and rural life. Turgenev, Maupassant and Chekhov, alongside others such as Gogol and Babel, all served as aesthetic founders of literary realism in the short story. (In his work cited below, Joe Cleary admits that 'the distinction between realism and naturalism has never been fully clear, and the two terms are often used interchangeably'. He further contends that there are many different varieties in the realist mode, 'of which naturalism is only one current' (112). Taking this point into consideration, this essay uses the term 'realism' as an all-encompassing reference to this particular aesthetic mode, while remaining cognisant of the fact that it is an umbrella term for a literary style that contains within it a broad range of characteristics.) The intellectual underpinning of this mode was influenced from the mid-nineteenth century onwards by the discourse of thinkers such as Darwin, Marx and Freud. It resulted in a realist envisioning that has as its philosophical belief the notion that 'what happens in this world is explicable in terms of the mechanical laws of biology, physiology, economy or psychology'. Literary practitioners of the form were viewed in a sense as scientists: their works of art could clinically examine and expose 'the deeper "laws" that governed human behaviour'. (Cleary, 114) Chekhov and Maupassant wrote their realist stories during the Russia of Alexander III and the France of the fin de siècle which was 'an age of scepticism, of tedium, and of that "conglomerated mediocrity"'. (Lavrin, 2) Moreover, Turgenev believed that 'the genius of a great writer can discover life's "living truths"... "[t]o represent, accurately and with power, the truth, the reality of life is a writer's highest happiness"'. Nineteenth-century literary realist representation of reality rendered it 'as organically emerging from the historical processes which determine[d] the life of that period'. As Turgenev in particular saw it, a work of art sprang 'from the life of a nation' and an artist's work could be 'a progressive factor in the development of... society'. (Terras, 23; 31-2) It was an ethos that was notably similar to O'Connor's outlook, and other post-independence short story writers such as Sean Ó'Faoláin, Liam O'Flaherty and Mary Lavin: their artistic conception was not to make Irish literature radically original but to delineate reality with a more critical precision.

Similar to his contemporaries, O'Connor in his respective way had experienced disappointment with post-revolutionary conservative Ireland and this put him into a situation analogous to that of his realist predecessors. In turn, the ideological conceptions promoted by these international nineteenth-century writers were akin to the historicist and instrumentalist formulations that O'Connor had started to repeatedly convey in his mid-to-late 1920s cultural criticism. O'Connor's critical work throughout this decade—before he came to write his first collection of short stories, *Guests of the Nation* (1931)—resonated with the sound of nineteenth-century literary realism's suppositions. His recurring arguments that the 'historical memory' of a nation naturally impacted on contemporary reality, his idea that the circumstances of a writer's epoch had a deep bearing on the artistic work, and his belief that art could play an instrumentalist role in social development and reform: all of O'Connor's 1920s literary theories indicated his deep philosophical adherence to the nineteenth-century form, and it was a position that he would thereafter maintain throughout his critical writing career. In O'Connor's seminal study of the short story, *The Lonely Voice* (1962), for example, almost half of the writers surveyed belong to the nineteenth-century tradition, with Turgenev, Maupassant and Chekhov occupying the first three chapters in the book. Gogol does not receive an individual chapter but O'Connor does locate him centre-stage in the introduction: 'We have all come out from under Gogal's "Overcoat"'. Of course, it is with O'Connor's introduction that critics have most closely engaged to date, in particular his well-known theory of the 'submerged population group'. This oft-cited foundational concept in O'Connor's theorising of the form was linked predominantly (with Anderson the exception) to nineteenth-century realist short story writers in his explanatory expansion—'Gogol's officials, Turgenev's serfs, Maupassant's prostitutes, Chekhov's doctors and teachers, Sherwood Anderson's provincials'. His formulation was thoroughly embedded with practitioners of the nineteenth-century short story and O'Connor himself went so far as to state that his literary view had been 'largely coloured and limited' by his study of nineteenth-century literature. It was a philosophy that would also play an unequivocal role in O'Connor's attitude towards modernist writings.

Notwithstanding potential contemporary critical connections between the Irish modernist and realist short story, O'Connor had reform in mind when attempting—in his cultural criticism at the time—to dissociate himself from Irish modernism. His realist standpoint was reflective of a broader European debate in the 1920s and 1930s. In the Soviet Union, socialist realism became the official aesthetic; Fascist regimes as well as the Soviet Union regarded modernist art as bourgeois profligacy. Because of this, modernism tended to be regarded at this time as a resisting form to political assimilation. However, realism was also viewed as the aesthetic capable of offering strong interpretative criticism of social issues and state policies. It led to expansive debate on the aesthetic and political values of realism versus modernism. (Cleary, 140-1) There is little evidence though in O'Connor's 1920s critical writings that he was even aware of this larger discussion and yet his reading material, epistolary references, creative and critical work, exhibited a developing coalescence with European realism. The nineteenth-century realist tradition of the short story and its ambition of providing an aesthetically faithful portrait of society while simultaneously proffering critique, as opposed to exploring radical literary experimentalism, held for him the greatest appeal. By 1942, in his infamous essay on 'The Future of Irish Literature', the ideological underpinning of O'Connor's 1920s creative and intellectual leanings had solidified into a doctrine which claimed the country needed a literature that was critically engaged with the reality of Irish life: 'there is no public opinion, and if the artists do not fight, who will?' O'Connor's promotion of literary realist writers in the same article would later lead to a charge that the modernist component was being covertly written out of Irish literature. With some exceptions such as his lauding of D.H. Lawrence, modernist writers did tend to come in for either sustained attack or disregard in O'Connor's writings, and it was a position closely bound up with his theorising of the material conditions of literary reception in mid-twentieth-century Irish society.

O'Connor's stories for the most part do not endow characters with individual agency and an imputation of literary determinism could be applied to his works. Instead, the focus of his reform inclined on instrumentally influencing the reader. Turgenev had similarly believed in the cognitive impact of art: 'Fiction's contribution to knowledge is mainly so-called "types", aesthetic universals which help man to know himself and his society [… types] created directly from observed socio-historical reality.' O'Connor linked the private act of reading to the broader socio-political context, which he in turn fastened to his theories of the short-story form: 'a private art intended to satisfy the standards of the individual, solitary, critical reader [… who will] see into the shadows' of the story. The gaps and omissions inherent in the genre left a far greater onus on the reader to complete the picture proffered; it created space for the reader's 'moral imagination' and 'moral judgment' to dilate into social considerations. For O'Connor, this art form demanded a direct relationship between the writer and reader in specific historical conditions: 'Dragging the reader in, making the reader a part of the story—the reader is part of the story. You're saying all the time, "This story is about you—*de te fabula*"'. (*Paris Review*, 1957)

This admission buttressed O'Connor's anti-modernist slights in his later writings, but it also echoed his earlier elevation of the instinctual over the intellectual writer in his *Irish Statesman* re-Gaelicisation criticism—the idea that it was the moral, humanist instinct and not intellectual stylistics that was the more valuable in literature. O'Connor for instance translated a poem of seventeenth-century Irish language poet Dáibhí Ó Bruadair, 'Is Mairg na Fuil 'na Dhubhthuata', in one of his *Irish Statesman* articles—'The Poet as Professional'—but he did so only to dismiss its 'lofty' air. He disdainfully compared the intellectual technique of Ó Bruadair to modernist literature: 'so much mischievous arrogant craft... And again one smiles, thinking what form the Expressionists, Joyce and the rest have produced, more modern, more ecstatically ridiculous than the forms used by this cynical tatterdemalion of the seventeenth century'. This allegation in turn echoed O'Connor's private letter to Hendrick, imploring him to help dispose of the 'literary language' of the Irish Literary Renaissance, and was further linked to his advocacy of 'simple language' in another letter. 'After all, are not words the first test of an artist's sincerity?... writing in English the cult of beautiful words has become so much a part of us that we have forgotten what sincerity meant'. ('The Poet as Professional')

It was the 'simple' lyrical quality of Ó Bruadair's poetry to which O'Connor imparted his respect: 'In his work, his intellect, his wit, his consummate mastery of the technique of verse, are always dominant. It is only at certain moments that the crust is broken, that we see behind the intellectual personality the personality of emotion, the passionate lyric power'. This promotion of 'simple language' by O'Connor could be better understood within the context of a nineteenth-century literary realism influence at work. Turgenev had championed a language of 'clarity' and 'simplicity', and Chekhov and Maupassant had similarly advanced a language of 'synthetic simplification', 'remote from "bookishness"', and all that was '"affected, pretentious or posing"'. O'Connor's later scornful labelling of Joyce as the 'rhetorician's dream' and the 'university man' resonated with Turgenev's account of Gončarov's novel, *The Precipice*: 'Rhetoric, nothing but rhetoric'. Turgenev's pejorative use of the word 'literature'—'Oh this literature, how it reeks of literature'—and his praise for Tolstoy—'[his] greatest virtue is precisely that his stuff smells of life'—also strongly foreshadowed O'Connor's 'literary language' and art coming 'into touch with life' critique of modernist literature.

Yet, it is worth noting that O'Connor did have a generally favourable disposition towards Joyce in the 1920s. This could be partly attributed to his instrumentalist approval of Joyce's declaration to forge 'the uncreated conscience' of the Irish race and write the 'moral history' of the country. The 'scrupulous meanness' and stylistic flair in *Dubliners* also stimulated O'Connor, to the point where his early efforts in writing short stories have traces of a Joycean influence—'The Peddler' (1926) and 'The Awakening' (1928), for example. In addition, Joyce's grimy realism, epiphanic moments, alienated individuals, and representational Irish communities, initiated a pattern upon which O'Connor reflected. Joyce's thematic attention, furthermore, to the Catholic Church, Irish history, and the country's socio-political strains, is repeated within O'Connor's own short stories. It is worth noting that in 1945 O'Connor also wrote a short story which directly references Joyce in the title—'The Dead'. Rejected by *The New Yorker* in January 1946, the story appears to have unfortunately vanished. (A rejection of a story by *The New Yorker* was not unusual, despite O'Connor being continually published in the periodical from 1945 until his death in 1966). In relation to Joyce's other works, the portrait of Dublin life in *Ulysses* also initially attracted O'Connor. Instead, the more experimental and extravagant Joyce's work became, building to the 'associative mania' of *Finnegans Wake* as O'Connor saw it, the more decisively he disengaged from it. Over forty years later, O'Connor would admit only to a realist concentration in his admiration of *Ulysses* with 'its description of the poetry of everyday life in the first decade of this century', predominantly valuable because: 'as that Dublin fades into history, this aspect will seem more and more important'. The 'ecstatically ridiculous' dismissal in his cultural criticism perhaps points in many ways to O'Connor's endeavours to publicly disassociate from his immediate Irish predecessors, particularly with such literary giants as Joyce. (This makes it all the more intriguingly regrettable that O'Connor's 'The Dead' is missing.) His retreat to the nineteenth-century short-story tradition conceivably created a space for O'Connor's engagement with the realist mode without his having to declare a Joycean debt.

At the time that literary realism was permeating his thinking, O'Connor was also cultivating his taste in medieval and modern Irish language poetry (he is still critically considered one of Ireland's finest translators) and his 1920s cultural criticism signifies his predilections. A distinct stylistic and thematic intersection between the literary realist tradition and his Irish language poetry preferences is discernible. Ostensibly, O'Connor's 1925 article, 'Life and Literature. The Poet as Professional', was a review of an excerpt from Sean Ó'Faoláin's Master's thesis on Ó Bruadair, published by University College Cork in *éarna*; but he also made use of the publishing opportunity to extol his own critical bias as he praised Ó'Faoláin for prioritising the lyric personality over the intellectual personality. O'Connor's greatest admiration for Irish language poetry lay in the early medieval period, when the lyrical personal element was at its strongest and the language was at its simplest. As Robin Flower observed in *The Irish Tradition* (1947): 'Language ceases to be decorative and ceremonial and grows simpler and more intense so that it almost comes to be the emotion it expresses'. Predictably, therefore, O'Connor critically bemoaned the rise of bardic schools and the resultant decline of lyric poetry. Dignified construction, complicated metres, and a dialect firmly protected 'against infiltrations of localisms in phonetic and idiom' were all part of bardic training. The trained intellectualism involved in stylistic composition, the avoidance of 'living speech', and the lack of personal passion in these poems was deplored by O'Connor: 'Ireland is never a name… it is harp-playing'. His praise of the early medieval poetry characteristics of simple language and 'living speech' were resounded in his critical applauding of literary realism.

However, what is also interesting here is that O'Connor was additionally emphasising the lyric as an important component of writing. It shows that O'Connor's imagination was in fact caught between a romantic inheritance and a realist philosophy. His retreat to early medieval poetry in search of a historically remote romantic influence was perhaps analogous to his retreat from Joyce: an anxious repudiation of any possible Yeatsian sway over his literary imagination. In a 1925 letter to the *Irish Statesman*, O'Connor rebuked Yeats on the grounds of his poetry embodying, as he saw it, a form of transcendental romanticism: 'I do object to the assumption… that this verse represents Irish literature, that in reading the Lake Isle of Innisfree they are doing ample justice to the twelve centuries or so during which the Irish race set down its trouble about the terrible mystery of life.' It was the romance of early medieval poetry that appealed, O'Connor argued, because it did not call for transcendence from life but instead looked to deepen the appreciation for the quotidian:

> When I use the word romantic I am not thinking of what it might mean in English or in German literature. Irish verse of the period is not the literature of an escape from life, for it is mainly dramatic and objective. Its romanticism lies in its appeal to a fuller life within the life we live; like Hamlet, bounded by a nutshell, it counts itself a king of infinite space, and always it will sound this double note of imagination and precision.
>
> —'Literature and Life. An Irish Anthology', *The Irish Statesman*, 12 June 1926

This double note of imagination and precision was located in romanticism bound up with a realist aesthetic; it was a form of poetic realism and it was this, ultimately, this essay argues, that O'Connor tried most to emulate in his creative writing (and critical works—his 'lonely voice' theory being one such example). His own atmospheric, lyrical but ostensibly realist short stories reflected this in-between stance. Poetic realism—lyricism combined with a socio-political reality—is what O'Connor strove to attain in his artistic style.

O'Connor was writing some of the stories for *Guests of the Nation* while working out his literary philosophy in his cultural criticism, including 'Guests of the Nation', and he had by then clearly honed the technical ability of poetic realism which manifested itself so demonstrably in the collection. Perhaps mindful of Joyce's lyrical moment of epiphany, O'Connor stated in *The Lonely Voice* that the axis of a short story centred on a single revelatory moment and he cited nineteenth-century Russian writer Gogol's 'The Overcoat' to illustrate this: 'If one wanted an alternative description of what the short story means, one could hardly find better than that single half-sentence, "and from that day forth, everything was as it were changed and appeared in a different light to him"'. The final line of 'Guests of the Nation', a story set during the Irish War of Independence, emulates Gogol's words and the reader is left aware that the memory of the action taken would ensure life has irrevocably altered for the two Irish soldiers:

> I stood at the door, watching and listening to the damned shrieking of the birds... Noble says he felt he seen everything ten times as big, perceiving nothing around him but the little patch of black bog with the two Englishmen stiffening into it; but with me it was the other way, as though the patch of bog where the two Englishmen were was a thousand miles away from me, and even Noble mumbling just behind me and the old woman and the birds and the bloody stars were all far away, and I was somehow very small and very lonely. And anything that ever happened me after I never felt the same about again.

In the story's ending, O'Connor isolates the atrocious encroachment of war on everyone involved, which lies in comfortable conformity with the characteristics of literary realism and a depicted powerlessness of the individual in the social system. The two Irish soldiers, Bonaparte and Noble, are as much victims of political ideology as the two English soldiers they had befriended and were subsequently forced to execute, Belcher and Hawkins. The devastating effect of war is the motif of this story, while difficult questions of loyalty and morality regarding the recent revolutionary past are directed at the reader, all lyrically heightened by the loneliness of the bleak and evocative language. Both the tragic reality of war and the romantic revolutionary quest are thematically depicted throughout the story.

Given his lack of faith in his poetic abilities, in many ways, the form of the short story itself presented for him the option of combining the varying strands of his ambitions: desiring to be a poet, offering socio-political commentary and inspiring reform, exploring and incorporating a wider European literary inheritance, imparting an instrumentalist impact, and wanting to establish his own artistic technique while navigating the influential terrain of his Irish literary predecessors. A poetic realist aesthetic allowed O'Connor the space to accomplish these aspirations, and the short-story genre readily lent itself, as he believed, to encompassing the diversity of pursuits. When asked by *The Paris Review* why he preferred the short story as his medium, he replied: 'Because it's the nearest thing I know to lyric poetry—I wrote lyric for a long time, then discovered that God had not intended me to be a lyric poet, and the nearest thing to that is the short story... a short story can have the sort of detachment from circumstances that lyric poetry has'. In the same interview, this romantic colouring was subsequently mixed with a realist cast when he declared that he was also a social 'reformer'. Thus did O'Connor balance his philosophical hybridity throughout his writing life.

WORKS CITED

Osborn Bergin, 'Bardic Poetry', in David Greene and Fergus Kelly, eds, *Irish Bardic Poetry: Texts and Translations, together with an introductory lecture by Osborn Bergin, with a foreword by D.A. Binchy* (Dublin: Dolmen Press, 1970).

Joe Cleary, *Outrageous Fortune: Capital and Culture in Modern Ireland* (Dublin: Field Day Publications, 2007).

Crowley, Malcolm (ed. and Intro.), Interview with Anthony Whittier, 'Frank O'Connor', *Writers at Work: The 'Paris Review' Interviews* (1957; repr. London: Secker & Warburg, 1958).

Robin Flower, *The Irish Tradition* (1947; repr. Oxford: Clarendon Press, 1973).

Heather Ingman, *A History of the Irish Short Story* (Cambridge: Cambridge University Press, 2009).

Janko Lavrin, 'Chekhov and Maupassant', *The Slavonic Review*, 5/13 (June 1926).

Frank O'Connor, Letter to Sean Hendrick (Wicklow: undated [early June, 1925]), Harriet O'Donovan Sheehy Collection, Dublin.

Frank O'Connor, 'Literature and Life. The Poet as Professional', *The Irish Statesman* (3 October 1925).

Frank O'Connor, 'Literature and Life. An Irish Anthology', *The Irish Statesman* (12 June 1926).

Frank O'Connor, 'Literature and Life. Classic Verse', *The Irish Statesman* (23 July 1927).

Frank O'Connor, 'Guests of the Nation', *Guests of the Nation* (London: Macmillan, 1931).

Frank O'Connor, *Towards An Appreciation of Literature* (Dublin: Metropolitan, 1945).

Frank O'Connor, *An Only Child* (London: Macmillan, 1961).

Frank O'Connor, *The Lonely Voice* (1962; repr. London: Macmillan, 1963).

Frank O'Connor, *The Backward Look: A Survey of Irish Literature* (London: Macmillan, 1967).

Michael Ó Donnabháin [Frank O'Connor], Letter to the Editor, *The Irish Statesman* (13 June 1925).

Victor Terras, 'Turgenev's Aesthetic and Western Realism', *Comparative Literature*, 22/1 (Winter 1970).

A longer version of this essay was previously published in *The Irish Short Story: Traditions and Trends*, edited by Elke D'hoker and Stephanie Eggermont (Oxford: Peter Lang, 2015).

The Black Proclamation

Eoin McNamee

The gates of DG Waring's house were rusted. The driveway overgrown. I turned a bend in the driveway and the house was on a slight elevation in front of me. The great empty windows overlooked Carlingford Lough. The house was partially burned in a reprisal attack. Blackened on the northern side where the flames took hold. To the right of the house there was a row of graves. The graves were small. Children, I thought at first. The earth on several looked fresh-turned, black with some malice I did not understand. When I looked at the headstones I saw that they were the graves of dogs.

Above my head the rooks sang the Black Proclamation.

My brother bought me a box of lead figurines of the Rising leaders. The figures rest in foam cut-outs. James Connolly. Padraig Pearse. Plunkett. The green uniforms. The Sam Brown belts. If you look closely you can see that they are in fact figures from some other war painted to resemble rebels from 1916. I want to believe in them but I can't. Need is not quite belief. I line them up on the windowsill and ask them to recite the Black Proclamation.

Willie John Cunningham was the Carlingford Lough pilot. His death notice was in the paper. *He smuggled the material for my wedding dress from Omeath to Greencastle across the lough,* my mother said. The dress hung in an old wardrobe for years. Hand-sewn sequins on a white background. At night the lost brides are out there on the mudflats and shallows. With the curlews and terns. You can hear them calling to their husbands.

The Black Proclamation is the history of the defeated.

I stepped through the ruins of the rear of the house. The kitchen appeared untouched. There were cups and plates on the table. Estate invoices spilling from a bureau drawer. There was a tapping noise from somewhere in the house. A branch against a window pane. I walked into the hallway. The fire damage was worse here. Charred timber. The staircase hung in the air. A black cat watched me from the top step as if its presence had been written some time before.

I ran away from Waring's house and stopped at Mary White's shop on the way home. The shop was small with a low ceiling. Mary asked me where I had been. I told her. She leaned over her dark counter. *The night I was born the soldiers took my mother to DG Waring's in the back of a lorry.*

In the basement of that house they stripped her naked and searched her. As they were stripping the pregnant woman DG Waring circled her. Mary said she was wearing *an Italian Officer's uniform and carried a cane which she tapped against her leather boots.*

Mary's mother went into labour on the floor of the lorry as it carried her from the house into the cold Easter night.

Men in crumpled suits. Tired-looking. Losing more than they win. *The bullet struck his pelvis and richocheted upwards through his heart.* Compromised. Disheartened. They are waiting in their buses. In the taxi ranks. At the gospel hall. In the hospital car park. In the dread night. At the dinner table. On their own street. In their own shops. At the checkpoint bookies school quiet streets where they once dreamed of love. They know their time is limited. The Black Proclamation calls upon the dead generations of the future, not those of the past.

Colm came to the door the night they died. My mother opened it. They had been to school together It was a stormy night. *Where is my chief my master this bleak night mavrone,* she said quietly. *Cold, cold bitterly cold is this night for Hugh. Its showery arrowy speary sleet pierceth one through and through, pierceth one to the very bone,* Colm said. *Recite to me,* my mother said, *the Black Proclamation.*

The Black Proclamation requires you to dishonour it with cowardice, inhumanity and rapine.

The Court Martial Prosecutor William Wylie wrote about Constance Markievicz in a private letter sent in 1939. *I am only a woman you cannot shoot a woman you must not shoot a woman… she never stopped moaning the whole time she was in the court room… We were all slightly disgusted. I won't say any more, it revolts me still.* But this is what people do in war. Men and women. They moan. They are paralysed with fear. I dream of soldiers running from a checkpoint explosion at the border, throwing their weapons away and squealing. They inform and denounce others that they might live.

The Black Proclamation requires that you revolt the Court Martial Prosecutor.

The text of the Black Proclamation contains language which some might find offensive. The Black Proclamation is subject to terms and conditions. The authors of the Black Proclamation bear no responsibility.

We lay awake listening to the bands and the preacher in the town at the bottom of the hill as he read from the book of death.

The Black Proclamation stands above you armed with an automatic rifle. The bullets pass through you and splinter on the floor beneath you and the Black Proclamation is afraid of being hit by a richochet. The Black Proclamation is waiting in a lonely farmhouse. The Black Proclamation does not torture but uses inhuman and degrading treatment. The Black Proclamation sets the tilt switch. The Black Proclamation makes the warning call using an identified code word. The Black Proclamation kicks down the door. The Black Proclamation cites national security. The Black Proclamation walks in the funeral procession weeping. The Black Proclamation controls the media. The Black Proclamation wouldn't have one about the place.

A few weeks ago a friend stood at his father's graveside. Like my own father, a beautiful, ruined man. His uncle turned to him. *You have to remember that we came from a generation of men who were destroyed by the North.* As they fade away they turn to look for their lonely wives but cannot see them.

Here at Greencastle the beach is scoured by the tide. Dark weed, empty paint tins from the boats. The southern shore is half a mile away. On the Blockhouse Island cormorants hold their wings aloft. It is said that they are messengers from this world to the underworld and that they hold their wings that way to hide their shame.

Forty-five years after I climbed over DG Waring's gates I hear her swagger stick.
Tap tap tap.
The skeletal dogs have broken from their graves. Teeth rotted. Bone eye-sockets askew.
Tap tap tap.
Where are you going she says.
I haven't finished with you.

The same people living in the same place

i

the first mistake was we believed our own publicity
we were gone and there was no finding us
not through protest not via mothers crying on TV
not through the spiel of indignation when elections loom—
we were gone so far from the seat of power that
this is what they call 'disappeared'
we held ourselves quietly, with dignity we thought
though there was no one to see, we waited
as a chip waits for a lucky draw,
as the back end of an argument waits for *the reveal*
we waited, until we almost forgot ourselves,
until the hum and the haw of prevarication
was the rhythm it seemed of the seasons.
Will we be left in the lime slide of time
and what will they call us then?

ii

Hell is an island of too many horizons.
A book called *Enquire within about everything*
has got to be framed by the devil.
The first ink drawing of the man with the longest nails in the world.
He cannot change his clothes, his nephews must help him to eat.

An overview of human teeth, separated by race,
herbivore apes on a sliding bar of comparison.
Twenty-seven varieties of sausage made from offal,
none including ground chicken feet.

Oh for the curlicue of an ornate majuscule.
Ah to feel a cursive stroke of light.

Here is the curl in N for New Ireland
Here is a list of the least important deaths.

Siobhan Campbell

War has been given a bad name

after Brecht

I am told that the best people have begun to say,
from a moral point of view, how it is difficult now
to believe in a cause. With international terror, the
home-grown sort was difficult to ignore. Of course
the finest of us were never in their target, being able
to justify the conflict for either side. But even the bishop
is concerned about absolution: perhaps a collective
blessing where nobody catches his eye. Business types
warn about recession, as most of those 'volunteers'
will need a pension. Some even think it better to maintain
status quo. But they do say we should attend the *Let go
and Forget* sessions, coupons free with national newspapers.
I believe they have someone there so mesmerising that even
those with holes through their palms may learn to pray.

Siobhan Campbell

Some Notes on Names and Deeds

Kevin Barry

1

I was named after a dead mod. My first cousin, Kevin Barry, came off his scooter in Gorleston-on-Sea, near Great Yarmouth in East Anglia, in the summer of 1968, and he was killed instantly. He was seventeen. I was born in June the following year, almost a year to the day since his death, and so I was called for him. By the age of twelve I was a mod myself. This was around the time of the revival led by The Jam. I loved the look—a fishtail parka, Sta-press trousers, Ben Sherman polo shirt, white socks, black tasselled brogues—and somewhere at the back of my mind I probably associated it with the glamour of tragic early death.

2

My cousin's father was also Kevin Barry. He was born around 1921 in Limerick city. It was a working-class family, with the males often employed on the railway, and the family lived near the station, in a laneway off Lord Edward Street. Going by the date, there seems a reasonable probability that my uncle was named for the rebel martyr. He moved to England for work in the late 1930s and he joined the army there and was shipped out to Italy. He was captured by the Nazis an hour after landing and spent the war at an open prison in an Italian village. He ate well enough and chased women for three years and came back in 1945 in the guise of a hero Tommy. He got a job then in a shipyard in Great Yarmouth. I have no idea if that side of my family was strongly political or if my uncle's joining the British army was frowned upon. Naming a child 'Kevin Barry' in Limerick city in 1921 might have been an expression of popular sentiment as much as an overtly political act, and anyway half the town would have wound up with sons or nephews in the British army.

3

The other side of the family had a blueshirt streak. They lived on Parnell Street in Limerick—they weren't long in from the countryside. My grandfather wore a blue shirt all his life. I remember him rolling up the sleeves of it to take apart his Honda 50 on the lino in front of the fireplace. Then he'd put the motorbike back together again and head for the pub on it. He had once gone to see General O'Duffy address a gathering in the city. I suppose there's every chance he raised a one-armed fascist salute to him. He wore a blue shirt until the day he died in the early 1970s and he always voted Fine Gael.

4

I went to a couple of the black flag marches for the hunger strikers in Limerick city as a twelve year old. There was death-glamour on the air: some of the local young fellas were suddenly very fervent and het-up about the North, or at least they were for a while. The IRA was known to be strong thirty miles out the road: the notorious west Limerick and north Kerry brigades. There were often stories in school about columns being seen on training runs at dawn in the Curraghour woods.

5

I only ever noticed my name raising a certain feeling when I lived in Edinburgh in the early part of this century. Sometimes it was smiled at and occasioned amused glances. I joined the Stockbridge branch of the library in the city in 2003 and when my name was presented on the form, the two lads behind the desk cracked up. That will go down well in some places, one of them said to me, and the other broke into a bar of the song.

Never having experienced anything like it in the Republic, I was amazed at the fervour of the hatred during the James Connolly memorial march in Edinburgh each May. Often there were assaults and stabbings and random attacks around the verges of the march and the day, and the atmosphere was toxic.

6

I am one of an army of Kevin Barrys, of course. When I was signing on in Cork in the mid 1990s, the woman at the dole office was searching for my file one day and told me there were six Kevin Barrys at that hatch alone. There is a bomb disposal expert in New York, a boxing trainer in New Zealand, a slide guitar player in Illinois, a retired Joycean professor in Paris—all Kevin Barrys.

7

In 1988, during a brief period of third-level education, at what was then NIHE Limerick, I found that the leftist students were very involved with Central America and the Sandanistas and all the rest of it, but they had nothing at all to say about the North.

8

I left the college and got a job as a cub reporter on the *Limerick Tribune*. One night I was alone in the newsroom and took a call from a man claiming to be speaking for the INLA. He issued threats to drug dealers in a couple of estates in the city. He had a very flat Limerick accent. The next day, two men from the Special Branch arrived to interview me about the call.

—What did he sound like, Kevin?

—He had a very flat Limerick accent.

—Could you do it for us?

—I could, yeah.

—Go on so.

—'How's-it-goin' there, I'm callin' on behalf o' the Irish National Liberation…'

9

In 2007, having returned from living in the UK, we bought an old barracks of the Royal Irish Constabulary in County Sligo. It had a waft of dead sergeants off it and I knew that sooner or later it would start trying to get into my fiction.

It is located about eight hundred yards beyond the village of Ballinafad, looking over Lough Arrow. The reason that it was built outside the village was so that it could keep an eye on the Ascendancy hunting and fishing lodges across the lake.

10

Some of the land around Lough Arrow was owned by Sir John French, of the Frenchpark, County Roscommon Frenches. He was a hero of the Boer War, a notorious womaniser, a man who incited big passions. He had a property at Drumdoe, just across the lake from the barracks. In 1918 he was made Lord Lieutenant of Ireland, and his was not a popular reign. There was a botched assassination attempt in the Phoenix Park in 1919. Faulty information led to a hand grenade being thrown into the wrong car. After the War of Independence, Sir John bought another estate nearby, at Hollybrook, a mile down the road from the barracks. But he was advised not to stay on in Ireland as his presence might incite difficulties. He returned to England and ended his days as (and see if this name incites even the tiniest frisson of ill-feeling in you) Field Marshal John Denton Pinkstone French, 1st Earl of Ypres.

11

The roof was burnt off our barracks during the War of Independence. It was one of those curiously courteous operations of the era—the Ballinafad RIC was given a week's advance notice of the fire. Thus nobody was on site when the blaze went up. When you read between the lines, it seems that many of the engagements of the era were made on the basis of these local understandings. It was the conflict of a small country, where everybody knew everybody else, and many of the actions were merely symbolic in intent.

12

I am currently sitting in what used to be the RIC's stable. It makes a good writing place, because the wi-fi doesn't reach from the house, and also there are no windows at the back of the house, so nobody can see when I'm not working. The original walls surround the barracks grounds but in one section the old stones have been replaced by breezeblocks—this was a gateway beside the stable, long since blocked up, that would have been used for the horses. Often when I'm digging up the garden I come across horseshoes, and lots of old brandy bottles, too. If you wanted to attack the barracks, the best way would be to come down the blindside of it, from the direction of Keash hill.

The N4 runs there now, but in 1916 it would have been just foothills. On the far side of Keash lies the town of Ballymote, a notable IRA stronghold in 1916.

13

That year, a Tuam man named Patrick Fallon was appointed sergeant at the RIC station in Ballymote. He made slow but steady progress against the activities of the IRA battalion in the town and district. He was a nuisance to them for four years. He was shot dead on his way back to the barracks from the Ballymote Fair in November 1920. Knowing that reprisals would be swift, the town went into a panic and there was a stampede of cattle as the place was cleared out. Eight lorries of Auxillaries arrived that evening and Ballymote was set on fire. They would have been able to see the smoke rise over the Bricklieve mountains from the barracks at Ballinafad or they may well have been involved in the operation themselves.

14

When I entered secondary school in Limerick city, the hunger strikes were not long over and classroom support for the IRA ran at one hundred per cent. I know this because we were questioned one day in 'Civics' class by a Christian Brother. He asked who among us supported the cause in the North and every hand was raised. The Christian Brother seemed happy enough with that. These are not the sons of blueshirts, you could see him thinking. The Christian Brothers seemed to me to have no interest at all in the Christ end of things—their chief concern was in marketing a specific take on Irish history. In the school's popular sentiment that year, Bobby Sands occupied a place I would say precisely commensurate with that of Bob Marley: legends.

The almost sexual charge of blood-sacrifice mythology works best on adolescent males. By Leaving Cert time, there were several young fellas around the school who were widely rumoured to be 'in the Ra'. They were usually big quiet hurler types from the county—lads who would have much more interest in the Harty Cup fixtures than in eyeliner and fey indie bands from the north of England. That there might be actual Ra men in our midst seemed unlikely, the North being so far away, being something that existed on the television news; but then you might note the ages of those arrested on active operations, and their addresses. It wouldn't be unusual for them to be teenagers from Munster.

15

I sometimes feel myself to be apolitical but I know this is nonsense. You lift yourself from the bed and breathe in the morning and you are a political being. As soon as you walk out the door there are decisions to be made. But sometimes to care at all seems difficult and uninspiring and I suffer a common disenchantment—I believe that national politics is largely just a distraction from the fact that we're essentially owned and run by commercial, financial and technological concerns, the same ones who own and run our neighbours across the Irish Sea. We are all cousinly under the yoke of our very modern oppression. In some ways I think local politics is more interesting now and maybe the place where more traction is possible. Not that I get off my hole about it.

16

If I was to draw up a story, I'd probably have a young man from Ballymote waiting on his moment in one of the caves at the top of Keash hill. His dilemma is the ancient one—does he possess physical courage? Is he able to steal by night across the foothills of the Bricklieve mountains and approach on the blindside the barracks at Ballinafad? Is he capable of using that revolver at last, or of poisoning a horse even? As the blood rises, and his heart thumps, as the darkness thickens, can he still feel the pulse of a motive force? Will it sustain him once the deed is done?

The Names

Kevin Curran

Maura English was like a ma to me. She made sure I was always looked after by giving me the main street. But once, when I asked for a change she freaked out in front of all those old gee-bags and said, 'I've put my faith in you these past years, Max. Don't be an ungrateful little shit and throw it back in my face.' It could've been worse, I suppose. I could've been on the hanging baskets with Rita Kilduff.

What I had to clean was fairly straight forward anyways: The Courthouse steps and doorway (sometimes a dog shit, maybe even a human dump), the Library's wheel-chair ramp (cigarette papers, butts, maybe a needle), the painted white windows of 'Rasta High Life' (posters for cleaners, childminders, lost dogs, DIY men), the old AIB doorway (crisp packets, bottles, lighter refill cans), the porchway to Caffrey's Jewellers (post, fliers and leaflets from people who thought he was still in business), The White Heart (they'd boarded up the windows and doors and painted them pink but Maura was always nagging me to make sure no posters or notices were allowed to stay up. 'Even the 'No way we won't pay' ones?' I'd say. 'Especially them,' she'd moan, 'it's an empty pub on the main street, not the Liberty Hall,') the entrance to the old shopping centre (always cans, a rank smell of piss and maybe socks or underwear—skidmarks once), and finally, back on the other side of the street—across from Deli-Burger and beside Jim's Cash for Gold—the small monument on the wall that had the names of those two local lads chiselled into it (the usual graffiti: a scrawled Lido and Abdel and sometimes a drawing of a dick and balls with a few pubes).

My da and his mate, The Brinnie, used laugh when they saw me with the vest and go, 'Ah, The Didye, cleaning up the mean streets of the Brig, one shite at a time.' I just ignored them.

All ye needed with you for the clean was a hi-vis vest, those thick rubber gloves, one refuse sack, one pickers, and for the placard monument thing a toothbrush and solution. That was it. Easy, really. Even though like, I'd have preferred to be doing the gardening on the roundabout beside Wavin with Maura English and her kids since like, I'd never been asked.

NEAR THIS SPOT
SEAMUS LAWLESS
AND
SEAN GIBBONS

There was a spot in Deli-Burger—inside the door to your left, at the high stools and half table—where ye could see from the monument across the road down to The Courthouse (my Tidy-Towns route). My da said he couldn't give a flying fuck what I could see from there once I could see the menu. But I'd learnt it off at that stage.

I was in Deli Burger that night getting my da's curry chips and batter burger and my brother Johnny's cheese chips and American burger—he was back home since he'd broken up with Charlotte—when it happened. Lido called over to me from the monument just before I went in and I nodded—not excited or nothing—since he was different when he was with Abdel. Abdel made him seem taller and older or something. 'Max, fam' Lido shouted, 'come here.'

So I went and said hello and all that, keeping my fist tight on my da's note. Lido was all arms and shoulders, real loose and he said, 'Relax Max—eeeyy,' and Abdel laughed at his rhyme (like I hadn't heard it before) and Lido said, 'Nah fam, I'm only buzzin with ye,' and he spat behind him into the canal and jumped down off the monument and patted me on the back—like he always did—and gripped my shoulder. 'Hey,' he said to Abdel, 'member I told you bout me and my neighbour's hand-shake? Watch.' Lido nodded at me, and I shit myself for a second. You see, we'd been trying it outside his house for a few weeks since he never liked to go in early, and, like, in fairness, neither did I, ever, cause my da's mate would be in there and he'd be taking the piss or Johnny'd be in his room balling over Charlotte riding Robbie Richardson's older brother. But I thought it was just for the craic. The hand-shake. Only for us, like.

Lido raised his hand, ready to go, and smiled, 'allow, fam, don't disgrace me in front of my boy.'

When they first moved in my da used to say, 'There goes Mrs Chiquita,' if he saw Lido's ma in all her gear going to their church on Sunday. I'd laugh with him, but I dunno, I sometimes felt kind of jealous, like, of Lido and his ma and his bro going somewhere together as a family (even if it was to a hall that used to be a carpet shop). At least they had memories, had each other. All I had was the memory of my ma on the couch with puke coming down her chin making a kind of pool between her neck and her chest and her cigarette after burning a hole in the carpet and the smell of it—the puke and the burnt carpet—being rotten. She had a vodka bottle on her lap (I was used to that) but this one was empty and I couldn't wake her.

Lido didn't really talk to me in school, yeah, since I was only in second year, but we'd nearly always meet outside his house in the evenings and have some bant. One night he was there with his headphones on rapping to himself and when he saw me he took them off and said, 'You know what he's rappin bout?'

'Who?'

'Lil Wayne, fam.' I must've just shrugged cause he tutted and went, 'Punany man. Pu-Nah-Nee.'

'Oh,' I said, kind of embarrassed and he patted my back and shook my shoulder.

'Fam,' he said, 'you've got to get yourself some swag. And you ain't never gonna get it going round them streets with those big yellow gloves and that vest. Ditch that shit. You look like a cop.'

'But my ma was delighted when I started it.'

'Fam, she was probably happy when you were doing it, like, as a ten year old.'

'Maura English says she'd be proud of me now too.'

'Oh my days, Max. Maura English. Do her kids do that yellow glove shit?'

'Yeah.'

'Well, do they do it with all that actual shit and needles an all? Does anyone other than you do that shit?'

Maura English and my ma went to school together. Maura had loads of funny stories bout my ma and since my da said nothing about her after she died apart from, 'She was a selfish bitch, Max,' and Johnny said nothing bout anything to me only, 'Fuck off, Max,' Maura was the best I had. And no, no one else did it. But that made me more important, didn't it?

A few weeks before it happened I was coming home from a late night walk—my da's mates and all were in the house—when I heard a voice go, 'Maxy baby,' and I shit myself since it was dark and the road was real quiet and no one was around. I stopped walking and there was a giggle—two voices—and I looked into the lane at the side of Lido's house but it was too dark to see anything. 'Max, bro, come here, fam.' It was Lido and since I'd nothing better to be doing I hopped the little wall between our houses and went into the lane, pure blind. I knew, like, there musta been a girl there since I could smell the perfume and I couldn't see a stitch and I heard her giggle and Lido whispered, 'Come here, fam, come here,' and he reached out of the darkness and grabbed my right hand and, I dunno, I went with it and he dragged me forward and I couldn't see for shit and suddenly he took my wrist, yeah, and pushed my arms onto something and the girl with him giggled and I felt a jacket or something and then after a second my hand was moved onto a hot, soft—so soft, man—handful of tit. It could only have been tit. I got a feel of the nipple and all and it was rock hard and, I dunno, I was on it for a second—less maybe—and whoever she was squealed and pushed me away and went, 'Jesus Christ, Lido, his hand's fucking freezing,' and Lido just laughed and went, 'Sshh, sshh—my mama'll hear you.'

I backed away, on top form, and Lido whispered, 'Lose the yellow gloves, fam,' and his voice was swallowed up by, 'Come on, baby,' and the sound of kissing and I knew then it was Eithne—Bartek's girlfriend. Everyone was talking about her after she tried to dye her hair blonde but made it bright yellow instead like a Manga girl. All those heads in school had a hard on for her because of it.

After that night Lido was my hero. He'd given me ammunition and, BAM! my world was changed. So to show him some appreciation and since we'd been practising that fist-pump, handshake thing for ages, I decided to do it in front of Abdel. When we did it—straight through, front slap, back slap, fist pump, grip the top of each others' fingers, fist pump again and finger point with thumb up (like a gun) and boom you're blown backwards by the force of the shot—Abdel fell around the place laughing, shaking his head and slapping his sides. Through all the shapes and noise I spotted their names in BIG BLOCK CAPITALS on the plaque thing—again. I'd only cleaned it like, two weeks before. And down at the bottom—again—was a massive cock and balls with the little spikey pubes. This wrecked my buzz since I knew I'd be there the next day scrubbing away at it with my toothbrush and solution.

I didn't say anything but gave them their stupid high-fives and went across the street to Deli-Burger mad thick cause Lido knew I cleaned there and his name was the biggest on it.

I'd ordered and was in my seat when I saw Bartek coming up towards them. I knew, like, straight away there was gonna be trouble since he had that big thick constipated head on him and sure, Lido had told me about Eithne's da seeing a text about a blowjob on her phone and her da thinking it was Bartek who got it and going ape-shit and marching down to Bartek's door and decking Bartek's da when he gave him beef.

Bartek was a psycho. He became a gym freak after his mate, that little shit Richie Nulty, gave him a beating outside the school over a spilt Yop. About a month later Bartek was back friends with Richie and invited him up to his house for a spliff or something and when he was at the front door about to let Richie in, didn't Bartek pull out a hurley from his porch and crack Richie over the head with it—for real, like. How do I know? Everyone knows since it was Bartek's da in his big Polish voice that recorded it on Bartek's phone. I heard the da was hiding across the green with the phone waiting for them to arrive into the driveway. I don't speak, what ye call it, Polish or whatever, but Lido told me someone told him that the da was saying, 'Do it, son, do it.' And at the end of the clip, when Bartek was all out of breath, you could hear the da say in English, 'Bartek, look camera, look camera. Say to people what happen if they fuck with us.'

Not long after that, when Bartek began getting all ripped and all, he started going out with Eithne. But Lido said Eithne got tired of Bartek thinking he was the man when all he used to do was jizz in his pants anytime he got a feel of her tit, and that's why she dumped him on his 15th birthday.

WERE BRUTALLY DONE TO DEATH
BY BRITISH FORCES, WHILE IN THEIR CUSTODY

I'm not sure how, but Bartek heard the text was about Lido and he musta been so thick he went and posted 'ur ded Lido' on Facebook and then Lido, taking the piss—he was probably with Abdel when he did it—posted a picture of stained tracksuit bottoms and wrote, 'dont blow it Bartek' underneath. I thought that was a bit of a stupid thing for Lido to do.

When I saw Bartek and Arek and Piotr coming up the street from my seat in Deli-Burger I was still pissed off, yeah, about Lido's name and the cock and balls. Yer one from behind the counter went, 'American burger, cheese chip, batter burger, curry chip,' and I stood up, like—I was about to open the door and shout across to Lido—and she screamed, 'Hey, pay now, you pay now: American burger, cheese chip, batter burger…' and I just turned to her and went, 'Relax the fuck,' and I was surprised at what I said but proud too since I hadn't stood up for myself like that before and the place was fairly busy and a hot girl looked at me and kind of smiled, like, as if to say, 'Fair play.' I got to the front and chips were sizzling in behind the counter and there was steam rising and that fatty gurgling sound from the pans was getting louder and another one was on the phone going, 'Deli-Burger, you want delivery?'

Since I was busy paying for the grub didn't I miss what happened. But my da was talking to the owner of the Cash for Gold and he said he had it on CCTV and it was pure fucking mental how quick it went down: That scaldy headed prick (Bartek) just popped around the corner out of nowhere and dived in at the poor young black fella (Lido) and legged it off and that was it. The only way you'd know he'd been shanked was the pool under him on the ground right there in the shadow of the monument.

My da shook his head after he told the story and said, 'Sure didn't they find the fuckin Stanley blade down the harbour the next day at low-tide, the fuckin eejit,' and The Brinnie just chuckled at Bartek's stupidity and said, 'Weren't you friends with the little black fella?' And I nodded, yeah, like, yeah I was, but I dunno, I wondered if I really was since I done nothing when I came out of Deli-Burger that night and saw all the madness across the road only grip the chipper bag tighter and leg it home, kind of freaked, not knowing what had happened, but, kind of knowing since I'd seen the head on Bartek coming up the street.

We didn't go to the funeral or nothing since my da said, 'sure, what's the point? We wouldn't understand a fuckin word they'd be saying.'

Maura English texted a few days after and since I didn't reply, in like, ten minutes, she rang. She was freaking out. The Tidy Towns inspectors were coming and a car had crashed into the roundabout and her display was in shite, The White Heart was covered in posters and loads of the funeral flowers had been left at the monument and Lido's graffiti was still there. She. Was. Going. Mental.

Ten o'clock on a summer holidays' Wednesday morning I marched up to the monument thinking I was the bomb with my gloves and vest and solution: Maura English needed me. Only Maura was there already with her boys, and the flowers were all gone. They were there the day before because I'd seen them and read some of the cards. A big refuse bag was in her hand and it was bulging and ripped and stems were sticking out of it and I said, 'What ye do that for, Maura?' Kind of angry with her, definitely disappointed. People had left flowers there for a reason and she didn't give a fuck. The dead don't ask for much. Respect their memory is all.

'Never mind them,' she said, reaching out for my solution, 'now, come on, get cracking on this,' and she pointed at a thin streak of blood smudged over the Irish words and then she just, like, gestured with a grunt at the grafitti Lido and Abdel had done on Friday night.

Fair enough, like, I knew she'd put a lot of work into all the Tidy Towns lark, but the flowers? That was bad out. Lido deserved better. So I said it to her again and she just pressed her lips, trying not to get angry, 'Could you, for once in your life, son, just do as I fucking ask,' and she stormed across the road with her kids and threw the bag in her boot and flew off. It wasn't about the flowers.

20th SEPTEMBER 1920
AR DHEIS DÉ GO RAIBH A N-ANAM

That plaque monument thing was a bastard to clean. When I said all you needed for it was a toothbrush and solution, I never said, like, what sort of solution. It was mine. Like, I made it, especially for limestone (not just the monument). A coke bottle filled with my da's WD 40, his paint stripper and old sunscreen was it. Know how long it took me to get that together? Fucking. Ages.

So I was nearly finished scrubbing the blood off—it wasn't much since he must've just got it on his fingers or hand and then put it on the plaque for like, a second or two max cause it came off easy with a bit of solution—when I realised: Lido'll never get a plaque like this. He couldn't even get flowers, for fuck sake. That was bad out. But on I went, ignoring it all, scrubbing the thick permanent marker, the letters—all capitals of course—into nothing, like a good boy for Maura.

I was bet into it, putting the real intense scrub on like I did on my ma's, when a shadow appeared over my shoulder and I turned and who was there with a little red rose and her hair all dyed black and looking like an Emo, only Eithne. We hadn't actually seen each other after the lane, (and even then we didn't really see each other) but I had met her in my dreams every night since.

She left the rose at the bottom of the wall and her top was real loose and I got an eyeful and she stood up all serious and then she frowned at the plaque when she saw what I was doing. She was a ride.

'What ye doing that for?' she said, all thick.

'It's for the Tidy Towns.'

'The wha? Leave it.'

'But Maura…'

I copped, I dunno, it just hit me: Maura English is a cunt. Not only that, but I was just as bad. No, worse. I might as well have thrown the flowers out myself with my poxy yellow gloves.

'Fuck this,' I said. Like, seriously, what was I doing? Lido was a mate and I was scrubbing the proof of his existence off the walls. 'Give me one second.' And I turned into the plaque and it reminded me again of my ma's gravestone and I gave it one more final going over, really went at it to clear everything bar his signature tag off.

I took the solution and the toothbrush and fucked them into the canal and reefed off the yellow gloves and looked at the shite all over them for a second and thought about Maura and her kids and all the flowers they'd arranged that I'd never smell and then fucked them into the canal with the hi-vis vest too. Sometimes ye don't need a ma, ye need a ride. Or a blow job. Or even another feel of a tit.

'Well?' I said, cool as fuck.

She didn't say anything for a second and I thought I'd blown it, but then she bit her lip and nodded, 'Deadly.' Shy kind of. And I thought, why not? So I said, 'You wanna go Deli-Burger for a milkshake or something?'

Her eyes went big, like she was surprised little me would ask such a thing and she shrugged and whispered, 'Okay, cool,' and we waited for two cars to pass and then crossed the road and I opened the door for her and showed her to the best seats in town and I got the drinks and brought them over and smiled, delighted, ye see, cause the cock and balls—even the little spikey pubes—could be seen perfectly from where we sat.

One Hundred Years

Easter
rising from your low stool
at the window you
brushed your hair
with the silver-plated brush
long-handled, the one
given at your christening
with matching mirror you sat
at the window for the light
was better there

my grandmother was

the bullet whipped
through the open casement
from the street (name it) below
the Easter Rising
though you didn't know it
then

at the back of the room

you were just 16 in 1916
Dublin, on your own
you got the train down
from the North yourself
digs in central Dublin, a teacher
training college, Blessed Virgin
I have asked for many favours
(name it)
recite three times, publish,
never known to fail

where the bullet stopped

2016 almost
Easter
I sit on a high stool
at the window in the Linenhall
to trawl through old news
papers online
(I only know the year)
there it is in black
and white your name
for the first time I know
and write

your name (name it).

Elaine Gaston

After 1916

North of the border
don't forget about North
of the border—there was always talk
even then, don't forget
there was no border then

but even so one night
men came and gave his grandfather
no chance to argue
just shoved the guns up
the chimney; here you'll hide

these for us or get a hiding
or worse
in the deep black and tan seam
that divides
bog from field on the edge of the townland.

Elaine Gaston

MiseryLit

Belinda McKeon

Kathleen was new. Kathleen was afraid of the newness.

Eileen, also new, was afraid of the noise, which (she did not know) was her own noise, and the noise of all the others who were new, and of the ones they had come away from, and of the other ones.

Joseph was afraid of the hands.

Michael was one of 234 Michaels, and Michael, at his beginning, was afraid of the noise and of the hands and of the feeling. Catherine, who was one of 194 Catherines, was also afraid of the feeling; the feeling was everywhere. The feeling was her. Something stayed away from her which could answer it; something stayed away from her which could clear it away; but something did not come, and anyway, Catherine did not know, did not get to know, what something was.

Josie knew. Josie was one of the ones who got to be no longer new. Who took steps. Long enough around for Josephine to become Josie; Josie was one of those ones.

Josie was afraid of the room.

Mary was afraid of the room. The other Mary was afraid of the room. The other Mary again was afraid of the room; the other Mary again again was afraid of the room. Mary Again Again Again was afraid of the room, and Mary Again Again Again Again was afraid of the room. And Mary. And Mary. And Mary. And Mary. And Mary. And Mary. And Mary. And Mary. And Mary. And

Mary. And Mary. And Mary. And Mary. And Mary. And Mary. And Mary. And Mary. And Mary. And Mary. And Mary. And Mary. And Mary. And Mary. And Mary. And Mary. And Mary. And Mary. And Mary. Mary-Kate was afraid of the room. Mary-Frances was afraid of the room. Mary-Elizabeth was afraid of the room. Mary-Catherine was afraid of the room. Thomas was afraid of the room, Patrick was afraid of the room, James was afraid of the room, Dan was afraid of the room, Johnny was afraid of the room, Jimmy was afraid of the room. Jimmy the other Jimmy; Jimmy the other Jimmy after that one again; Jimmy the next Jimmy; Jimmy.

The room was end. The room was silence, except when the door was open and it was not silence, it was sounds, sounds of needing, sounds of ending. Only others were put in the room.

Andy was afraid of becoming an other.

Rose was afraid of the feeling. The feeling was Rose. The feeling was Rose when it was the daytime, and the feeling was Rose when she was down in the dreams. The feeling was this: that the next moment to come to you would be something bad. That the next moment would be a roar. Grip and roar and plunge and lash and hammer hammer hammer, though hammer was not the worst, and kick and tear and strip and scald, and that could be the next moment; that could be the next moment, and there was no one who could say that it could not.

Bridget was afraid of the eyes.

Eamon was afraid of the floor. The floor was what was done to you. The floor was what you did.

Seán was afraid of the dark. There were 84 Seáns, and 67 of them were afraid of the dark.

Oliver was afraid of the dark.

Martin was afraid of the dark.

Emmanuel was afraid of the dark.

William was afraid of the dark.

Maureen was afraid of the dark.

Anna was afraid of the dark.

(Are you tired yet of hearing which of them was afraid of the dark?)

Patricia was afraid of the dark.

Noreen was afraid of the dark.

Brendan was afraid of the dark, and Gabriel was afraid of the dark, and

Kevin was afraid of the dark, and Connie was afraid of the dark, and Nancy was afraid of the dark, and Peg was afraid of the dark. Róisín was afraid of the dark. Hannah was afraid of the dark. Trevor was afraid of the dark and John Patrick was afraid of the dark. Mick was afraid of the dark and Mike was afraid of the dark. Sarah was afraid of the dark and Sophia was afraid of the dark.

Mary was afraid of the dark. Mary was afraid of the dark. Mary was afraid of the dark. Mary was afraid of the dark. Mary was afraid of the dark. Mary was afraid of the dark. Mary was afraid of the dark. Mary was afraid of the dark.

Anthony was afraid of the mornings.

Seamus was afraid of the forms.

Padraig was afraid of the sounds.

Sonny was afraid of moving, and of what it might bring on.

Francis was afraid of the ground.

Liam: of footsteps; Larry: of words. Maura: of the tall thin one; Janie: of the paint on the wall. Iggy was afraid of the corridors; Gerard was afraid of the fire. Theresa was afraid of the man with the red rash of tiny holes on his nose, because Theresa was afraid of the pain. Theresa was afraid of the pain Mary was afraid of the pain Mary was afraid of the pain Marian was afraid of the pain Marie was afraid of the pain Bridget was afraid of the pain Catherine was afraid of the pain; Harry was afraid of the pain Michael was afraid of the pain Johnny was afraid of the pain Thomas was afraid of the pain.

Jonathan was afraid of the tails.

Peadar was afraid of the air.

Noel was afraid of the water. Monica was afraid of the bowls. Breege was afraid of the curtains. Raphie was afraid of the fields. Honora was afraid of America. Cissie was afraid of the dead. Philip was afraid of the moonlight; Christopher was afraid of the flies. Kitty was afraid of the school; Enda was afraid of his hair. Douglas was afraid of Paddy Toner; Paddy Toner was afraid of Hedges Rourke. Lily was afraid of Mary Prunty; Mary Prunty was afraid of Assumpta Joyce. Tomás was afraid of uneven surfaces. Brian was afraid of his own hot, stinging shit. Maisie was afraid of singing. Dermot was afraid of the hole. Imelda was afraid of dirt left on the floorboards; Clare was afraid of the bars of her bed. Niall was afraid of the man with the creases on his face; Dessie was afraid of the man who riz up the gold. Conor was afraid of the long dead man, thin; Edward was afraid of the nails.

Kathleen was afraid. Eileen was afraid Joseph was afraid Michael was afraid Michael after that again was afraid. Catherine was afraid all the Catherines after that Catherine were afraid. Josie was afraid. Josie got to two. Mary was afraid. Mary got to four. Jimmy was afraid. Jimmy, eight months. Andy was afraid; Andy got to be fairly tall. Rose was afraid; Rose, at five, had shocking, defiant-looking blonde curls. Bridget was afraid; Bridget never moved off the flat of her back. Eamon was afraid Seán was afraid Oliver was afraid Martin was afraid; Martin had weak lungs, and Martin was afraid of the spread of them across his pillow. Emmanuel was afraid. William was afraid. Maureen was afraid Anna was afraid Patricia was afraid Noreen was afraid; Noreen was afraid of the things if you looked behind. Brendan was afraid Gabriel was afraid Kevin was afraid Connie was afraid; Nancy was afraid Peggy was afraid Róisín was afraid Hannah was afraid Trevor was afraid John Patrick was afraid John Michael was afraid Mick was afraid Mike was afraid Sarah was afraid Sophia was afraid Mary was afraid Mary was afraid. Mary was afraid. Mary was afraid. Mary was afraid Mary was afraid Mary was afraid Mary was afraid—

1916, you're asking me?

Evelyn Conlon

Some years, when written down, have a look about them. In their mathematical, tidy visuals they bring their own particular questions, giving off whiffs of what has come since—and the parts of it we've talked about—because that's what history is. As I have tried to address this 1916 question I have marveled at the pressure it has put me under. I realised that you could get defeated by the effort of answering for a number of reasons, some of which made me want to plead the secret ballot. This in turn has led me to understand more fully just how extraordinary it was as an event, not necessarily in itself but in its aftermath and in what it eventually achieved. So I chose to leave the thorny aspects aside, sweep away the dissenting voices, gloss over the parts that the secular me find difficult, and see if I knew what it meant to me on an esoteric level, and yes, I do mean exotic.

My first reaction to the question is to be instantly transported to the fiftieth anniversary in 1966 and how that shaped some of the ways in which I saw myself in the world. It's impossible of course to fully measure that sort of thing, because time of day, place and questioner will affect the answer, but clearly now is a good time to have a think about it, reluctant and all as I may have originally been. This reluctance comes from the tensions I see gathering, the black cloud that some people insist on bringing to the table, the thunderous unspoken blame for how things have turned out. It may also come from the unfinished nature of the entire affair.

But let me take you back a bit. On Easter Sunday 1966 I was aged around about 14 and a half, becoming aware of myself as someone other than a girl in a grey gymslip, although what that was I had no idea, and indeed often still don't. Looking back I can see that I was a detached sort of child, in love with things like history, stories well told, and even the aura that poetry could create—I had fallen for Baudelaire, of all people. Boys came in and out of my landscape fleetingly, but they were an idea that was hard to hold on to—I occasionally regretted having no brothers who would presumably have had friends that I could have watched without effort, outside of school hours. There were no boy neighbours either—well there was one half a mile away, but for some reason or another he didn't count.

I had gone to a two-teacher school, Mrs Cassidy downstairs for the first four years and for the last four years upstairs a Mr McGill who would now be up on common assault charges at least, such was the vigour he put into his daily use of the cane. He was an equal opportunities man and used it on girls too, although there is one day in his battery of some boys that stands out all on its own. I often take a look at fifty-plus-year-old Irishmen and am astounded that they can even hold on to a conversation never mind have emotional relationships. Mr McGill told great stories though and I do remember grappling one day with how the two sides of him could reside in the one person. I can't remember how I resolved it, but I know I still enjoyed the stories, particularly the history ones. Around our parts people still don't want to talk too much about Mr McGill, mainly because he died young from cancer, and perhaps they're afraid of what they might say after that. Also, possibly, they don't want to offend the widow who had to rear the five or six children following his demise. A few years ago I was asked to write a short piece for a local historical chapbook about the days in St Mary's National School, Coravaccan. Funnily enough they must have felt that my view didn't really sit right with the rest, so they declined to print it.

At the age of eleven in 1964 I left the country school and travelled by bus for one year to 'The 7th Class', in the St Louis Convent primary school in Monaghan, into a roomful of about thirty girls, some of whom, including me, would be doing the Scholarship, the only possible way for me to get what was then a fee-paying secondary education. I had never seen a nun before and was a bit taken aback, but soon got used to the look of her and that of the dozens of others that I began to see in the distance, veils flowing behind them, flitting about in that place of awe, the secondary school. It was my first experience of being an outsider and I rather liked it. Sporadic, isolated, hitting continued—sometimes unexpected low blows to the back of the head. I don't remember a cane. But I do remember learning a ferocious amount of wonderful things and getting a beautiful County Council Scholarship, the most important thing I have ever won.

As a result of that, I took my place in the all-Irish secondary school, one of a few day pupils among what was mostly Gaeltacht boarders from all sorts of counties on the West Coast of Ireland and Dublin, a place I knew little of, although I knew lots about the Bronx and Long Island, having a plethora of American cousins who visited during the summers. I was so enamoured of the jigsaw that was secondary school that it was some weeks before I realised that no one, nor me, had been hit. My what an experience this was going to be. Getting the hang of it was like watching snow falling. And into this came the 1966 Pageant, an event exclusive to boarders, if I remember correctly, but then that would make sense, they lived there and had all evening to rehearse. While they were busy practising their lines, the rest of us were treated to the Proclamation. Quickly a rumour went around about an tSiúr Brigida: it was said that she'd had a boyfriend who was shot in 1916, and that she had subsequently turned her back on the temporal world and entered the convent. I thought that impossible but it could have been true— after all my own father had been born a month after the executions had taken place and she was older than him, or was she, it was hard to tell. So the ages could have fitted. Thinking about this I understand how short time is, how a lifetime has turned out not to be so long at all. I thought about the executions too in a compressed time sort of way when I was entering Death Row in the US on my research for my novel, *Skin of Dreams*.

So here's what happened. A month or so before the Easter Sunday parade we were directed to the Proclamation and we read it. *Irishmen and Irishwomen…* Immediately we were included. It is impossible to explain how important that made the entire experience. This was at a time when we were willing to accept that 'Man' and 'He' applied to us, but really in our hearts our English-language understanding was better than that, and we knew. But in our hands was a document that had actually set out to speak to us. To this day it's my greatest curiosity. Who first suggested that women be included and how did the conversation go? Is it true, as is generally believed, that there was only one man who had a problem with the calling out of Irishwomen? My what a bunch they were. We set to learning it off by heart. And my what a bunch we were, girl-citizen children, many of us of the poor, sitting at polished desks with the opportunity of having a second-level education. A proclamation, in other words a declaration of ideals, makes you bigger than yourself. And that's what it meant to me. It did seem exotic, way more elevating than everyday things.

It was pointed out to us that the inclusion of the word 'Irishwomen' was an astonishing thing and I was willing to take their word for that, even though I couldn't figure out why it should be thought so. As you can see I had a bit to learn about exclusion. In all the years since when I hear the query 'Who suggested that the word women be included?', I go back to that time of my innocence when I presumed that it would be a given. Lest you think I was uncritically carried away by the rhetoric of the entire experience I do remember questioning whether the sentiments in 'The Mother' could be truly ascribed to the subject of the poem, how could we be sure that was what she thought? And I brought it up. Perhaps that was not appreciated. I was getting well ready for the next Proclamation that I would read with interest, which was the Charter of Rights from Irish Women United. I missed *Change or chains*, being firstly too young and then too immersed in flight rather than fight.

So there was a before and after reading of the Proclamation and a later learning of how it had been let down, its ideals at least partially destroyed by those who eventually came to power, those who would use shoddy dishonesties to further themselves, while beside them worked men and women still imbued with a notion of civil service.

But the words of it still stand for what is best in aspiration to the greater good above personal greed. With hindsight I think I can honestly say that the sentiment expressed in it turned me towards a view of the world that spreads out rather than in. I was fascinated by the fact that people would do something for their country. It's not that I didn't know about other uprisings, but this one had been successful, that's what made it different. Hadn't they talked about it at the crossroads in Hungary and India? (Mind you in our house it was considered only partially successful, we had our hinterland cut from us, by the eventual Treaty. We looked across the border with a sense of loss.) And hadn't it caused all sorts of rumbles in the Conscription Debate in Australia, the echo of which is still heard where people talk of these things.

My reluctance to examine the place of 1916 in my thoughts might also have something to do with my fear of anniversary as a concept. I have occasionally written short stories in reaction to something that can only be addressed by fiction. 'Reasons That I Know of That We Are Not Allowed to Speak to My Grandmother' is a reply to the sheer nonsense and depressing pointless guff around weddings, where people behave as if this is the only day in their lives worth living. (Take it easy, you've just been lucky to have met someone that you, still, like, and you might even be really lucky and continue to like them, and they you. Only time will tell.) I've recently been at a humanist funeral which was just as bad. Spare us from the uncontrollable weeping of a relative, which should be done not from the pulpit but in the front row with a sympathetic arm being occasionally passed over the shoulder. But I digress. Sometime around 1997 it became apparent that the Millennium was going to turn into the equivalent of twenty weddings on one night. 'Escaping the Celtic Tiger, World Music and the Millennium' began as a reply to this phenomenon but veered off into the further reaches of lexicography. A decision was made early in our house to fine people if they mentioned the word Millennium. In the end we threw together a lovely quiet evening, some poets, a painter, a musician, an open invitation to two sons and their friends, and Mary Holland, who funnily enough was the only one who cracked and thought after a few glasses of wine that it might be an idea to go up to the roof to see the fireworks.

A further problem is the looking back at what has happened since 1966, the viciousness of the war, the so called Troubles, which is a slightly more serious word than the Emergency. I feel a whiff of the closing down of discussion that accompanied those Troubles. But that's the burden that our history has. Our very geography decided our fate. We were after all a tiny island beside a larger one with notions of achieved Empirical grandeur and its subsequent queasy superiority. It's an interesting thing also to wonder about the effect of place on one's thoughts. I started writing some of this essay while gratefully squinting out at sun on the Dordogne River, free of dissident voices, but looking at it now back in Ireland, where it takes on a different complexion, I suddenly long never to have been asked the question or to have refused to reply. Talking of place—I've noticed too that Northerners can be more interested in 2016—there's a touch of the 'If you were in Belsen you'd eat it' about this. They are more appreciative of the reality of being a citizen rather than a subject precisely because they haven't got it. Doris Lessing visited two schools in the same week, one out in the African bush where the teachers were scraping out the alphabet in the dust, no books, and the children were hanging on to every word, the next in a comfortable classroom in London, next door to a library, where the students looked bored with privilege and never dreamt of going into the room with the books.

Talking endlessly about the I, not putting it in a wider context, has a parochial narcissism about it that holds no interest for me. I dread emotional incontinence so this is not an autobiographical essay but it is about how I came to see myself as Irish. There is pre- and post-reading of the Proclamation and there is pre and post the European Schools Day Essay, both of which took place within the two years of me being aged between fourteen and sixteen.

Now, let me try to get my head around this. This was an essay competition run in the countries of Europe. The year I did it the title was 'Changes I would like to see in Europe, their effect on the educational system and thus the formation of citizens'. Fancy that. Generally this competition, like the learning of games and being part of the 1966 pageant, was open only to boarders but a new, rather radical nun had arrived in our midst and she decided that I should do it. In the evenings the boarders went to the library to research the topic, in the evenings I went home. I don't think I intended to do the thing at all, but on the appointed day it was remembered that I had been signed up. Because I would not be there in the evening I was brought, alone, into the office of the Mother Superior, given a desk, a pen and told I had two hours.

The experience was so novel—no one was ever in this office except for matters of a most serious nature—I enjoyed the challenge. I had in my mind Brendan Kennelly's poem 'Apostles of Possibility'. I have no idea where I could have come across that. So, armed with the poem, the pen and the strangeness of the surroundings, I set to. A few weeks later I was returning from a wander around town, slipping back into school to collect my bag, having given some class a miss, when I met departing pupils, leaving the premises much too early. It transpired that the entire school had been summoned to the hall to announce that there had been two winners from our school, one of them me. They were then allowed to go home early, hence the exit of the day pupils, as I slipped back in. Obviously it was a bit of a disaster that I wasn't present, but in the circumstances it wouldn't have been politic to do anything serious about my behaviour.

Then came one of my first lessons in class, although I didn't know that's what it was. I had to fill in a form for the upcoming journey to Germany, the prize given to the winners. For hobbies I truthfully answered, reading and dancing—a truth that lasts to this day. Mother Dorothea, who was cursed with a particularly unsweet voice, whined at me, 'No, no, do you not play tennis, put down tennis and we'll teach you.' I suspect that they were reading 'boys' for 'dancing' and that certainly would not do. I put down tennis—although I insisted on keeping dancing in. Perhaps the tennis would take the common look off it. And they did give me two lessons that got no further than me being baffled as to the point of the entire thing. I was sent out to the hairdresser's to have my hair done for the passport photograph which explains the bouffed up appearance in my first document for travel. And then on our journey to Dublin, to Coláiste Mhuire, to be formally announced as representatives of very young Ireland, I had to be kitted out in a boarder's Sunday outfit, clearly my own day-pupil one not being seen as acceptable. Did any of this bother me? Not one whit. Somewhere, perhaps in my solitary nights—I didn't sleep at home, that's another story—I had learned not to mind too much about the strange behaviour of my betters.

The prizewinners arrived and were assembled in Bodensee, Lake Constance. On checking through a truly fascinating labyrinth I discovered that much is lost of the records of this event but I do know that there were ten winners from Ireland. Each country's group had with them at least one teacher and a member of its parliament with an occasional visitor, which included Denis Healey. And yes I noticed his eyebrows. Our man was Richard Burke. Among our ten winners were Nuala Ní Dhomhnaill, perhaps already becoming a poet with her matching notepaper, and Declan Kiberd, definitely already becoming an academic, I would say. Each morning we had roundtable discussions for which we donned translation headphones. I was stunned by the entire thing. Now that I think about it, it was a kind of youth parliament—if I'd been a little older I might have got more out of it than an evening with an Italian, who taught me 'O Bella Ciao', and my first alcoholic drink to go with the experience. When the time was up all the students headed home but we Irish were treated, by Ireland, to an extra few days. We were brought to Strasbourg to look at the EU building and then by train to Paris. We were very aware that our country was treating us well. I mention this because I do believe that gratitude had something to do with feeling that we belonged to a new country. Forget the niggling fact that we weren't an entire country (always there with Ulster people), the proclamation had been learned off by heart and still tripped lightly off the tongue.

There are many things wrong with this republic of ours, particularly at the moment. The greasy till made a spectacular reappearance there for a while, the obligations of privilege were forgotten by many. And covert fumbling for more than a person could possibly need was carried on arrogantly by all sorts of people, some of whom I might even have once called friends. There were many things wrong with the Republic when I was carrying the stigma attached to the life I was living in the 1980s, and yet even at that time I remember doing a reading in London and while roaring with rage at home, exhausted on picket lines, I answered there that it was not such a bad place strangely enough, its natural resources were rain and women. You'd have to have lived then to know why that was important. What I meant was that it was, and still is, a place that has idealistic people. The Proclamation is still an issue, suggesting human rights and enfranchisement, and about to be become more so as it is laid out on school desks once again. This time around different things will be talked about. It will not be such a shock if some smart-arse girl remarks that De Valera wouldn't allow women into his battalion, she might be able to get a copy of Margaret Ward's *Unmanageable Revolutionaries* from her mother and it might even be discussed.

What of my fear of anniversaries? I thought that I might have had to disappear for this one. I had a terrible dread that the shouting about who owns 1916 would prove impossible to live through. (Can someone please explain how anyone can own an historical event? Perhaps they mean understand it. Or were part of it. A bit like people who now claim to have been in favour of contraception all along and of having put their heads above the parapet in the Eighties, when actually they crossed the street as we stood selling condoms at the top of Grafton Street, having our names put down in Garda notebooks and, no doubt, on job interview 'Additional Notes'.) But somehow this is shaping up a bit better than I had expected. The fact that poets and teachers were among the signatories of the Proclamation might just give the artists of today their deserved say. They, after all, are the people continuously involved in public service, most of them living on the scrapings of tin in order to give us a better understanding of what life means.

But back to the polished desks and the Proclamation. We were getting ready for our own revolution as we read it in 1966. In the beginning we may have thought parts of it were quaint, just as today we ourselves could be called that very thing. The point is that the Proclamation might have ended up being like a Baudelaire poem except for what happened afterwards. It is an astonishing wonder that three quarters of this tiny island did indeed manage to get green post boxes. And because the days are gone when you went inside the green telephone box outside on the street with your change lined up to speak your private conversations, some people think that it doesn't matter. I think it does.

I don't want to claim retrospective smartness, but I do believe that the Proclamation's effect on me was to leave me open to the notion of a place way outside myself, which has been an interesting enough planet on which to have spent the subsequent fifty years.

Blessed

after P.H. Pearse

I grudge them—
more than any of you will ever know—
my two strong sons
and their stupid, bloody protest.

I have cried all day and all night,
every day and every night
since then, ever and forever—
no amen on my tongue—

for Pat, our melancholic prophet,
fainting at a drop of blood,
but calling out for insurrection
over an old warrior's grave.

He set off that morning,
his pawn-shop sword
threatening to catch the spokes
and throw him off his bike.

And Willie. Will, my baby boy—
his big brother's shadow—
took the tram to town
to throw away his life too.

You must not grieve,
You too will be blessed,
Pat wrote to me
that terrible day.

Blessed. Ha!
I tend the graves.
I feel the burn of lime
on my boys' flesh.

A.M. Cousins

A Liffey Swell

Seamas Keenan

A full year past, and the lingering stench of dampness and wood smoke hung in the air. People said that basements were smouldering in the city centre, small fires re-starting, oak beams glowing red in the dark. I nudged Farren, slowed my pace, coughed into my hand. He knew the drill.

'Don't look round, don't speed up, and try not to sweat,' Farren whispered. 'Remember your training. Don't signify guilt. To an experienced observer, furtiveness is proof positive of nefarious intent.' That's the way the man talked. I think he was a Latin teacher in a previous life.

It had been a busy week. For four days, I'd attended intensive classes in the derelict cottage on the outskirts of the city. Small-arms and explosives lectures in the afternoon, military theory after tea, and, to test our mettle, mock skirmishes with an imaginary enemy after dark. Farren was the Training Officer, and for some reason, he'd taken a shine to me. I think my father and he had once worked together on some bilingual sketch-show or fund-raising amateur dramatic production.

On the fourth night, Farren took me aside and handed me a ten-pound parcel bomb with a length of fuse inserted in the middle stick of dynamite. He told me not to look for risky targets, but to place the device in the first available back-alley, light the fuse, and get away as quickly as I could. According to him, I was too valuable an asset to be used as cannon-fodder. Certain gentlemen, he claimed, had big plans for me. They were always on the lookout for well-spoken, well-educated young men. The war wouldn't last forever, and opportunities were endless.

The houses looked deserted, so I placed my bomb on a bottom step, touched a match to the fuse, listened to the sulphur hiss and catch, and walked away.

It's true what the experts say. In moments like that, your mind goes blank. In a second I'd lost all sense of myself and my plans. I didn't faint, or run, or freeze but I imagined myself a recalcitrant racehorse in need of blinkers to get from A to B. I could see ahead of me a cobbled street and a pale light. Nothing else. I had no peripheral vision, no consciousness, not even a premonition of imminent extinction. My mind was a snow-shaker, full of flurries and scudding clouds. No grand medieval cathedrals, no hallowed grottoes, no pine-trees bending in a gale.

And now, I was having a similar sensation.

'I think you're imagining things,' Farren said.

I hoped he was right, but saw little sense in arguing. If a bullet was coming, let it come, and let it enter my skull swiftly, accurately, and painlessly. All the lads were agreed on this point. If you ever get the choice, the best way to die is to be shot point-blank in the brain. You won't feel a thing.

For an older man who'd already spent time in prison, Farren was gregarious. He hadn't stopped yapping since we'd crossed the footbridge. For a blooded operator and senior officer, he possessed little awareness of danger. Once the river was behind us, he relaxed, considering the area we'd entered a safe territory, a zone of watchful sympathisers. I could see few signs for optimism. No flags flew on lampposts, no rowdy, bosomy women in hastily smeared lipstick ran to embrace us. It struck me that the groups of ill-dressed, lethargic men at street corners might harbour enemy agents.

After a minute, Farren glanced around, covered his mouth, and whispered.

'You've never met the big fellow, have you? That's why he wants you for the job. You're anonymous, no one knows your face. An unknown quantity. That means you can go anywhere. He leaves nothing to chance, the big fellow.'

If there's one thing in this world that I detest, it's a man whispering in my ear. It's unhygienic, that heat-swarm of breath, and the millions of germs that splatter on your face. I turned my head away from Farren.

'He's a massive man, you know, built like a tank, all chest and neck! And he was only a wisp like yourself in his youth. As a boy, he'd sit up half the night licking stamps for election literature. And deliver the letters before dawn. Hail or shine. He's also a genius at mental arithmetic. Your own mother, God rest her soul, was very fond of him.'

*

I'd never been to this part of town. My mother would have killed me if she'd thought I was frequenting the slums. I stared at the narrow street and the nose-tickling turf smoke spiralling above every chimney pot. Plaster statues of the Virgin and Saint Anthony flaunted their robes in uncurtained windows. A raggedy Papal flag flew from a pole nailed to a window frame. Not a paving stone remained intact. Farren led me over a jigsaw of cracks, weeds and crevices, past dirty mongrels with crudely docked tails cavorting with troupes of unwashed children.

We turned into a lane half-blocked by an eruption of brambles, nettles and ropey weeds. I could see the crimson glint of honeysuckle tips glowing like Sacred Heart lamps in the gloom. Farren counted the back doors. Satisfied, he dragged back a sheet of corregated tin, rolled up a sleeve and slipped his hand carefully through a punched gap in a wooden fence. With a finger at his lips to silence me, he eased back a creaking bolt and pushed. A mildewed gate scraped open.

The backyard was upholstered with coal-dust mould and discards of hairy turf. A rusted wheelbarrow blocked an open lavatory. The makeshift path to the house was dry, compacted mud, grooved in parallel lines. A child's vest and a woman's undergarments flapped from a length of thick cord that ran from the topmost branch of a neighbour's tree to a six-inch nail embedded high on the fence. The windows of the house were smeared with a streaky, putty-like substance that obliterated the interior. Farren tapped the glass with a knuckle, then wiped his fingers on the windowsill.

*

I would consider myself a cautious follower of James Connolly. I studied his writings, attended some meetings, grieved at the manner of his death. I give you my solemn word, I am not a snob, but I would never, ever, offer a guest of mine a grey woollen blanket.

Bluish veins stood prominent on the woman's cheeks. Her face looked raw, scourged by close exposure to open turf fires and constantly boiling pots of steaming water. This was a woman who hung out her laundry in windy, drying weather, who dragged lumpy bags of coke from colliers' yards, who tramped the streets with a rickety, swaying pram.

I thanked her for the blanket, smiled at the inquisitive child in her arms, and closed the bedroom door. I knew that this was a hard neighbourhood and that life was a constant battle for the poor. I knew that. That's why we fought for them, to take control of the state and eventually, the means of production, and ensure no more inequality, or poverty or child neglect. Until then, we were taught: be happy with what the people have to offer. They live on pitiable amounts of food. Sometimes, I admit, I was not convinced of the people's commitment to our cause.

The bed was a narrow cot squeezed between a metal filing cabinet and a wall. In impoverished communities, people furnished their homes with odds and ends picked up in pawn shops or hucksters' stores. All around the district were buckshee operations, sales of illicit items conducted in back alleys. To supplement their paltry stipends, soldiers from the nearby garrison resorted to stealing from their quarters. Articles that weren't nailed down eventually found themselves on a stall. Farren, and some of the company commanders, weren't happy with this, worried about the high levels of collaboration between the military rank-and-file and the local populace. I understood that concern. Once you deal with the enemy, at whatever level, a line is crossed. One thing leads to another and next thing it's a bargain in exchange for a snippet of gossip.

It was impossible to sleep. The minute hand on my watch entered the hour of midnight. I'd gone straight to bed, preferring not to engage in conversation with the woman. She seemed in awe of me, and I knew nothing of the rearing of children or the many diseases that afflict them.

My usual billets were on the other side of town, in the semi-detached mansions of poets and academicians, language enthusiasts, the occasional genealogist. I enjoyed their company, their nonchalance and cynicism. And I found their preference for expensive liquors stimulating. We'd sit up half the night, talking about freedom, art, philosophy and radical economics. Without sounding immodest, I believed they found me fascinating, dashing, a young man of considerable intellectual stature.

I'm not claustrophobic, but that room was a tomb. I was too tall for the cot and the woollen blanket sparked a rash on my chest and arms. The mattress was damp and the heat of my body drew tiny bubbles of moisture to the surface. My ankles, thighs and waist were covered in a wet sheen. I tossed away the blanket and examined the undersheet, a thin strip of yellow cotton with spreading archipelagos of water, estuaries and canals criss-crossing.

The air was clammy with the milky-scented urine of an incontinent child. The soiled perfume of boiled cabbage rose through the floorboards. I could smell lino peeling, dishcloths steeping, sodden wood murmuring as it warmed. The crayon slicks on the walls were infantile stick-people, horses, cows. I dried my legs on the corner of the blanket and pulled on my clothes, bone thirsty, a headache thumping. Despite the house's microscopic dimensions, I knew I'd get lost looking for a glass of water. I also knew what was causing the migraine. The countless sticks of dynamite wrapped in greaseproof paper under the bed and the hundredweight bags of fertiliser mix beside the door.

I sat at the bedroom window and stared at the fields behind the house. As dawn broke, squares of trampled grass grew bright with heather and thistle, and on a slope, black indentations where fires had ravaged the earth resembled the mascaraed eyes of the women who gave recitals for the cause. On a leafless tree, creamy-feathered birds swayed like clothes pegs on a washing line.

Defiled by another's urine, and agitated, hungry and thirsty, I searched the small room to kill slow time. In a cardboard box behind the metal locker, I found a .38 Webley revolver and four rounds of ammunition. I loaded and unloaded the gun. I wasn't happy to be here, but a job's a job, and an order's an order, and I was proud to have been selected. I had no real complaint about my assignment. It's only for a day or two, Farren had promised, and to complete it, the big fellow needs you close at hand. All the same, given my present unhygienic situation, there was something inhospitable about the lodgings afforded me.

*

'Memorise that,' the Big Fellow said.

I was disappointed that it wasn't Mick. Just another big fellow. Oddly, since the reorganisation of the Army, it had become common practice for any officer over five-eight to be described as a Big Fellow or a Long Fellow.

I studied the scrap of paper he held before my eyes.

1 J XL, 1 PT, pleated, 34W, 31IL. Green, military cut.

A code, I assumed, the internal dimensions of a barracks, or vantage points for an ambush. Eleven words, none too complicated. I concentrated for a few seconds, and nodded to him.

He struck a safety match, touched the paper and held it between his thumb and forefinger as it burned to ash. He didn't flinch when the flame puckered his skin.

I stepped back a pace, saluted him. He smiled, and punched me on the upper arm. The muscles froze, a local anaesthetic, paralysed from shoulder to wrist. Farren was laughing. Where did he learn to punch like that, I wondered.

'Never salute a superior officer in public. A sniper could be watching. Don't acknowledge my rank or address me as sir. You're not trying to have me whacked, are you? Not being paid to set me up?' He winked at Farren. 'I thought you'd trained this cub better? We're just the same, son, skin and bones, cut from the same cloth, and with a bit of luck, we'll both be buried in wooden caskets when we snuff it of old age in our family beds.'

Most reassuring, I thought, but kept my mouth shut. He didn't seem the sort of man who'd appreciate a touch of irony. He rooted in his tunic pocket and offered me a hand-rolled cigarette. I hoped it wasn't his last. His ashy fingers had transferred a line of grime to the gummed paper. I sucked in the harsh nicotine of shag tobacco under his unsettling gaze, like that of a mature predator gauging my meat potential.

He shook my hand in dismissal. His grip was firm, the palm cold. He could sense my fear, conscious of his effect on me. That, I supposed, was why he treated us all so casually, like drinking companions or old pals casting a leisurely fly on a slow-moving river. He was ruthless, Farren had warned me, a man who'd shoot his own mother in the head if she stepped out of line. Farren's words were typically exaggerated, but not uttered as a criticism. He admired this big man, and that anecdote was an ultimate tribute from one soldier to another.

The Big Fellow whispered something to a teenager at the door. He had something actorly about him, the consciousness of a man who'd perfected stagecraft. Beneath the melodrama was a smart, coiled operator who knew exactly what he was doing. A violent man who understood the play and had learnt his lines.

There's nothing wrong with that, nothing aberrant or transgressive. From my own studies of military theory, I'm convinced that all successful leaders must be single-minded. The sternness, and occasional brutality they show their own troops are necessary when conducting wars of apparently insurmountable odds. Unlike a regular army, our forces have no recourse to legal niceties, no opportunities for debate on the morality of our actions. Insurrectionists cannot engage the enemy on the open field. We have neither the personnel nor the armaments for such engagements. We are, at best, a part-time soldiery left to our own devices. So, to maximise resources, we rely on tight internal discipline.

*

Farren was angry that I hadn't bothered to shave. I told him I'd forgotten my razor and that the woman didn't have a man about the house. When I stepped out of the car, he handed me a folded envelope for my contact and warned me to stay out of the public house at the corner of the street. I guessed, from the feel of the envelope, that it contained discs of metal, detonators or primers of some description. I placed it in my shirt pocket and buttoned the flap.

I remembered my training, tried to make myself invisible. My coat was belted, my collar up, my flat cap pulled forward. In my waistband was the Webley I'd borrowed from my billet. I didn't know why I'd taken it, but it made me feel good. There'd be ructions, but the cold barrel felt reassuring against my groin. I lingered at a fruit stall in the outdoor market, weighing fat oranges and dark plums, sniffing them, doing my best to avoid the trader's eye.

The street was mid-morning busy, women swinging netting bags, women exchanging greetings and pleasantries with neighbours, some pushing prams, some escorting cantankerous toddlers by the hand. A couple of middle-aged men stood in doorways, sucking juice from overripe peaches. Golden liquid dribbled down their chins onto knotted scarves. They might have been waiting for wives, but I had my doubts. I watched one of them read a hand-printed card in a shop window, and the other shuffle his feet as he sucked greedily on his cigarette, anxious to be rid of the noxious distraction. Farren had told me that the city centre would be under covert surveillance. I was sure that these two men, the bargain hunter and the smoker, were aware of my presence and expecting me. When they first saw me, they had become animated, bouncing on the balls of their feet, rubbing their hands together.

When a high-sided furniture-delivery van slowed at the kerb, I ducked behind it and raced across the road, into the building, up a flight of uncarpeted stairs and along a narrow, dimly-lit creaking corridor. No one appeared from the rooms, no one heard my carefully placed footsteps. Cobwebs shimmered on the ceiling. Third door from the left, Farren had said. Which side was left? I stopped outside a black door and prayed that I'd memorised correctly the entry code. Two palm-slaps, two knuckle-raps and two cracks with a closed fist. Some of these codes were pointless.

A rake-thin man in baggy dungarees ushered me into a high-ceilinged room, as spacious and echoing as an empty warehouse. A circular porthole in the ceiling admitted a column of light onto a long rectangular table. Two boys emerged from an annexe, carrying on their shoulders a rolled length of cloth. As they tramped across the room they reminded me of pallbearers at a pauper's funeral, impassive and dutiful. They placed their bundle on the table and stepped away as a stooped little man brandishing a curved knife sliced the bindings, pocketed the cords and unrolled the material. He spat blue-headed tacks into his hand and nailed each corner of cloth to the table edges. When he'd smoothed all the creases flat, he beckoned me forward.

I handed him the folded envelope and recited the code I'd memorised. He listened intently, then, with a pencil stub, scribbled on a sheet of thick brown wrapping paper. I found it impossible to believe that this unassuming, unprepossessing little man was an expert in military strategy. Of course, it was none of my business.

I found the atmosphere of quiet, purposeful concentration very impressive. These workers were serious men, and they glided from table to annexe to cupboard like acolytes preparing a holy ritual. And not one of them was tall. It must be the darkness and the constant exposure to dust, thread and dye that stunted their growth. The little fellow with the knife took my arm, held it out, manoeuvred me into the beam of natural sunlight. He laid a sample of cloth on my sleeve, studied it.

'What colour would you call that?'

'Green,' I hesitated, 'bottle-green or… dark olive, or… is there a colour called Lincoln Green?' I was struggling to remember my greens.

His compatriots were smiling. They knew their boss was testing me, playing with me. I might be young, but I'm not as green as I'm cabbage-looking.

'Good lad. Green it is. Nothing but green for you boys. Is it for the big man? That fellow's chest's out of proportion to the rest of his body. Did you know that? He needs his jackets specially tailored to hold all the medals he's expecting to win. Don't tell him I said that. He's a fine soldier, but… well, no sense of humour.'

The others laughed. I refused to acknowledge his contemptible stab at humour and was just about to chastise the midget for his effrontery when one of his apprentices issued a high-pitched, single whistle. We gathered round the boy at a window. Down in the street, a troop carrier blocked traffic and armed soldiers unloaded crossbeams of wood decorated with coils of barbed wire. A trooper ran into a fruit stall and overturned it, wheels buckling, striped awning touching the gutter, wooden trays skidding on the kerb. Apples, oranges, cabbages, tomatoes and carrots rolled and bobbed and sank in a rivulet of filthy brown drain water.

'Out the window,' the leprechaun screeched at me, 'Out the window, down the fire escape, down the lane and across the wasteland. They'll be there for an hour or so. Be back in, say, two hours.'

He returned the unopened envelope to me. 'Take that bloody thing with you. Trying to get us all hanged, is that the game?'

Fifty minutes to kill. My trousers were ruined, muck to the knees and one of the seams had split. I stood in the lane, splashing dirt from my clothes with handfuls of rain water. No one to blame. My own fault. If I hadn't brought the gun, I could have simply strolled past the soldiers, nodded to them, doffed my cap, inquired as to the time, borrowed a light for a cigarette, passed the time of day with a captain or lieutenant.

Unfortunately, I had in my possession a loaded weapon and that was a capital offence, so I had to resort to alleys, untended back gardens, rough fields, high brick walls topped with points of embedded glass.

The pistol would have been useless. I wasn't even sure how to operate the safety catch. I'd never been in a gun battle, never fired a gun in anger. I had a basic knowledge of the Thompson submachine gun, could strip it down blindfolded, but that was a training procedure. As Farren would say to us all, there's a world of difference between firing at tin cans and firing at a target that can shoot back at you.

Farren had said that the pub was out-of-bounds. Well, he wasn't here. With my pint, I ordered a bowl of vegetable soup and a ham sandwich. I lifted the bread and stared down at the pink veined slab of meat wearing an overcoat of thick yellow mustard. The stout was sour and sharp, drawn too quickly by the barman, and the froth had bubbled itself flat. Through the window I could watch the roadblock. The soldiers seemed relaxed, ready for lunch, impatient to be off. Some of them whistled at passing convent-school girls. At least they had something to occupy their minds. The pub was quiet and the only other customer had buried his face in a newspaper. When I looked up, a soldier was squinting through the window, rapping the glass with the foresight of his rifle. The instantly animated barman stuck a bottle of whiskey under his apron and hurried to the front door.

I slipped the folded envelope from my pocket and weighed it in the palm of my hand. I picked at the seal and hooked back the flap with a fingernail. The soldier had vanished and the barman was changing a barrel, so I cautiously emptied the packet's contents onto the table. Some of these new-fangled detonators can be so ultra-sensitive, a dirty look can set them off. I opened my eyes and stared at six brass buttons, each identical and each embossed with a tiny harp and shamrock.

Uniform buttons! I had no problem with uniforms. In fact, I'd hope, in time, to have one of my own, something dark green with square pockets, epaulettes, and a discreet flourish of cut and tuck, a touch of colour to offset the blandness of plain cloth, crossed rifles or swords in silver, or a tiny tricolour stitched above the breast pocket or across the shoulder. I'd be telling a lie if I denied that the thought of promotion hadn't crossed my mind, but, given my socialist credentials, I wanted nothing capricious or ornamental, nothing ceremonial or copied from comic opera, no plumes or feathers, no cocked hat or regimental cap.

The barman was watching me and the boozer had folded his paper. Medals and badges and buttons, strips of coloured cloth, discs and triangles of brass and imitation silver. I could hear Farren's voice. 'Image and presentation, boys, image and presentation. Keep that in mind. More important than rifles and field-guns. Don't believe that wars are won on firepower alone. We're not a rabble, or a posse of cowboys. One day the Big Fella will be kissing the Bishop's ring on the steps of the pro-Cathedral.'

The Butcher's Apron

Lisa McInerney

Pup is indignant about the flag. It is indignation that swells and spills over and it provoked in him, in the fifteen minutes between then and now, a dreadful need of being with his own people. The tribe at Justy's do not let him down. They lift their heads; they share his shock; they call his pint. First he is animated. His indignation asserts itself in arms arcing through the pungent, carbonated air of Justy's, ten minutes to seven, Friday evening, late April. Then he is pensive. He is melancholic. He shifts in his bar stool, lugging its legs an inch over the tiles. He has relinquished the mass of his story but is momentarily lost in its absence. This is Pup. He is young and he is gangly and there is an awful lot he doesn't know.

Sparky luxuriates in Pup's ignorance with the imposed ecstasy of a condemned man tackling his last meal. Pup's constitution will one day match what houses it, but for now he lopes and leans and baulks and scratches. He is only just gone twenty-three and works in the warehouse of a place that sells uPVC doors. He is six foot two or three without the bulk to make it look right. He has a young wan in the housing estate on the arse of the town; she is rubicund and mostly sullen and whenever she comes to Justy's with Pup, Sparky asks her if she thinks she's on The Missions or what? Sparky would have plans for Pup if he thought the young wan would let him. Pup is sincere and possessed of a laugh that lays waste to everything around it.

Now Sparky tries to jog Pup from his gloom. He unfolds himself from his over-bar hunch, leaves one forearm on the counter and the other on his hip and aligns himself so that his belly shrinks. 'And they just have it flying there?' he says. He is loud and sure and his voice has the desired effect. 'Fucking unreal,' says Pup, and he uncoils also and looks around at his audience. 'Like it was always there. The fucking cheek. The fucking…' he doesn't know what.

Boom bust boom. There is an economic recovery, the news says; *in Dublin only*, the news will not concede. The management of Justy's—Justy himself being long dead—never knew the sound of a full till and so they do not know how hard a fall it was when the fall came; Justy's never attracted the kind of patrons susceptible to fiscal undulations. They have a day trade: no busy times, no lunchtime surge, just a steady current of the same old same olds. This allows for certain liberties. If the customers want a lock-in, there'll be a lock-in, during which the smokers light up. Clandestine services can be pitched in the beer garden—from two regulars in particular: the cur who sells the dope and the malkin who sells the suck-offs. If Sparky has a want of a bit of grub but no mind for the road home, he can bring in a snack box or a takeaway dinner from the hot counter of the Topaz on the lower road or even a cooked chicken from SuperValu and and eat it at the bar. Justy's looks after its own and its own murmur and tut at Pup as he relays his story.

He starts, as before, from the point at which his lift dropped him after work. He strolls in along the lower road towards the town square, considering the fresh weekend; he crosses at the roundabout; he spots to his left the gaudiness of it, its flashing in the damp breeze, its fucking audacity. He peers, shades his eyes, squints. He comes a little way up the path towards it. It flies to the right of the EU flag, which flies to the right of the Tricolour. It is a Union Jack, hoisted on a flagpole at the entrance to the Kilcreehy Castle Hotel. It makes no sense. It is like there is a glitch in his sky.

'What reason could they have for that, now?' ponders Cullinane from the cluster. A man of many scars and few head hairs, a pragmatic man. He submits that the hotel is to host a wedding tomorrow—is one of the families British?

'Sure someone must be going,' Sparky says. 'Someone must have been asked to the Afters.'

No one in Justy's has been asked to the Afters.

This wedding occupies the tribe for a small time—*who* is going, if they are not; who is signing the nuptial contract; where this British family get off tramping into the Irish heartlands with their inglorious cloth. And the concession then to rationale—it might not be all that bad. As a gesture, y'know. As a nod towards friendship between natural foes. Perhaps it might have been a good thing, in another time. It is, the tribe at Justy's decide, just *too soon*.

Sparky is surest of all that it is just *too soon* to fly a Union Jack in Ireland; if it wasn't too soon then why did they all get such a shock on hearing Pup's story? It is not usual for groups numbering more than, say, five souls to share the one reaction. Sparky is a thinker, though he might not look it. He likes to believe that it is for this reason he's nicknamed 'Sparky'; *I'm not an electrician at all,* he laughs, often, *ah but I'm a live wire.* Those who ask about Sparky's nickname are rarely acquainted with those who know that Sparky is Sparky because Sparky was his dog's name when he was a boy. Nevertheless, Sparky is sharp enough. Fierce cute, even. He reminds himself often: *I'm no fool.* The thought that he is a fool and so too stupid to know that he's a fool gives him terrible anxiety.

'The Butcher's Apron,' he says. 'That's what they call it above,' and he flicks a thumb, as if Northern Ireland is the attic atop the manor where they might tuck away their loons and malcontents.

It is *too soon* and it is an affront and so action needs to be taken but the shock resonates and it's too strong to allow for thoughtful planning. And so tactics need to be charmed out, whetted by emphatic reminders of their history, of the ties that bind compatriots. Reminiscence is a virus hopping from host to host and strengthening; one by one they succumb to it, Pup, as the instigator, first. *My granddad was in the IRA.* Everyone's granddad was in the IRA. *My father's great uncle was shot by the auxiliaries. That Mass rock up off Gogarty's Lane, that was our land one time.* They spin yarns from old battles. They lament hardships suffered by ancestors. They are connected by ambassadorial grief, and through the thickening fog—for they drink as passionately as they talk—Sparky feels loss. Like something has been yanked from his grasp. The loss of a birthright.

Talk turns to other invaders. The new crowd come not with pikes, swords or firearms but with impudence. They set up businesses and primarily serve their own. They send their children to the local schools and secure exemptions from compulsory Irish lessons. They drive taxis—*almost all the taxis,* keens the chorus. Sparky shifts in his seat. This kind of chatter always ends in cacophonous ignorance, each voice shoring up and adding to its precursor's woes; the predictability of it saps him.

'We'll go have a look,' he says, and waits to catch Pup's eye. 'We'll go have a look, will we?'

That he has stirred Sparky into action cheers Pup greatly. He swigs the dregs of his pint and belches, leaving his jaw swing for longer than is necessary. He stands, grinning now, as if he's forgotten the alien colours.

Their town is of an unremarkable layout: a spine of pubs, chippers and dentist surgeries, capillaries stretched out to a Lidl on the west, an Aldi on the east, sheathed by a vellum of pebble-dashed housing estates and fields patched with burnt circles and sodden depressions. There is only one route Sparky and Pup can take and so they take it mechanically, each locked into his natural gait—Pup to his bouncing, stretching getalong, Sparky to his heel-knocking, clipped swagger, like a man afraid to trust his own knees. And there is a clamminess to the wind and to their surroundings, dankness to the concrete under them: the earth is nervous.

The castle of Kilcreehy Castle was never more than a stone framework around which was propped and plastered the necessities of the hotel: the castle houses only the lobby and reception desk and two suites above, suited mostly to American genealogy enthusiasts. Sparky and Pup do not make it that far, their crusade interrupted at the eyesore on the flagpole.

Well, what do we do now? thinks Sparky and the thought's incompetence upsets him; he is not used to being useless, not inside his own head.

As if in sympathy Pup breathes, 'It's a shock, isn't it?'

The flag is lurid in artificial light. It is bold and mocking and in its overlapped crosses it clashes even with itself. It is, notes Sparky, an empire's flag, an arrogant thing. It is bigger than he thought it would be.

He knows the Tricolour should not be flown after sunset. He doesn't care so much for the other two but knows that reverence is meant to be extended to them as well: the cold new European empire, and the brutal old.

He walks away and Pup catches up and keeps pace.

'What do we do now?'

Sparky says, 'We ruminate, Pup.'

They do not return to Justy's. They head instead to a pub closer to the hotel. This is owned by one Terry Corrigan, who's twenty-four stone and mobile only in the gravest of circumstances, so Sparky and Pup are served by his son Darren, who inhabits the role of landlord with studied precision. He dispenses one-liners. He is fluent in politics, county rivalries and the Champions League. He is a master of ambiguous responses. He has walnut-coloured eyes and has never managed to grow a decent beard. 'Sarcastic fucker,' Sparky says, cradling his pint in the sweep of his right hand, and Pup agrees.

A band has just finished setting up and its frontman conducts soundchecks as Sparky and Pup get cosy. Sparky hopes for patriotism. The Wolfe Tones. Paddy Reilly. Songs about revolution, emigration, bloody fraternity. Pup fidgets and looks around, twisting over this shoulder, then the other, like a man trying to free himself from a mangled car. 'Will you calm your tits?' Sparky says—a wisecrack he learned from a nineteen-year-old niece—and Pup guffaws. The band start their set but they play 'Pumped Up Kicks', then Olly Murs. Little in the way of rumination has taken place but Sparky wants to move. 'Come on,' he says and Pup apes him, swigging back the final third of his pint and stretching ceremoniously.

Sparky is not yet drunk but he is itchy for it—the haze and the loss of heed, inhibition drowned; drunkenness feels like being submersed; he likes that. It takes time and effort to get Sparky drunk, because it's the one sport where practice makes the player worse. It means that nights out have become expensive, sometimes crushingly. Pup's nights out too, but for different reasons: Pup always buys rounds of shots at closing time.

The upside to the protracted sobriety that defines his fifth decade, Sparky thinks, half-bitterly, is that he can outlast Pup or any of them at funerals, christenings and weddings.

Which reminds him again of the flag.

'I wish,' he tells Pup, 'that they'd played some of the old songs, that band. It's all trendy these days. It's all fuckin...'

Pup knows what he means.

There is not much light left now. A smudged ribbon of cloud separates the sky from its khaki horizon. Sparky clears his throat.

He is less a singer than he is a chanter, his voice trained by tipsy nationalism and the camaraderie of Saturday afternoon football terraces. But he tries to give it meaning. He tries for sweetness, even. Soul sound. The way the monks mean it, or the Welsh.

I was eighteen years old when I went down to Dublin...

And Pup joins in, just as solemn and sincere.

There is a point where Sparky realises they might make each other cry, far as they are from intoxication. They are under the influence of the song or of what the song means, what any of it means... They are custodians of a history, Atlas to its weight, and the tune is just one of many, a sinew of great heritage, of a country, a family compelled by the border of sea, thirty-two counties, *thirty-two*, each as much part of the whole as the next.

Sparky and Pup slow their steps but the song ends; songs do not go on forever.

'What'll we do now?' asks Pup.

Sparky is loathe to return to Justy's. He has unfinished business with the enemy banner. He tilts his head to the right, to the door of another pub. Three houses down, four more to go—five if he counts the hotel bar, and he might yet. 'I haven't been in here in a long time,' Pup says as they cross the threshold.

They settle down by the soot-stained fireplace. They have two more pints apiece and Pup then moves to the vodka Red Bulls and gets even more fidgety, bouncing on the balls of his feet and watching the women. He is not old enough for fidelity, Sparky knows, and Christ, distraction is hard enough to come by, there should be concessions made. It's a small town and a big world and he knows that Pup is stuck here, that he has no mind for travel and even if he did, no fucking money and no chance of coming by it. He suspects that Pup's young wan is tolerant of occasional, whispered betrayal, so long as she's not poked on it, so long as he doesn't get anyone pregnant. She'll marry him some day; they'll get a mortgage; he'll quieten.

But Sparky isn't lax on Pup's wandering eye tonight. He is in need of attentive company tonight. So he says to Pup, 'Did you know that the Fianna are only sleeping?'

Pup is instantly and gratifyingly wide-eyed. 'How's that, Spark?'

'Fionn mac Cumhaill never died, they say. He's in a cave and he's asleep and the Fianna sleep around him. They'll wake again in Ireland's most desperate hour, and put what's wrong to rights.'

'You'd think,' says Pup, 'the Anglo thing would've gotten them moving.'

'Sure then there must be worse to come,' says Sparky with satisfaction, and while Pup sits enchanted and chewing his bottom lip he finds a two-euro coin and brings it to the jukebox on the wall by the bar and sifts through Metallicas and Rihannas for 'Uncle Nobby's Steamboat' and 'Carrickfergus' and 'Come Out Ye Black and Tans'. And so the magic is extended and Pup's eyes glint with clannish fervour and not with the notion that somewhere in this place is hidden the chance of a feverish ride against the back of the town grotto.

The lights are flicked off and on for last orders and Pup leaps forward for a couple of sambucas and, with Sparky refusing his measure, downs both.

They leave and move with purpose towards Mighty Bites where Pup orders taco chips and a chicken burger, and they sit outside so Sparky can have a fag, and there aren't many people out, it being only Friday and an unremarkable weekend, but they make a carbuncle to a small mass in their late teens. Sparky tells them the story of the sleeping Fionn, but they seem uninterested and he spots one of the girls smirking at another. 'You think it doesn't mean something,' Sparky says, trying to sound sage, 'but it'll mean something to you soon enough.' Where are the young people to go, he wonders, if not to London or Melbourne or Toronto? They are dressed too well for this town and they know it and it pleases them. He feels it like a burning in his throat. Or his gut. He'd like to lift a cheek of his arse to relieve himself but decides against it.

'How are things with you, Paud?' trills one of the girls and Pup brightens and tries to answer with calculated, masculine nonchalance, and Sparky winces on his behalf; the girl is seventeen or eighteen, glittered and spiced, and she has no interest in Pup beyond the pallid cruelty of deceit. He watches Pup sit straight and the girl sidle closer, watches her winch her neckline so that her breasts thrust for her chin, watches her eyes settle on the fleck of special sauce at the corner of Pup's mouth. 'Let's go,' says Sparky, and Pup blinks and says, 'Sure, you jog on if you like, Spark,' and there's a pang flipped in Sparky again. He reminds his friend that they're not done with the night yet, that there's a great impudence they have yet to challenge. 'Oh yeah,' says Pup. He announces darkly that they have something to take care of and doesn't notice that the young wan neglects to react.

So Sparky leads them back to the flags, and now in the early hours they are still slapping the breeze. And maybe, he thinks, swaying in queasy accord, if the hotel people had done their duty by the Tricolour and taken it down at sunset, and taken its rival with it, maybe he would have allowed himself home to bed. He's irritated, then incandescent that the protest's been pressed on him, after the week he's had, because the hotel people won't follow the rules, can't be bothered to do what's right.

He pushes on down the hotel driveway, Pup in tow.

The lobby light is dimmer than he expected, late and all the hour. There is a dark stone floor, brocade upholstered couches, mahogany. A broad-shouldered man in a gunmetal grey suit behind the desk, arms moving, hands busied with office implements. Laughter travelling from a distance, orphaned sounds, strangers' merriment.

Sparky lays his hand on the polished desk top and his hand looks pink and his fingers stubby.

'Do you not know,' he says to the broad-shouldered man; his badge sports no name over the embossed title of Night Manager, 'that the flag is supposed to be lowered at sunset?'

The Night Manager frowns. His actions slow. And then 'Oh!' and almost indiscernibly a breathy stream of *f* sounds; he stops what he is doing. 'It should have been done, lads,' he announces. 'Sorry about that,' but he doesn't look at either of them and Sparky's not sure whether this is out of curtness or shame but either way it emboldens him. 'Are you not going to do it now?' he says, and Pup to his left puffs his chest, a manifestation of Sparky's valour.

'I'll see what I can do,' says the Night Manager.

'And while you're at it,' says Sparky and his voice cracks, 'You can take down that other one and leave it down; it has no right to fly here; long enough we were trying to get rid of it.'

'Ah,' says the Night Manager. 'Well. We have a wedding tomorrow, lads; he's from England; it's a courtesy.'

'It's an offence,' says Sparky.

'Well it isn't,' says the Night Manager.

Not having the benefit of intoxication, how can this broad-shouldered man see the heart in Sparky's objections and travel, in his mind's eye, back to when this land was raw and the bloody rituals that birthed it appreciated? And Sparky, so usually persuasive amongst his own, has in fuelling this beautiful devotion tied his tongue: he slurs, and staggers once, and loses words. And Pup cannot help. Sure what would Pup know; he lopes and leans and baulks and scratches; he's young and weak and vulnerable; he is not even used to his independence.

They are defeated and insult on injury they retreat back to the Union Jack, that symbol of a great history denied to Sparky and to Pup, to all of them.

Sparky thinks, *how many of us died to send that yoke back where it belonged*? He imagines laid out before him a battlefield, he sees young men fall for honour, he imagines them clean-shaven, in dull grey waistcoats, in flat caps to a man.

He weaves between the flagpoles. 'Where's the rope?' he says. 'There's a rope to bring it down.' But the halyard is inside the pole, secreted behind a locked panel, and he cannot get at it. He steps back. He looks up.

'It flies there,' he chokes, 'as if it means nothing anymore.'

Sparky cannot bear the thought that he missed out on its meaning something. He has had a thorough education in its significance; he passed with flying colours Inter Cert History and Italia '90 and *Was It For This?* and he has travelled, Sparky, he has lived in Liverpool and Chicago, he has felt his Irishness, he has known meaning in it, and—

'Hold on,' Pup says.

He starts in the raised shrubbery in which one too many flagpoles were planted. His abundance of joints and limbs makes sense for once; Pup is lithe, Pup is a machine. Sparky stands into the shrubbery after him. He sinks a little into its soil as he cups his hands for a leg-up. Pup begins to ascend. He coils around the metal supporting the flag of the European Union, sticks out the sole of his runner and balances against the pole on which is hoisted the Union Jack. He strains, pants, and makes progress and Sparky is almost overcome.

A good lad, Pup. No cop on, but a steady compass, a sense of right and wrong, a willingness to learn, a heart unrivalled in the town. *And look,* Sparky laughs, *up he shimmies*! And when he reaches the flag there will be the feeling that a great deed was done in a small gesture, and Sparky waits for it.

But there is no gesture. There is no pride plucked from the sky; there is no evil vanquished. There is only a fall. Down he comes again in great disarray, limbs bunched, face to the dirt, and Sparky stands over him, 'Pup? Jesus. Jesus, Paudie,' but there is no answer, and he knows that's the end of it.

Bird Man Spawns (reprise)

'Therefore it is God's decree
Bare to the world he'll always be.'
Seamus Heaney, 'Sweeney Astray'

1

I, post-hatch, half wild, part man, King Cock, beak fed.
Crowed upon the dawn of the roost of the high-stool-born,
Womb-shell cracked in blazing red
Cradle-crowned in twisted thorn, stout-spittle and shit
Who was hushed-up proper by a bishop's limp crook
To the froth-born yak of my unhallowed-be mush
And nailed by the claw-hooked hand of each wing
To a shattering stained-glass notion of gospel
The Devil's own pack, half Jokers and Jacks.
A straight card flush, part magic trick stroke truth.
Strung-up by the neck in the sheds of my youth
And condemned for the out-of-line cut-of-my-jib
To live in the liminal gloom of the chatterbox darkness
Tied up in knots by slivers of iridescent light
To the hoot of the moon in the conjuror's night
By the whispering, whispering, whispering world

2

I am who am you who is they who is us
Who is molten cerebral beneath the skull's crust
Half cut, part gay, translucent, silent, still, come what may.
Who hovers in midair, brass-bollock-bare and brazen as fuck
Beneath the frenzied spotlights of the raving sun.
Naked and deranged in candy bar towns besprinkled with visions
That burst into wildfire, lynched upon pitchforks
Trembling in asylums of unsullied flesh
In black debased basements caught in the tangle
Of a fine spun cobweb of shuddering chills
I shrank out of sight in a bottle of pills
And bled from the ear to the nightingale's tune.
Who could fly off your cliffs to the song of your grief
Then perch upon branches, light as a leaf
In the gathering, gathering, gathering storm?

3

I who can ride on the blustering steeds
Of Caorthannach winds until bitter words bleed
From the fresh open wound of my jabbering mouth
Blabbering absurd incantations of naught
I post upon pedestals, grinding my teeth as you stand
At the pulpit or kneel on your penitent knees at the pews
To crucify Gods you would worship and whip
And then like a virus go spread the good news
Of your suffering souls condemned to restraint
Beloved by demons and cursed by the saints
To live in my head away with the birds
Yes it was I that taught them to sing
And I heard thunder clap in the silver-washed beat
Of a mid-May meadow-bound butterfly's wing
And was lost for a while in the wilds of myself
In a riddle of shadows that lunged from each wall.
Who was lead by the hand through the dark by the blind?
It was I of the muttering
Muttering, muttering mind.

4

I who could fly with the shadows of dusk
Wept for the sun when the sun turned to rust
Who could see every world in the maddening clouds
Knew the lore of the crows for I taught them to talk
Who was picked up and worshipped in out-of-town town bars
And burned every love by the fire of the soul
That kindles the mind set ablaze in the stars
Thus was I judged in your hollowed out eyes and confess
To the blessed congestion of what you believe
Is carved in the stone of your corpse-fed creed
Yes I confess, I confess, I confess.

5

It was I who was tarred and then feathered
And hung upside down by the unbroken bread of my body
Left in the stocks of apostates and thieves
Where the red-necked, half-witted, deaf, dumb and blind
Thoughtless and flightless minstrels of misfit
Gathered to brand me the beadledom's leper
For displaying in full feather the wings of the mind.

6

So I soared in my dementia on the keening of the wind
With the landscaped bludgeoned and the red sky skinned
I wailed at the flowering song of the shrub
I hooded the rook and bespeckled the dove
When the Cardinal cursed what the Morrigan blessed
I lay with the robin and reddened her breast
A fine holy madness to wreak amongst men
For the pennies they gathered to bury the wren
In the harrowing, harrowing, harrowing muck.

7

And here, at last, with our rainbows spent
I sang in the full plume of my bedlam
To the adolescent seed of the gobdaw state
To the blue clad batons of the gombeen law
And the bone-headed puppets of the amadán Dáil
And my song was a Godless land without faith
That the fat of the lamb spat back in your face
And poisoned with sorrow the seed of your men
Piping my sickness from furrow to glen
For I danced on your grave well before you were dead
And I spray painted red: *not right in the head*
Then I skipped through your mirror and with a tip of my hat
I died in a dream and then never came back.

Stephen Murray

The Multimedia Revolution in Poetry

Dave Lordan

Poetry is undergoing its second great, global revolution, self-transforming from a dominantly textual art form into a dominantly digital and performance one. The first revolution, during which poetry mutated from a wholly oral art into a dominantly textual one, began around 4,500 years ago in the courts of the ancient tyrants of the Middle East. Textual poetry then emerged as a byproduct of the invention of writing, itself developed to enhance the practice of accounting. From the off poetry, politics, economics, ideology, and social power are inseparably intertwined.

This first revolution took aeons to complete, during which the 'civilisation' birthed in the fertile crescents, founded on accumulation, mystification, and domination spread like a slow cancer across the globe, assisted as much by the weapons of writing and accountancy as by the might of conquering arms. Yet the oral foundation of poetry remained and remains strong, if very patchily so, in unconquered parts of the world, and among subaltern artistic milieus in the heartlands of empire—e.g. the beats, the black arts movement—and is now rising again as part of the multimedia revolution in poetry.

The twenty-first century, multi-medium poetry revolution is taking place in the space of decades and it is much needed. By the close of the twentieth century poetry in its text-only incarnation had brought the art into extremely marginal territory, and very close to complete disappearance, save as a state-subsidised heritage format. Dana Gioia recognised this in a 1991 essay for *The Atlantic Monthly*, 'Can Poetry Matter?', writing that poetry was 'no longer part of the mainstream of artistic and intellectual life, it has become the specialised occupation of a relatively small and isolated group. Little of the frenetic activity it generates ever reaches outside that closed group.'

Gioia notes that page-poetry is only kept alive by a complex network of state subvention; it is on life support, in other words. Page-poetry has had to pay a high price for its dependency on the neo-liberal politicians who, by and large, have run the State in the English speaking world since the 1970s. Far from revivifying page-poetry, state-regulation has tended to aggravate its morbid symptoms of public irrelevance and in-group confinement. Long-term state subvention of a select number of publishers, administrator-poets, and literary quangos has given rise to a poetry bureaucracy which wields control over nearly all available channels of state funding and mainstream publishing and broadcasting and which will generally give in to the temptation this produces to advance their own narrow sectional interests within the artform, at the expense of new forms and their new audiences. Only the political influence of sectional interests within poetry can explain why virtually all state funding and institutional support in the English-speaking world goes to page-poetry, when the majority of the publicly accessible work of new and emerging practitioners and of voluntary public engagement with poetry now clearly takes place in digital and performance mediums.

That state-entwined networks overseeing and regulating poetry have, aside from occasional tokenistic or face-saving gestures, set about ignoring the digital and performance revolution is perhaps the best piece of circumstantial evidence for it. For it is in the nature of revolutions that they take place outside of and in contradiction to the institutions and networks with a vested interest in the continuation of the old ways of doing things. Thus, with few exceptions, the revolution of poetry has also been a revolution of autonomy, of proving that twenty-first century poets require neither the support nor the regulation of the state, nor the patronage of vested interests within the literary world to make original and impactful work that reaches a wide audience. Digital and performance mediums have therefore offered a much needed path of independence from the neo-liberal state and state-regulated arts bureacracy to many poets.

This independence then is partly a matter of inclination, and partly born of necessity. Lack of official recognition and support of mediums such as performance and film poetry forces poets working in these mediums to rely on their own and community resources. Given the vast institutional imbalance in favour of page-poetry, it is remarkable how much public engagement with poetry is now dominated by the unfunded digital and performance mediums. Lack of official interest in, and therefore statistics on, new poetry mediums make their popularity difficult to assess with clinical accuracy. However, it is obvious that the live poetry event is now far more engaging to and popular with the poetry public than the poetry book is or perhaps has ever been.

According to a state-funded Irish publisher I recently raised this issue with, most of the poetry collections now sold go to libraries, collectors, and family and friends of the authors. In other words there is no readership for the average poetry collection worth talking about. This is not to argue that poetry collections should not be funded, but that they should be funded on an honest and proportional basis, as the heritage medium within the overall art form. It would also be part of a clear-thinking, artist-centred, audience-expanding funding strategy to offer training and support to all poets who wish to learn how to work in these contemporary mediums.

While book sales are in the ditch, attendances at live poetry events, of which there are now dozens per week to choose from in Ireland alone, are increasing at a high rate. Lingo 2015, run by volunteers on a shoestring, with a minimum of public funding, attracted 1500 paying poetry supporters. This makes Lingo, in its second year, with no paid director or staff, easily the largest poetry festival in Ireland. Performance poetry has also very quickly become the main way young people participate in poetry. Stephen Murray's Youthspeaks programme, to mention just one of several thriving independent school's programmes, has in eight years visited upwards of 400 secondary schools—half the total—and enabled thousands of young people to make poetry—again without any institutional support or valorisation.

Figures for public engagement become even more encouraging at the level of the poetry film, a medium whose rise is allied to that of performance poetry, and often involving the same practitioners, but which has distinct aesthetic challenges and audience potential. Even the simplest of recording technologies, accessible and usable to anyone with a bare minimum of computer skills can enable a contemporary poet to reach a potential audience of millions through YouTube. The number of poets that have reached four- and even five-figure audiences for their work on sites like YouTube and vimeo runs into the thousands.

Although Dana Gioia remains broadly correct in his ominous assessment of the increasing marginality of the text-only poem and poet, he couldn't have been more wrong about poetry considered as a whole.

These new and enlarged aesthetic and audience possibilities are perhaps most exciting to those of us who write politically—like Bertolt Brecht did, or Milton, or Neruda, or Adrienne Rich, or countless other canonical figures in the past. In fact the new situation seems to have been made for the political or, if you wish, public poet. It is not just that the potential audience for public poetry has increased hugely as a direct result of the new media poetics, but that this new audience is politically conscious and hungry for well-made and topical work in a way that has not occurred for many decades. Social movements such as the anti-water charges and the Repeal the 8th movements in Ireland, which have analogues in many countries across the world, are creating a new and transformed public appetite for socially engaged art of all sorts. It's a multimedia audience to which both the old text-only packaging of poetry and the largely quietest content of that poetry over the past few decades is irrelevant. This global audience reconfiguration—a shift to political enagement at the same time as a migration towards digital and live consumption of socially-engaged art—explains why the space in performance and video poetry is taken up so much by political poetry and poets.

Poetry, perhaps the most mutable and adaptable of all the art forms, has always been political and the range of ways it can be political has mutated constantly through time and is mutating again today—under pressure from and in response to political and technological change. So far as we know, the very first written down poems were written by temple priests on the orders of tyrants, with the purpose of glorifying the tyrant and elucidating the cosmic justification for his tyranny. The lyric, born among the Greek city states, developed as part of competitions between blind lyre-strummers as to who could most effusively praise the ruling members of their own city-state. The foundational documents of 'western civilisation', that Gandhian joke, are, alongside the Bible, the two epic poems of Homer, and one by his Roman Imperialist imitator Virgil. From the earliest days of the Roman Republic, up to the present day in private schools and universities, the ruling elites throughout Europe and in its many conquered lands have learnt the 'values' of the glory of war, the passivity and inferiority of women, the dispensability of the poor and the working masses, the justification of absolutism and aristocracy, the inferiority of non-white races and the justification for conquering them above all from the epic poetry in which these values were first inscribed and beautified for the purpose of reproduction by future generations.

Poets have tended to write politically in three different, often complimentary ways. To begin with there is a long tradition of counter-amnesiac poetry, that is poems memorialising instances of injustice or struggle which otherwise might be wilfully forgotten by the dominant culture—a canonical example worth much study is John Milton's 'On the Late Massacre in Piedmont'. Connie Roberts's recent Arlen House collection *Little Witness* redresses a shameful lacunae in Irish poetry with its focus on the experiences of working-class children abandoned to clerical institutions. Elsewhere, award-winning Israeli poet Aharon Shabtai offers many striking and courageous contemporary examples of counter-amnesiac poetry, such as this:

Culture

The mark of Cain won't sprout
from a soldier who shoots
at the head of a child
on a knoll by the fence
around a refugee camp—
for beneath his helmet,
conceptually speaking,
his head is made of cardboard.
On the other hand,
the officer has read *The Rebel;*
his head is enlightened,
and so he does not believe
in the mark of Cain.
He's spent time in museums,
and when he aims
his rifle at a boy
as an ambassador of Culture,
he updates and recycles
Goya's etchings
and Guernica. (*translated by Peter Cole*)

The second kind of political poem, and poetics, is one which elaborates a set of countercultural values in opposition to those held by the powerful. Such poetries, if they develop in tandem with a mass counter-cultural movement can provide strong points of coherence and identity formation for the social movements as a whole. The High-Romantic movement in poetry was based entirely on such a project—the French Revolution created the Romantic movement and its ideals inspired the best of them until well into the 19th century, just as their poetry inspired masses of activists and social reformers and continues to do so. The history of poetry is replete with such examples of mutual feedback between social movements and poetic trends. The poets of 1916, although less impressive artistically than the Romantics, also obviously fall into this category.

Thirdly is the style of political poem most absent from mainstream discourse in Ireland, and most prevalent outside it. This I will call the interventionist poem. The interventionist poem addresses in a more or less confrontational manner a current political issue involving a just conflict between the weak and the powerful. The interventionist poem clearly takes the side of the oppressed and encourages them to continue to struggle. The interventionist poem puts the writer of the poem at the same or worse risk of backlash as others involved in a struggle. Interventionist poems are provocations, not invitations to contemplate. They are not prayers, but rallying calls. Shelley's 'Queen Mab' and 'The Masque of Anarchy' might be English poetry's two great interventionist poems. Both are responses to mass persecution, and both were underground bestsellers, in pirated copies, among the politically restless and relentlessly persecuted English working classes in the 1810s.

Perhaps the clearest and most resounding example of an interventionist poem in recent times is that written by the much imprisoned 82-year-old Egyptian poet Ahmed Fouad Negm while he was fighting in the battle of Tahrir Square in 2011. The poem has gone around the world a thousand times since, inspiring many people to join the struggle for freedom, wherever they are:

> The brave ones are brave
> The cowards are cowards
> Come down with the brave
> Together to the Square

The master of the broad range of political poetry—the counter-amnesiac poem; the poem of countercultural values, and the poem of intervention—in the twentieth century was Bertolt Brecht, someone who we can be sure would be working primarily in digital and performance media were he around today. In cases, he wrote poems which combined all three main elements of political poetry to produce works of monumental stature and ever-echoing resonance:

Questions for worker who reads

Who built Thebes of the 7 gates?
In the books you will read the names of kings.
Did the kings haul up the lumps of rock?
And Babylon, many times demolished,
Who raised it up so many times?
In what houses of gold glittering Lima did its builders live?
Where, the evening that the Great Wall of China was finished, did the masons go?
Great Rome is full of triumphal arches.
Who erected them ?
Over whom did the Caesars triumph?
Had Byzantium, much praised in song, only palaces for its inhabitants?
Even in fabled Atlantis, the night that the ocean engulfed it,
The drowning still cried out for their slaves.
The young Alexander conquered India.

Was he alone?
Caesar defeated the Gauls.
Did he not even have a cook with him?
Philip of Spain wept when his armada went down.
Was he the only one to weep?
Frederick the 2nd won the 7 Years War.
Who else won it?
Every page a victory.
Who cooked the feast for the victors?
Every 10 years a great man.
Who paid the bill?
So many reports.
So many questions. (*translated by Michael Hamburger*)

In his 1935 essay 'Telling The Truth: Five Difficulties', written while in exile from the Nazis who had removed his citizenship, Brecht wrote his most important contribution to the theory of interventionist poetry:

> Nowadays, anyone who wishes to combat lies and ignorance and to write the truth must overcome at least five difficulties. He must have the courage to write the truth when truth is everywhere opposed; the keenness to recognise it, although it is everywhere concealed; the skill to manipulate it as a weapon; the judgment to select those in whose hands it will be effective; and the cunning to spread the truth among such persons. These are formidable problems for writers living under Fascism, but they exist also for those writers who have fled or been exiled; they exist even for writers working in countries where civil liberty prevails.

Thankfully, we have no shortage of poets outside the quietist establishment who have courage, keenness, and skill in relation to speaking truth to power about injustice and oppression. What is perhaps somewhat lacking is the judgement and the cunning—the German word for which connotes cleverness, craftiness, and ability. Both craft and craftiness are necessary to connect interventionist poems with the relevant audience so they can be heard and reacted to by as many people as possible.

The activities of several contemporary interventionist poets will provide examples of the range of possibilities available. Hollie McNish, the English performance poet, made a lo-fi, no-budget film of herself reciting her anti-racist poem 'Mathematics' which has now been seen by close to two million people and can justly claim to have had a positive political impact on a crucial issue for working class people in Britain. It cost nothing to make, no forms were filled, no permission was asked for or given.

Besides the explosion in live poetry events and audience numbers, more and more poets—Stephen Murphy and Sarah Clancy are just two of the best known—are beginning to perform work by invitation at political demonstrations. Both Murphy and Clancy have performed in front of tens of thousands at anti-water charges demos. The opening lines of Clancy's 'Look How Our Leaders Tremble When They See Us Together' can be construed as a comment on orthodox 'leadership' in poetry, as well as in politics:

> Our leaders would like to inform us
> that they are fine with protest in fact they really respect us
> so long as we follow their rules and do it
> without any disruption of business, (preferably at home
> in our own bedrooms where no one can see us,
> and without any unnecessary shouting
> that might upset the neighbours) they're fine with it then,
> so they are.

A third example of a successful interventionist is Kevin Higgins. Higgins is Ireland's most accomplished political poet and satirist. Not despite this, but because of it, he gets few invitations to read at Irish literary festivals and fewer still to appear on radio or in mainstream newspapers. Yet he is likely the most widely read living poet in Ireland, precisely because he has concentrated with an admirably Brechtian craftiness on building an audience for his skilfully-written, provocative, topical poems in a wide range of non-literary digital publications in Ireland and the UK. On The Bogman's Cannon, for example, the alt.culture website I help to edit, poems by Higgins, who is our satirist-in-residence, have been read close to ten thousand times in an eight month period. Given that The Bogmans Cannon is only one of a dozen or so well read extra-literary websites Higgins publishes in on an almost weekly basis, his annual readership may well stretch into six figures—a fantasy figure for the page-poets who are so often falsely and unthinkingly represented in mainstream cultural media as being the major public figures in contemporary Irish poetry.

As in Brecht's time then, a spiraling crisis of capitalism and imperialism has raised political consciousness worldwide and created mass movements attempting to address the front-line symptoms of the crisis. In the most optimistically Brechtian of scenarios these mass movements will evolve, through many ups and downs, into a global revolutionary wave. They will be the vigorously evolving audience for a Brechtian poetics of intervention for the foreseeable future. They can realistically be addressed only through the range of dynamic and daringly contemporary methods—although spoken word is more accurately described as a revived method—some of which I have exampled above.

The task facing interventionist poets is not simply one of writing poems, but of finding ways for these poems to reach the audiences for which they are intended and whose interests they are written in and best serve. We owe it to our art, our audience, and ourselves to use every available medium. Naturally, there is no funding (and certainly no corporate brand prizes!) in Ireland for making subversive poetry films, for managing online interventionist publications, or for establishing sustainable countercultural performance spaces. We should of course campaign for such funding—it is our democratic right to be afforded a proportion of available public funding which reflects the public engagement and taste for our work. And it is blazingly obvious that funding models for poetry have to change if they are to become a support rather than a hindrance to the twenty-first century poet. What we don't need however is a new bureaucracy—any funding supports for new media poetries need to be democratically and transparently administered and not merely middle-managed by a chosen few who go on to propagate a new orthodoxy with themselves at the helm. In any case, don't hold your breath for official backing for radical cultural forms of any kind. Our state's chronic institutional inertia, resulting from a hundred years of right-wing and occasionally centrist government, i.e. government by vested interest elites and their excrescent bureaucracies, is likely to continue for some time to come in much of the arts as it does in just about every other field of Irish public life.

To be sure of making their mark then, the interventionist poet must forgo any reliance on support from within the ranks of the bureaucratic quietist establishment, from the state, or from the neo-liberal academy. Thankfully, mutual aid between interventionist poets, together with support from within the mass movements their work addresses, can and does do away completely with the need for establishment backing of any kind. Working together, with the shared goal of speaking the passionate truths of our time to the broadest possible layers of the population, we can and will be part of turning the world upside down, and so right-way-up, again.

Casualty

after Seamus Heaney
i.m. Professor Gordon Hamilton-Fairley (1930-1975)

At home that autumn morning
the radio began to blur…
'a car bomb… no warning
Campden Hill Square
man dead… device set off
by his dog…' *please God*
don't let it be the Prof.

I used to wonder what
he thought of me,
his daughter's boyfriend
pitching up post-party,
toothbrush stuffed in denims,
squiffy, slurring words.
Yet he was always gracious
although he'd been on wards
all week, staring at death;
or conducting seminars
on lymphomas, leukaemia;
or lowering the blood pressure
of staff at St Bartholomew's.
I felt as if I'd lost a dad
again—the adult listener
I'd never really had;
a soulful empathiser.

I can see him at their cottage,
light fading as he pokes
a bush to find a guinea pig
and save it from the fox;
nineteen-fifties retro
side-parted auburn hair,
an open face, crooked elbow,

attentive, ready to share
the countdown of his days;
for we had no idea
that he, a cancer specialist,
was fighting cancer too.

'The Murder of a Life Saver'
the headlines shouted—
the bomb was for a neighbour
delayed from going out.
The dog had sniffed the car.
The windows imploded
in the square; from body parts
they identified his elbow.
I went to Holland Park
and joined the family
delirious with shock
crying, laughing, alternately;
that night the four of them
collapsed to sleep in one bed,
a tangled heap of limbs
like the raft of the *Medusa*.

The evening of the service
Mum and I met Dad
in his Fleet Street eyrie
a trinity re-glued
for a couple of hours.
Dad was quiet, sheepish,
perhaps all too aware
of being lynchably Irish;
he asked about my tie
and looked a little miffed
when I replied
that it had been the Prof's.
We headed for St Paul's,
the sky gunpowder grey,
Dad musing on the war
when bombs were two a penny.
We thought a hundred souls
would come, but thousands
filled the floodlit cupola:
it was as if all London
was in mourning, the dome
rising like a huge balloon
on a myriad candle flames
and breath of hymns.
Afterwards we went home:
Dad to his second wife
me to my single Mum;
the Prof's four children to a life
without their only Dad.

In the cathedral crypt,
Dear Prof, your plaque
declares in stone that it
matters not how a man dies
but how he lives:
a bomb may vaporise us
but cannot even bruise
the memories of gestures
and acts of love or malice
that stamp us thereafter.
Like placing a device
behind the wheel of a car;
or searching a bush to save
a guinea pig. You cared
for Life, and gave your days
helping others to survive;
and to forgive.

James Harpur

All The Children Equal

Mike McCormack

A couple of years ago I sat in a room in which I lost everything. I was there for less than two hours but when I walked out of it I had lost my child, my identity and the life I thought was mine. Also set in train were those circumstances which would end my marriage, twelve months later.

I had accepted an invitation to address a symposium at UNICEF's global headquarters in Paris on the theme of Citizenship in the 21st Century. The letter—yes, the invitation came by way of a letter—made it clear the organisers would like me to recapitulate some of the ideas I had explored over the years. These people were familiar with my work, and a good part of the letter brought me on a lightning tour of those pieces which they said touched on the theme of their gathering. Some of these pieces I had not thought of in years—the whole Self-shooter with Botox series is so long ago now I can hardly remember it: the same also with the Neurocloud cycle. I was flattered by the invitation and pleased to accept an opportunity to vent some of my ideas before a learned and influential audience. As if cued in by these happy thoughts my phone went off as I was reading the letter; Nathan was checking in.

'Hello Mum.'

'Hi Nathan, everything okay?'

'Everything's fine, just coming off shift so I said I would give you a call.'

'I hear birds in the background.'

'Seagulls: I'm throwing them the last of my sandwich before I get a few hours' sleep.'

'You back on later today?'

'Yes, back on at midnight.'

'What's the weather like, it's nice here.'

'Nice here too, blue skies and clear seas, forecast says it will hold up till the end of the week. I'll scope it for you.' And he turned the vid-phone away from him to sweep a broad arc over the sea which stretched towards the horizon. In the distance I could see the six other platforms which marked out the Corrib gas-field.

'Nice and peaceful,' I said.

'Yes, for as long as it lasts; what are you doing today?'

Our phone calls were always like that: chit-chat and small questions. It was something to be thankful for—my son in his mid-twenties calling home every day for no reason other than to hear his mother's voice. Today I was glad to have something to tell him.

'I got a letter this morning.'

'A letter, Jesus, that's a blast from the past.'

'That's what I thought too. Anyway, UNICEF have invited me to give a talk in Paris on the expanding idea of citizenship.'

'Sounds good: are you going to take it up?'

'Yes, public speaking is not my thing, but this is important. Especially as it concerns my baby boy.'

'Aaww thank you, Mum,' he mugged.

'You're welcome.'

'But is that all you're going to do, make a speech?'

'That's all I'm asked to do; all they want is a speech.'

Nathan was suddenly impatient. 'For god's sake mum, with all due respect there are any number of theoreticians they could have asked to do the same job—there must be a queue of political philosophers champing at the bit for a prestigious gig like that. If you think you can get up and make a speech and then walk away from the lectern, job done, you're mistaken. You will leave a whole lot of disappointed people in your wake.'

'What do you want me to do?'

'Mum, they've invited you, Agnes Conway, to address the issue—Agnes the Unhinged for God's sake—you won't be thanked for a fucking lecture or a moving plea. I'm surprised you're so dim on this, you're usually a better gauge of the moment. Me and my tribe should send someone better out to bat for us if that is the best you can come up with.'

He was seldom so worked up.

'Don't tell me you're too old for this shit now,' he charged.

'No,' I bristled, 'and this shit as you call it is my life's work—as you well know. So what do you suggest, one of my greatest hits.'

'I don't know about that, but you have to remember that you are fronting for a small, vulnerable tribe.'

'Okay, don't go telling me my job. I may be looking down the barrel of a free travel pass but this is my work you're dissing. So have you any ideas?'

'You could go all old school. Standing there at the lectern, and start pissing yourself, as a protest against my exclusion…'

'No, I'm definitely too old for that. What about my tattoos—hologram one of my tats over the auditorium.'

'No, too gimmicky, not pointed enough. Do you have a date for this conference?'

'It says the seventh of May here.'

'That's good, it gives you two months to think about it, plus I will be rotated out of here the following week.'

'Are you coming home?'

'Where else would I go?'

'I don't know. Young men have things to do, they don't always have to return home to their mother.'

'No, but some of us like to. Okay, I'm going to go now to get some sleep. Kick ass in Paris.'

'I'll do my best, take care.'

'One moment, what about a song? You could sing a song, an ould come-all-ye. *Come all ye droids and clone-boys*… you could take it from there surely. You're still worth listening to, one of the few singers in the world who can sing chords. You have to make that vocal chord splicing pay its way.'

'Okay, I'll give that some thought. Bye.'

'Bye.'

I threw the letter on the table. Later that evening I replied to the email address on the masthead.

Two months later I set out before dawn to get a mid-morning flight to Paris from Dublin airport. I was in a good mood and driving along the M6, I was already thinking forward to the speech I would make the following day. What questions would I face, what objections would I have to contend with.

Researching the other speakers had warned me there would most likely be strong objections from the mittle-European and African delegates.

I drove in silence, avoiding my usual habit of listening to the radio. The far side of Athlone my good mood was suddenly cut across by a bolt of panic which forced me to pull over onto the hard shoulder and rifle through my shoulder bag. There it was, thank god! My inhaler plus a spare canister, nestling safely in the depths of the bag. The incident boosted my confidence—I took it as evidence that I was fully prepared and I drove on.

The early morning crowd in Terminal One was thin and listless. Check-in had not yet opened so I decided to have coffee and a scone. It seemed ages since I had last eaten a scone and I do not know why I thought it was a good idea to start eating one now. The coffee dock was quiet, only two other travellers sitting with their hand luggage dropped beside them. A table near the windows gave me a clear view over the runway where ground staff were going about their work in green hi-vis vests; some of them wore noise protectors on their heads.

By the time I had finished my coffee the notice board was telling me it was time to go.

There were only a couple of people ahead of me in the passport control channel. I dropped my watch and mobile and shoulder bag into the bins and pushed them through the X-ray machine. Stepping up to the metal detector I handed my passport to the officer who sat behind the desk. A few quick waves of his detector up and down my body and I walked on. The bin with my bag and stuff had already passed through and I was about to retrieve my passport from the officer when he looked up and waved his arm ahead of me.

'You need to go with these two gentlemen.'

'What is this about.'

Two airport security police had positioned themselves on either side of me and they had already begun to usher me towards a corridor which led away from the control area. From the corner of my eye I caught sight of a guard handing my passport to a man who appeared to be the ranking officer. I lost sight of them as I was led down the small corridor and shown into a small room with just a table and two chairs.

After a quick search through it one of the guards handed me my bag and left the room, pulling the door shut behind him.

*

The uniformed man on the other side of the table had a name tag which identified him as another member of airport security. He did not inspire confidence. The whole thing seemed to have caught him off guard. He arrived into the room shuffling a wad of papers which he had obviously picked up in a hurry. After a bit more shuffling and straightening he pushed one of them towards me and told me to fill it out.

This form ran to three pages with plenty of open fields waiting to be filled in. It was a demand for the usual information—personal details followed by a statement of destination and the purpose of my visit. My wish to be helpful and to move things along bent me to the task of filling it out. Ten minutes later, when I pushed it across the table to the officer he seemed relieved to get it. He looked me full in the face for the first time. Then followed a comedy routine with such a smooth series of exchanges it belied the fact that we had never before set eyes on each other.

'Can you tell me what this is about?'

'No.'

'I have been here over an hour, I think I deserve some sort of explanation.'

'Yes.'

'So you're going to tell me.'

'No.'

And while his gaze was unblinking there was something to it beyond professional scrutiny, something soft which put me at ease.

'An anomaly has occurred,' he offered.

'An anomaly?'

'Yes.'

"What sort of anomaly?'

'It's hard to say,' he ventured cautiously.

'Try.'

'That might not be wise.'

'For me or for you?'

'For both of us I would say.'

'But it concerns me.'

'Possibly.'

'I'm being held here in this room, so it either concerns me or it does not.'

'It's not that simple.'

'It is from my side of the table, it either concerns me or it does not.'

'I see how you could think that.'

'What does that mean?

'It means that if I were on your side of the table I would have exactly the same kind of reaction.'

'So you understand.'

'No.'

'Why not?'

'I'm not on your side of the table.'

'This is not getting us anywhere.'

'So it would appear.'

He seemed dismayed by these exchanges—more put out by them than I was. And I wanted to help him; the sooner this was cleared up the sooner I would get out of this room and be on my way. He rose to his feet, picking up the document I had just completed.

'A moment,' he said, 'I will be back.'

My mouth was open to protest when, at that precise moment, the phone rang in my pocket. James, my husband, sounded surprised to hear me.

'Oh, I thought you'd be in the air.'

'So why did you ring me.'

'Where are you?'

'My flight got delayed,' I lied, 'what's wrong?'

A long pause followed in which it was possible to sense James's confusion and anxiety on the other end. Finally, he blurted out.

'There's been an incident.'

'What sort of an incident.'

'News stations are reporting that Red Star has been captured by the Norwegians. It happened overnight, the incident is now over twelve hours old. They're holding hostages, Nathan is among them.'

The details are well known by now—how Norwegian marines breached the security cordon around the gas field during the night and took control of Red Star, the largest of the seven platforms, the very one on which Nathan was working out a twelve-month contract. We know now that they had already informed the government of their demands: the networking codes for the seven platforms which would give them control of the whole gas-field.

'And have you heard from Nathan?'

'No, there's been no official news from anyone, I'm just watching it on television and hearing things on social media.'

My thoughts were scrambled now and my confusion must have communicated itself to James.

'There's nothing you can do for the moment,' he assured. 'Just keep your phone on and I will call you as soon as I get word. God knows how long this might go on—days or hours or weeks or it might be over in the next few minutes.'

'Okay, keep me up to date if you hear anything.'

There must have been a time lag between the end of that call and the moment the airport guard returned to the room. During that interval, I relapsed to an old habit of recording messages to myself on the phone. Nothing more than a few short sentences, more words of assurance than anything else. My message was complete and the phone was on the desk when the guard re-entered.

'This passport,' he began.

'Yes.'

'This passport is legitimate?'

'Of course it is.'

'I have never come across one like it.'

A wave of relief passed through me; this would now be easily cleared up.

'It's a special issue one. A full biometric one with a retinal scan and full genetic signature sweep on it. It's very rare, it was issued to commemorate the mapping of the human genome back in 2006. There are only 100 of them world-wide… scanning it should have unlocked a verifying database.'

He nodded. 'That's all true. We've checked and everything you've just said has been verified.'

'But there's still a problem.'

'I'm afraid there is. According to our security network this passport has cleared Charles De Gaulle two hours ago.'

'That's crazy.'

'It might be crazy but it is also a fact—look at this.'

This new document was the copy of a passenger manifest for an Air France flight which had flown out at eight-thirty the same morning. And it did indeed have an Agnes Conway listed among its passengers. Like myself she had pre-booked a window seat in the left aisle. Her passport number was identical to my own.

'This is crazy,' I repeated, aware that I was repeating myself to no affect. Trying to gather my thoughts into a coherent next step. 'The chances of my passport being successfully forged are way out on the margins of disbelief. The degree of accuracy needed to render so many different signatures is astronomical.' And then, in a desperate inspiration, I declared, 'It would be easier to forge me than my passport.'

My outburst seemed to have focused the guard. He pointed to the document. 'This speech you're making in Paris. It says here that your son is…'

I let him dangle on the word; the moment and circumstances had made me cruel.

'Say it,' I urged finally.

It was as much as he could do to choke it out.

'A clone.'

'Yes, my son is a clone.' And I leaned toward him to deliver the coup de grâce. 'Not only is he a clone and my son but, he is also my brother.'

'I don't want to…'

'Yes you do, of course you do.' I was snarling now, leaning across the table with my teeth bared. 'You will torment yourself with this tonight so I am going to fill you in on the details. We can start with my twin brother; strangled by his own umbilical cord and dead shortly after birth: my twin brother whose various organs were stored without consent in the same hospital we were born in. Then the long judicial process we went through to reclaim them followed by the even longer process by which Nathan was cloned from them. How about that for a story? And you can rest easy knowing all that and talking about it because Nathan knows every word of it. His very own creation myth, and he's fiercely proud of it.'

Only when I'd finished did I notice how I had so completely demolished him, driven him back in his chair, slumped and pale. He was a good twenty years younger than me and I felt sorry for him. Christ knows, I would not have liked to have got into a fight with me at that moment. I put a hand out to comfort him.

'My speech in Paris is part of the ongoing campaign to get full citizenship for clones and the broader family of synths. Ireland is one of those countries withholding citizenship for these people—a hangover from the immigration experience earlier in the century. And with me it is personal, this is about my son.'

I don't know how I expected him to react to my speech—as a bid for sympathy it was totally undermined by my harsh tone. He straightened himself up in the chair, looking dazed and bruised.

'I don't know,' he swallowed, 'nothing about this day makes any sense.'

'Tell me about it. You're too young to remember this but I'm of a generation which would never have envisaged us going to war with Norway. You've grown up with that conflict but my generation still wonders what sort of fucking country goes to war with Norwegians.'

My phone went off on the table. It was James. For some reason I stood up to take the call.

'Okay,' he choked, 'things have escalated in the last hour or so. The Norwegians are now using Nathan as a bargaining chip. They have made their demands and the whole thing is time-sensitive. They have said they will kill him if the government do not turn over the network codes to all platforms.'

'And has there been a response from the government.'

'Yes, a government spokesman has repeated their position. They will not negotiate with terrorists.'

A strangled squawk resounded through the room. It took me a moment to catch hold of myself and realise that I had sobbed. I tried to hold my voice steady. 'Why Nathan, he's just a technician on that platform, he knows nothing.'

'That's the point—the Norwegians start small. They open the bidding with the life of one technician and ratchet it up from there.'

James's voice did not sound assured. Nor did he sound as if he had finished.

'They also know that Nathan is not an Irish citizen so he is a perfect opening bid in this exchange. If he is killed it will not provoke the diplomatic outrage that would follow from the death of a passport holder. But it will focus the government's attention.'

'So they know Nathan's a clone?'

'Yes, they know it from your work—all the pieces in which you have referenced him and all your campaigning on his behalf. They have already released onto social media chapter and verse of your work which shows how much they know, your history of his life. Right now they have him suspended by the ankles over a gas vent. If they flare that gas our son will be carbonised in seconds.'

The phone flicked up out of my hand and skidded across the table to the floor. My breath flittered in my throat and I sank to my knees. A few moments scrabbling in my bag brought up my inhaler and I pressed it to my mouth for two swift shots. My breathing levelled out after a few moments. The guard was looking down on me with a terrified look in his face.

'Did you hear that,' I implored, 'did you hear any of that?'

He helped me up, grasped me under the arms and lowered me to my chair.

'You're in shock,' he said, 'we can get you to a hospital.'

'No. I have work to do.'

The guard touched the side of his head with the tips of his fingers, as if to make a small adjustment there. 'I'm afraid you're not going anywhere,' he said, 'your case is now a national security issue. Very soon now you will be taken away for questioning.'

'My son,' I said, 'he needs my help.'

'I know. There's nothing you can do for him at the moment.'

I broke down then. My head tipped forward and I started to cry uncontrollably. I gave myself over to it completely, head down in my arms across the table. Time slid away from me but at some point the guard placed a cup of water and a box of tissues by my hand. I was grateful for his kindness. I called James two or three times but he wasn't picking up.

Two plain clothes-officers led me from the room. My guard fell into step behind us and I was glad of his presence. They escorted me back through passport control and out into the public concourse which was now thronged with the mid-day crowd. No one noticed the four of us moving towards the exit. I halted suddenly and turned around to my guard.

'Give me two minutes here,' I said, 'please.'

'No.'

'Two minutes, that's all I need. I've been scanned and searched, you will be right here, just two minutes.'

My appeal got through to him. He turned to the two detectives.

'What does she want to do?' one of them asked impatiently.

'I'm going to sing,' I replied. I had already taken a step away from the guards and started my throat clearing exercise. The extended, ullulating chords turned several heads towards me. Within moments some of them were already holding up their phones towards me. When I was sure I had my audience I started to sing…

Come all ye droids and clone boys
A tale to you I'll tell…

The crowd gathered and my voice rose out over them. The song took hold of me and I could feel myself stepping into a confident performance. But I did not finish. In the third verse I made the mistake of turning towards those people who stood behind me. That left me facing a television screen that was broadcasting one of the twenty-four-hour news channels.

What happened next has been captured from several angles by those who uploaded the clip to various social media sites. You hear the cry go up from the people watching the television. Their hands fly to their heads, their faces.

Some recoil from the screen; all are shocked. You can see the precise moment when the song locks in my throat. I turn my face into the fireball which blooms towards me from the TV screen. I understand immediately; my son, hung upside down, wrapt in flame, turned to shadow in the space between two heartbeats. You see my face engulfed in terror, a split second before I twist to the floor in a faint.

Yesterday was a proud day: proud and sad and joyous and a bit weird

Yesterday I was one of a crowd of people who stood in an aircraft hangar on the edge of Dublin airport to witness the state confer full citizenship on a gathering of clones and droids and various AI constructs. All told, their numbers swelled the census by eight hundred souls: eight hundred new citizens. It was a happy gathering. Droids with their shiny faces and graceful on their polycarbonate frames, stood shoulder to shoulder with clones whose varied age and appearance emphasised just how long they have been among us and how unobtrusively they have gone about their lives. Many of them appeared shy in the sudden light of the occasion. Shy but very happy one of them assured me. Also in attendance were several proxies standing in for all those incorporeal souls who manage our health service and our legal system. Everyone stood to speak their names and declare their fidelity to the nation, their loyalty to the state and its democratic values. 'Amhrán na bhFiann' was sung and everyone applauded at the end.

The minister's speech was thoughtful. He reminded us that these souls had freely chosen to take out citizenship in this state and they would now bring their unique energies and imaginations to our common endeavour. Our country was more open, more generous and pluralist for their presence.

It was nice to hear my son being remembered, the part his death played in bringing forward this day. I will remember forever the cheer and round of applause which greeted the mention of his name. Nathan was a gregarious young man, he would have enjoyed the whole thing. He would have felt at home among 'my fellow synths' as he called them—they were his tribe and he was pleased to call them all his brothers and sisters.

Before the ceremony closed I was asked to step forward and sing my song one final time: to put it to bed once and for all. So I did; I sang the version I never completed in the airport, the version which had its first full airing over the phone to Nathan the night before he died. My voice held and I managed it, just about. It was kind of so many people afterwards to come and thank me for my efforts and to express their sorrow at his death. On the journey homewards I pulled onto the hard shoulder and cried for his loss and mine. It is not the first time I have done that this last two years; it will not be the last.

I live alone now, the house is bigger and colder these days. My marriage ended shortly after we buried Nathan. It foundered on the part my work played in his death. James and I may come to a reconciliation sometime in the future but at the moment that does not seem likely. Too much grief, too much anger between us.

New rituals fill the emptiness. After the late news—the war with the Norwegians continues to claim lives—I sit with a whisky and watch a twenty second piece of CCT footage from Charles De Gaulle airport. The low-res footage shows a crowd of people streaming through from baggage reclaim into arrivals. The woman is heavy but she moves with a roll of her shoulders which suggests she is younger than me. Her walk is not my walk and her clothes are not my clothes. But her face is the sort of face I might have if I had lived a life which had taken no risks; the face of a woman who had held onto her marriage; the face of a woman who had kept her son alive. The footage holds her till she disappears through the exit. Twenty seconds, that is all I know of her before she disappears out of shot and dissolves into the world beyond.

I have watched the clip a thousand times now and I see we are nothing alike. But apparently we are identical.

Tomorrow Never Knows

Glenn Patterson

I was born in 1961, chronologically, you might even say, anagrammatically a grandchild of the 1916 Easter Rising and the events leading up to it North and South, as we would say now, though then those were purely geographical terms.

In 1962, a couple of Saturdays before Easter, I was taken in my pram to Belfast's Balmoral Showgrounds for the 50th anniversary of an Easter Tuesday anti-Home-Rule rally attended by Andrew Bonar Law, leader of the Conservative Party, and, among 200,000 others, the Lisburn Conservative Flute Band with lead-flautist and arranger Jack Patterson, my grandfather—who walked to the Showgrounds again beside my pram that April 1962 day.

Or so I am led to believe.

Where childhood memory is concerned it's always a little difficult to separate the bespoke from the off-the-peg or hand-me-down. I will stick my neck out, though, and say I do have at least a hazy recollection of my own of the blowing up of Nelson's Pillar on Dublin's O'Connell Street in the early hours of March 2nd 1966, five months before my fifth birthday by a group of former IRA members to whom the Admiral's continued presence, half a century after the Easter Rising, was a clear affront.

Within days, it seems, a group of Belfast schoolteachers had—as the Go-Lucky Four—released a single on the Emerald label, 'Up Went Nelson!', which according to one popular online encyclopaedia topped the Irish charts for eight consecutive weeks that spring.

I went looking, elsewhere on the web, through the Irish charts of the period, but couldn't find trace of it. (I said popular online encyclopaedia, not 100 per cent reliable.) I did find that at number 1 for the weeks spanning the 1966 50th anniversary celebrations was 'Black and Tan Gun', by the Johnny Flynn Showband, featuring Pat Smith on vocals, one of the most lachrymose of a tear-drenched genre of Irish rebel balladry, being the dying wishes of a soldier of Ireland, cut down by the gun of the title, that he be buried out on the mountain, near the town of old Bantry ('where most of the fighting was done') so that he could see where the victory was won.

The Johnny Flynn Showband's own victory reaching the pinnacle of the Irish charts was achieved despite a blanket RTÉ ban on 'rebel songs' over the Easter period, which does seem a little like banning red coats, white beards and Slade singles over Christmas.

I should point out that at the same time in the US charts Staff Sergeant Barry Sadler was at number 1 (number 24 in the UK) with the 'Ballad of the Green Berets', a song which moves to the beat of a different, military snare drum, but which nevertheless builds to—guess what?—the dying wish of a Green Beret, in this case that his son should become a Green Beret in his turn.

The lyrics were inspired by the death of Green Beret James Gabriel Jr, who was executed by the Vietcong on April 8th 1962, the day, as it happens, before I went with my grandfather to the Balmoral Showgrounds. The tune was a variation on 'The Butcher Boy', which coincidentally had been a 1965 hit for the Carrick-on-Suir trio the Ludlows, who in spring 1966 displaced the Johnny Flynn Showband at the top of the Irish charts with Dominic Behan's 'The Sea Around Us', a more tongue-in-cheek take on Anglo-Irish history and antipathies: 'The sea oh the sea… Long may it stay between England and me, it's a sure guarantee that some hour we'll be free, thank God we're surrounded by water.'

On April 6th 1966, the Beatles gathered at Abbey Road studios to start recording the tracks that would become their seventh studio album, *Revolver*.

They finished on June 21st with 'She Said, She Said', a John Lennon song. (*Revolver* was the first of those seven albums to reveal the reality of the Lennon and McCartney partnership by listing the lead vocalist, and therefore principal songwriter, next to each track.) They began, that weekend before Easter 1966, with another Lennon song (although it, not 'She Said, She Said', closed the album), 'Tomorrow Never Knows', the sessions for which—on the 6th, 7th, and 22nd of April—top and tail the Easter Week commemorations

Ian McDonald, in *Revolution in the Head,* concludes his analysis of the song—one of the most socially influential the Beatles ever made, introducing LSD and Dr Timothy Leary's psychedelic 'revolution' to the young of the Western world—by saying that the drug that inspired it left Lennon a mental wreck: 'only the scepticism that balanced his questing gullibility warded off a permanent eclipse of his reason… Many others like him never came back.'

I want to say I stray, but the events of spring and early summer 1966, the period roughly of those *Revolver* sessions, set the tone for the next half-century in Northern Ireland in particular. They didn't dictate it, but starting with the bomb in O'Connell Street, they reintroduced into the vernacular certain terms that had appeared moribund since the IRA had abandoned its 'border' campaign in 1962.

North of that border, the initials UVF, dating back to 1912 and the anti-Home Rule protests, were also revived, to murderous effect.

Between June 11th and 27th, two men—John Scullion and Peter Ward, Catholics both—were shot dead and an elderly Protestant woman Matilda Gould died from burns sustained in an arson attack aimed at the Catholic-owned bar next door to her house off the Shankill Road.

Talk about an eclipse of reason.

I had a notion early in 1999 to write a story called 'The First Anniversary of the Bicentenary of the Rising of the Society of United Irishmen'—get ahead of the game for once in your writing life, I told myself. I never got further than the title, largely I suspect because the title was pretty much the whole of the story… Which reminds me I have been thinking of late of abandoning narrative altogether in protest against politicians' increased appropriation of the word. There is a long history, after all, of musicians objecting to the use of their music at political party conferences—Johnny Marr, Radiohead, The Horrors to name but three. Maybe writers should petition to get narrative back, or maybe we should just let the politicians get on with debasing it and revert to stand-up: old-style stand-up, a string of one-liners, no patter, no context, make of them what you will.

The idea behind 'The First Anniversary of the Bicentenary of the Rising of the Society of United Irishmen' story—or at least title—was that we were getting to the point, and that long before this 'decade of centenaries', where the commemorations were being hugged too close, that even the best intentioned were distorting the present. As the saying goes up North—or at least in that bit of up North that maps on to my house—if the Titanic hadn't existed they'd have had to build it.

What I did end up publishing the year I didn't write the story was a novel, *The International*, set in January 1967, but reaching back to the previous June (five days after the final *Revolver* session, as it happens) and the murder of Peter Ward, a barman in the 'Blue Bar' of the hotel from which the novel takes its title.

Around the time I was starting to think about writing *The International*, the Provisional IRA, officially on ceasefire, used the cover name Direct Action Against Drugs to murder twelve men, including Paul Devine, shot as he sat in his car one Friday afternoon a few hundred yards from where I was having coffee with friends. How we respond—or had failed to respond in the past—to the murder of our fellow citizens was much in my thoughts.

There is a passage in the novel where another type of international, a Northern Irish footballer, called Ted Connolly (I was doing the equivalent of the *Guardian* cookery section's 'one ingredient, four meals': 'one word, four meanings', or as many as I could squeeze out of it), in drunken conversation with another of the hotel's patrons mentions an English friend of his who had been in Dublin, having an affair, the Easter of 1966. He was taken aback, this friend, by what he witnessed, the commemorations: Ireland walking backwards into the seventies is how he describes it, prompting Ted Connolly to ask the man he has cornered in the International, 'Do these people ever stand back and think? Does it ever occur to them how this all looks to loonies like Paisley, never mind my mate?'

Ted Connolly is, I have to stress, a fictional character—he's a Northern Irish centre forward who scores hat-tricks, of course he's fictional—so he's allowed to say 'loonies like Paisley'.

In the spring of 1966 Belfast City Council gave in to pressure and prevented an Easter Rising commemorative event from being held in the Ulster Hall, which was instead allowed to host a rally by Paisley—the Reverend Doctor Ian Paisley (for I am not a fictional character)—an expression, Dr Paisley said, of disgust that any Easter Rising commemorations were being permitted anywhere in Northern Ireland. Among those who attended that rally were several of the gang who, taking to themselves the name Ulster Volunteer Force (and it cannot be repeated often enough that all such organisations are self-designating), killed Peter Ward.

Fast-forward half a century and Belfast City Council now has a nationalist majority that begins to look irreversible, although the office of Lord Mayor continues to rotate between the parties and across (dread term) the sectarian divide. It is spending several hundred thousand pounds on cultural events to coincide with the centenary of the Rising.

There has not been, that I have yet heard, much opposition voiced from within what is these days referred to as (dreader term) the 'Protestant Unionist Loyalist Community'. (This place, if they can't claim you one way, by hook or by crook or outsize-umbrella-term, they'll claim you another.) I did have fears from that quarter (half?) in the run-up to the 2014 referendum on Scottish Independence, not least because of the calls from another quarter that a referendum on Irish reunification follow what, in the final days, looked like being a 'yes' vote.

Talking of referendums, time was the chief attraction of travelling south of the border from Belfast was it gave you somewhere to feel superior to. Yes, Belfast was bombed to fuck, but at least it had (in between their being melted by bonfires and burning-bus barricades) proper roads, phone boxes that didn't require you to press button A to speak, button B to retrieve your unused coins. (God, how we laughed at those.) And as for attitudes to sex and sexuality… I give you the 'condom train', which brought forty-seven women from Dublin to Belfast in May 1971 to buy the contraceptives banned under Irish law.

The overwhelming Yes vote in the Irish marriage-equality referendum on May 22nd last—the first popular endorsement of same-sex marriage anywhere in the world—confirmed that the rest of Ireland had in recent decades left the North behind.

I had to travel to Dublin on May 24th for a celebration of the life of poet and novelist Dermot Healy. It was Eurovision the night before: the votes had taken longer to count than the Irish referendum's own. I fell asleep on the bus and woke as we came into Drumcondra on the north side of the city. Looking up, my face pressed against the bus window, all I could see were rainbow flags—in windows, on lampposts—and instantly I thought of, and revised, the old Unionist slogan: *We will not forsake the blue skies of Ulster for the (forget grey!) red, orange, yellow, green, blue, indigo, violet skies of the Irish republic: we'll bring them up here!*

What was remarkable in fact in those days after the referendum was the instinctive identification—the fellow feeling—evinced by many, many people north of the border. I would go so far as to call it unity of mind: this was a land they—we, for I was and am of like mind—wanted to live in.

On the second Saturday in June we marched in our thousands—tens of thousands (well two tens)—through the centre of Belfast partly in celebration of the southern Yes vote and partly, more pointedly, to demand that the same marriage rights be afforded all our citizens too.

We chanted for a referendum of our own, like a polite version of the Clash calling for their white riot, although most of us knew that there can of course be no such referendum. The best we can hope for under our current carefully calibrated political structures is that the matter will be brought—even more politely—before a committee that might, but most likely will not, bring it to a vote in the assembly, where if a 'petition of concern' (a sectarian veto in all but name) doesn't kill it the resulting cross-community vote undoubtedly will.

Time and again of late it is our anomalous nature, on the island, in the United Kingdom, that strikes one. The reforms to the libel law enacted in Great Britain in the 2013 Defamation Act—and cited by Alan Rusbridger in his leave-taking from the *Guardian* as one of the highlights of his two decades as editor—did not extend to us in Northern Ireland. The fact that Northern Ireland, whose own citizens have been known to go out of their way to be offended is now an open invitation to citizens of other countries to go even further out of their way to be offended, and to threaten to sue for it—as lawyers for the Scientology movement did in respect of Alex Gibney's *Going Clear* earlier this year—is almost enough to make you smile.

But not quite.

The atmosphere in the south, post-referendum, reminded me of the atmosphere at home in the years immediately before—note before, not after—the 1994 IRA ceasefire, a sense abroad that things could not simply go on as they had been going on.

The euphoria seemed to—I was going to say seep, but in fact it poured—into every area of southern Irish life. In early June my wife was in Sligo at an All-Ireland Performing Arts Conference whose strap-line was 'Question Everything' and whose logo was a giant question mark. The conversations around as much as in the conference were about what not just Irish artists, but Irish citizens, could and should do now.

They might have taken note of the Skype presentation—'The Artist as Activist'—by Birgitta Jonsdottir, a poet elected to the Icelandic parliament in the wake of the banking collapse there, and, in particular, her suggestion that after six years in power the politicians who had been voted in to replace the old corrupt order were themselves corrupt, or at least compromised.

I was in Dublin again on June 23rd, for a book launch, and met up with two friends: the writer Carlo Gébler, born in Dublin, long resident in the north, and the publisher Edwin Higel, a blow-in, forty years ago, from Germany. We went for dinner in the Kimchi/Hophouse (one side bar, one side Korean restaurant) formerly the Shakespeare, which was once, Carlo assured me, a meeting place for the IRA, which might account for our conversation turning from the state of Europe in general ('I am encouraged,' said Edwin, 'by the dialectics of European history: the movement towards one extreme triggers a movement in the opposite direction') to the state of Ireland in particular, or the State of Ireland.

Twenty-five years ago when I first met him, Carlo, who was then in the process of moving from London to Enniskillen, had told me he had not moved south because he would not allow his children to grow up in a place where they could not have access to contraception. One of them, as I recall, was still breastfeeding.

Carlo is nothing if not thorough in arriving at his decisions, and opinions. 'I recently read the 1916 Proclamation of the Irish Republic,' he said. 'Not one article of it has been met.'

(Said it as we walked, dinner over, down O'Connell Street past the giant spire—'the Monument of Light'—on the site of the pillar that was blown up by the men, or possibly women and men, immortalised, at least according to the popular online etc etc in the song by the Go-Lucky Four—and how misplaced with repetition and at a distance of half a century of louder explosions that 'Go-Lucky' sounds.)

And yet he acknowledged that Ireland is much changed for the better.

The question was, had it changed despite its political classes rather than because of them?

Carlo attributed part of Ireland's success to English being its predominant language, the same as the island to the east and the greater landmass to the west: no check on the flow of ideas. There had been too in recent years—we all acknowledged and rejoiced in—a steady flow of newcomers to the country. (Well, it seemed like a steady flow then: a drop in the ocean of need it seems now, a tiny, tiny drop.) We must have talked faster than we walked. By the time I arrived at the Merrion Square club-cum-guesthouse where I was supposed to be staying the desk was shut: I was too late to collect my room key, so I walked back through the city at approaching midnight asking at hotels along the way whether they had any rooms free, or at least any rooms that would otherwise be lying empty that they would allow me to occupy for, say, half the advertised rate, as opposed to the double they seemed inclined to charge me.

My mini-odyssey led me eventually to Busáras, the main bus station, half an hour early for the one o'clock Goldliner Express to Belfast, or led me I should say to the wall outside Busáras, the concourse already being locked for the night.

And of course it being a mini-odyssey—and Dublin, and June—it was only appropriate that I should encounter a middle-aged Hungarian man who told me that I wasn't safe hanging about there. I pointed out the Garda station across the street. 'I wouldn't be pinning my hopes on them,' he said. 'In Hungary the police hit first and then ask questions, here they have you fill out a form before they can leave the station.' The weather also, he told me, although I had the evidence at my (numb) fingertips, was pretty shit.

What was clear, though, from the way he spoke, was that it was his useless police force now, his shit weather, his country.

It is not just the to-be-expected January-looking-at-June-ness that makes me feel wistful already thinking about that night, but the fact too that it belongs to a window of time when it seemed the lead-in to 2016, the centenary of the Easter Rising, might just after all not be dominated by the politics and language of 1916, or 1966 for that matter: post-referendum, pre the shooting dead in Belfast of Kevin McGuigan, in the middle of August, in revenge it is widely believed for the murder of Gerard 'Jock' Davison, one-time Officer Commanding of the IRA in Belfast and a former comrade of McGuigan's. Both men's names have been associated with Direct Action Against Drugs, the IRA cover name for for the murders carried out at the time I was writing *The International*.

John Lennon supposedly took the title 'Tomorrow Never Knows' from a Ringo Starr malapropism: 'you never know what tomorrow will bring', is what Ringo meant to say. And you don't of course.

But now and again, really, you can have a pretty fucking good guess.

Appropriations of Michael Collins

Therese Cox

On Knocknarea, near Carrowmore, I climbed to the craggy top of Queen Maeve's tomb, cradling a rock in my hand. When I reached the summit I set the rock on the stack. At sea level I'd singled out this rock and carried it all the way. But when I backed away from the cairn I found I'd lost sight of its jagged edge, its network of black lattice. I lit a cigarette, squinting under a foreign sky, and took stock of the limestone heap. I drank a sip of Lucozade, gone warm and syrupy from the sun. Then I climbed back down.

There was no reason to be here, exactly, but there was every reason not to go back.

'I have signed my own death warrant.' So said Michael Collins the day he penned his name to the Anglo-Irish Treaty. I didn't know what it was to face Winston Churchill in Downing Street or to do the dirty work of Eamon de Valera, but I knew what it was to be bone-weary from the strain of failed negotiation. I knew what it was to not want to go home because someone at home wanted you dead.

To escape my troubles I'd taken a month off work and booked a one-way ticket from Chicago to Heathrow. In London I met up with a girlfriend. We spent a week tramping through damp streets, posing in bright red phone booths, trying on silk dresses in Portobello Road. We lit candles in draughty churches and drank coffee with Croatian dissidents in cafés. We climbed onto the sturdy backs of motorbikes with men we'd just met and heckled speakers at the Marble Arch. After seven nights tossing in rickety hostel bunks, we parted ways in Paddington Station. She'd landed a work visa and was staying on in London to make a go of it. I boarded a late flight to Ireland. There were no plans made in advance, but somehow I knew how to get on certain buses going to certain towns. There was always a payphone, there was always a tourist office and a hand-scrawled map directing you to the nearest hostel or B&B. I never worried about where I would spend the night.

The plan was to land, get my bearings, and head west. After the week in London and forty-eight hours in Dublin I checked myself into a bed and breakfast, slinging my army surplus backpack in the corner. In town I rented a purple bike for a tenner and took it through the woods of Sligo. Lunch was a stack of custard crèmes smuggled from the B&B. I lay the purple bike in the long grass and read it lines of William Butler Yeats. From time to time I'd glance up from the nicotine-yellowed pages to take stock of where I was. I languished in birdsong, in branches that swayed in the breeze, in the reedy stillness of the lake. You could imagine it, a 'bee-loud glade', going on right here. There were no internet cafés and I'd promised no postcards. The important thing was being alive, I guessed.

As I sat in the stone circle I was not thinking of many things. I was not thinking of the man from Texas who'd pushed my face against the glove compartment of a Ford Thunderbird. I was not thinking of home, a place thousands of miles away that tended to rise up in my mind as a dull mirage of retail outlets and parking lots. I was not thinking about the fella I'd met during my stayover in Dublin, the one who'd told me the story of Michael Collins. Safe among the burial mounds, I hadn't taken stock of what a fight for independence might look like on even the smallest of scales. My idea of protection was wearing a crystal and hoping for the best. I had no affinity then for the assassin, for the man who made Ireland, for the fugitive on the bicycle who was forever on the run. But that would soon change. One day, and for many of the days that would follow, affinity for an assassin would be all the protection I'd have.

I am standing on a street in Dublin in front of a big fuck-off building. I am twenty-two. I'm dressed in steel-toed boots, faded jeans, and a black chenille jumper (though back then I called it a sweater). I have an army surplus bag on my back and a six-string in my hand. There's a fella beside me. He's fair-haired and young, beanpole lean, a smattering of barely-there freckles on the bridge of his nose. A Dubliner. He wears a battered leather jacket with twenty Marlboros stashed in the pocket, a soft black guitar case strapped to his back, a thick Tallaght taint to his voice.

Our story starts like this. He's scouring Grafton Street for a female singer for his band when he spies my opened guitar case, my upturned knock-off Kangol cap. Bound back to Chicago at month's end, I can't sing with his band, but he charms me with his compliments and his fancy-a-pint. We slip into a pub, slinging our axes. By the glow of a broken jukebox we lean over pints, knee grazing knee. When the talk turns fast to old souls I peg him as a Pisces, then write the word on a Heineken beer mat. He flips it over to my dead-on guess. The luck is with us. The night along the Grand Canal lasts till the lager-coloured morning. We brush the dew from our guitar cases, the grass from each other's backs, and swan into an ill-lit Rathmines café. Over crêpes and burnt coffee I start to brace for the slow bus home and the no-hard-feelings when he grins and says he's something he wants to show me.

Now we're standing outside the General Post Office. He's tracing the contours of the pillars, his fingers long and thin and calloused at the tips. He's brought me here to tell me the story of the bullet holes. I've been to Dublin once before and have heard the story of the bullet holes but I don't tell him so. He is my lover, we are newly in love, and while we are huddled by the GPO, or knees touching in the snug, or stretched out on the green rugby pitch, I want him spinning stories, I want his version of everything.

I am also twenty-two when I first imagine being killed with a bullet. Despite the fact that I am an American, a gun is a thing in action films till I am faced with the threat of one. I have found myself mixed up with a man from Texas eleven years my senior. That's the only way to describe it: 'mixed up with a man.' Because thirty-three is too old to say boyfriend, because anyway he isn't really a boyfriend, just someone who I was attracted to who sometimes I'd let be rough with me, someone I am now trying to estrange myself from. Co-worker, boyfriend, stranger, ex. It's a confusion that won't help matters when I sit down with the public defender, when I need shorthand to describe who, exactly, is trying to put a bullet into me.

Each morning before leaving for work at the bookstore I'd kneel down and check the undercarriage of my car for a bomb, one of those improvised explosives rigged to go off when you turned the key in the ignition. I didn't know what such a device would look like but I'd check for it anyway, I supposed I'd know it by its blue and red wires. It was a shitty hand-me-down cobalt blue Buick, a grandpa car, with a shattered transmission and left rear hubcap you had to kick to keep it from clattering off. When I'd turn the key in the ignition and the car didn't detonate, I'd slip a cassette into the deck and ratchet up the volume. I'd peel out of the parking lot of my apartment complex and for ten to fifteen minutes, depending on traffic, I was alive. Because there was a whole other life I was leading, an alternate life where I was not on the run from a jealous ex. I was sipping a mint julep in a rocking chair, I was swing dancing in a ballroom with a debonair paramour.

Never again will I love as fiercely as I do in this moment, in the slate-grey light when my Dublin lover shows me the bullet holes in the GPO. Or as recklessly as the moment when, after knowing him less than forty-eight hours, I trust him with my guitar and tell him to meet me in a week in Galway after I've done the stone circles and the Yeats. My blind trust of strangers. When I think of it now, it makes me want to claw my nails into my skin.

His Ford Thunderbird is in the parking lot again, between the bookstore and the discount fabric warehouse. His car is in the parking lot and he is not. Where is he? He might be in the café, he might be in fiction, he might be in sci-fi or business and finance. Or he might be hospitalised again, which would explain why his car seems to have been there for twenty-four, forty-eight hours straight. Does it make me feel safe to know he is on a locked ward?

There is a version of this parking lot where his car never moves. His car is in this parking lot forever collecting rust, and I am watching the car, approaching the building, checking over my shoulder for him to appear with a gun, flinching as I wait for the flash of my assassination. Fiction, sci-fi, business, finance.

I had graduated from a good university. I had a useless major but respectable grades. I wanted two things: I wanted a story for myself and I wanted to write. These did not seem like unreasonable things to want.

When I was twenty-two I sought to end a love affair with a thirty-three-year-old man by stuffing a break-up letter through the slats of his workplace locker. He found the declaration of independence penned in purple ink and cornered me in the break room. The door shut. The back of my head hit a locker. We went shoulder to shoulder as he put a slow, hot drawl to my turned-away ear. Unlike my letter with its haws and hedges, its alternate endings and cul-de-sacs, his side of the story was more to the point. If I tried to leave him, went the gist, he would goddamn kill me.

An easier thing would have been to find somewhere else to work. A telephone would ring, an ordinary phone, and I would startle. He'd leave books of black magic out on the counter where I was sure to find them, or wait till I was in earshot to get on the phone to place his special order for *The Anarchist Cookbook*. There were days when the only thing that gave me the courage to put on my department store suits in the morning and show up to shelve books was to pretend I was Michael Collins.

The threat was still fresh, my hands unsteady. I was shelving books in history when I spotted the book. It was a biography of Michael Collins. I was not typically someone who read biographies of important historical figures, but at the sight of the tricolour cover I thought of the lover I'd taken in Dublin and recalled his tender reverence for the man they called the Big Fellow. I took the tome in my hands. At home, under the covers, I fanned through the pages and traded my life for another. Instead of an ex I was dodging the Cairo Gang. A bad guy for the Irregulars. For the blue Buick and red Thunderbird I substituted armoured cars and Crossley tenders. The conflict between two opposing sides, so terrorising in the present, would one day be historicised: there was comfort in this fact. Of course historicising is its own kind of violence.

Historicising is a kind of violence. I cannot excuse what I have done with this story, only to say I know this much: it is a story that saved my life.

I'll try again. In the year after I graduated from college, while I was minimum waging at a bookstore in the suburbs of Chicago, I found myself mixed up with a co-worker, a man from Texas eleven years my senior. He had a prominent scar on his forehead and hailed from a family of preachers. I was drawn to the novelty of him, his southern drawl, his old-school gangster haircut, the way he rolled the sleeves of his shirts. He didn't give a pigeon shit for my love of big books and Brit pop. Our compatibility was founded on darker grounds, an attraction planted in the soil of a dangerous empathy and watered by curiosity and a cross-referencing of symptoms in the *Diagnostic and Statistical Manual of Mental Disorders*.

He was attractive in a used-car salesman kind of way. There was something he was selling me and that something was himself. Cocaine and years of binge drinking had probably decimated a few crucial brain cells, but he was a good listener. He opened doors and paid for my dinners. Mostly I was drawn to him for his stories. He was an ambulatory cautionary tale, the consummate bad-idea boyfriend, an ex-bartender who had attracted every type of injury and anecdote, trailing across state lines angry ex-lovers and brushes with death. He'd once spent a night in jail. Though my stories lacked his rattlesnake swagger we did share a history of self-cruelty, and I had mistaken this discovery as a suitable foundation for follow-me-home.

He'd been with too many lovers for me to want to legitimately sleep with him but we worked our way around this prohibition in other ways. Typically this all went down in the detached garage at the far end of the parking lot from his condominium. There was a padded bench for bench-pressing, a cracked concrete floor. The door slid shut on massive casters. I stalked back and forth over the concrete, smoking expensive Nat Sherman cigarettes. They were 101 mm, gold filter. I wore high-heeled boots and used a fake name. The things we did to each other were things you'd do in a garage with a broken car. A broken car you liked taking for a ride but goddamn it you couldn't help it sometimes you had to give it a kick because it was a piece of shit. It coughed, it cheated, it let you down. Sometimes I was the broken car on that bench, back arched, ratcheted up to the roof. Other times I'd be the one knee-deep in elbow grease, a twenty-two-year-old girl mechanic with a bike chain for a bracelet, an extension cord coiled in my hand.

It went wrong at the end of that summer. I'd played a solo gig one night at a coffeehouse, a divey sort of joint in Rogers Park. In my three-chord repertoire was a song that hit the wrong wavelength. He'd thought it was about X. It set him off. He began cultivating a jealous fantasy that I was sleeping with a lanky, shaggy-haired bookseller named X. It was true I'd gone to see an art-house movie with X, but there'd been no romance in the way we traded names of directors. Next he suspected a bookseller named Y, a prematurely balding guy with wire-rims and a pickup truck. Gradually his jealousy spread to Z and then to every male I came in contact with: co-workers and customers, ex-boyfriends and men I might meet if I went out unsupervised.

Nursing this paranoia, he showed up the next Friday to the suburban bar where I went drinking with my co-workers. The place was packed with minimum wagers like myself from nearby retail outlets. Just before midnight he appeared at the head of the table like a lugubrious figure from a German Expressionist film. X was wedged in beside me. All conversation skidded to a halt. The party stuttered back to life but this man stayed at the head of the table just glowering at us, knocking back bottle after bottle though I knew he wasn't supposed to drink anymore. X made his exit first, tapping Y's shoulder, the two men exchanging low words before making their getaway. By the time I slipped out to the parking lot, a shadow was following fast at my heel. I stopped when I saw the rusted wheel rims of his dark red sports car.

'Get in,' he said.

A door slammed. He lurched the engine to life and launched into a tirade. He steered wildly, at full speed, down the streaking road. I dug the lit end of a cigarette into the back of my hand to make him stop shouting. The pain seared with white heat. At a traffic light by the all-night car wash I threatened to jump out of the car but he hit the locks. I cranked down the window and tried to crawl out of it but he grabbed me by the ankle and dragged me back into the passenger seat. Something struck my back, a fist or a flashlight. My forehead pummelled the glove box with blunt force. You burned yourself, he was yelling, you hit your head.

In the end he dropped me back at the parking lot where my blue Buick sat waiting. He gunned the engine and was off, his wheels screeching burnt traction. I unlocked the car and got in. I gripped the wheel for a long time, my shoulders heaving. I imagined a man in uniform, an officer of the peace, finding a young woman sobbing at the wheel and setting things right. A cup of coffee, a warm blanket, a promise of protection.

I took a leave of absence from my job. I gathered what was left of my savings and went to London, then flew to Ireland by myself. In the windswept west I hiked through stone circles and read pamphlets of local lore. I sat cross-legged in the lumpy grass near ruined abbeys. I was moved by scenes of rural simplicity, a red-faced farmer in overalls, a blind kitten tumbling and mewling in the tall grass. From time to time the strap of my backpack would graze the sore spot, but I did not think much about the jealous man I had left behind, the one who delivered lectures at me at full speed about X, Y, and Z.

In Galway, as arranged, I met up again with my Dublin lover. I never once doubted that he'd meet me in Eyre Square, guitar in hand, because he'd promised he would. We met by the statue of the poet and embraced like long-losts. An unmarried couple knocking on doors, looking for lodging: in those days it was still frowned upon. We rented a room in Salthill from a white-haired tongue-clucking proprietress, a fussy upholstered double room with baroque floral sheets and a bed with creaking springs. Among the scattered souvenirs from my travels I'd ended up with a flyer for a Dublin walking tour. He picked it up, a glimmer of admiration in his eye. He had two idols: one was Jimi Hendrix and the other was Michael Collins. I knew less about Michael Collins than I did about Jimi Hendrix so I asked him to tell me about this hero of the Irish Republic. He undressed me with his calloused fingers, and he did.

The bugle sounded at 11:45 AM at Liberty Hall. The rebels stood to attention. By the midday Angelus their march was well underway, a motley assemblage of comrades dressed in dark green and bandoliers. They dragged handcarts of smuggled German guns towards the GPO, wheels clashing on cobblestones. In the basement of Liberty Hall they'd cranked out their proclamation on a warhorse of a Wharfdale Double-Crown. The set of metal type trafficked in from Capel Street had lacked letters, so they'd improvised, cutting a C from an O, dabbing sealing wax on an F to make an E. Inside the GPO, they staked their flag, clearing the main concourse of customers. A gun went off, blowing out a piece of stucco ceiling. In the lobby a policeman buying stamps begged not to be shot. Michael Collins, steering the throng towards safety, revolver in hand: 'We don't shoot prisoners.'

After six days of defending their posts, the rebellion is clearly failing. The khaki uniforms have closed in. The city has been burning steadily for a week. The air on Moore Street is thick with gutted timber, the cobbles below deckled with wreckage and broken glass. Collins picks through the rubble, ash on his coat, his boots flecked with debris. Surrender is certain. He rages. His fury is that it has come to this. If they aren't all rounded up and shot at dawn, as many of them will be, he swears one thing: never again will he wait for the enemy to close in.

Face the mirror and don the regalia: the eyeliner, the armour. On the morning of the court date, I trade the crystal for a Celtic cross. The silver links slink round my throat as I fix the chain in the mirror. As I'm fastening the clasp I realise the public defender is wrong, that my ex will appear in court. Of course he will appear. A restraining order for such a man is not an end to the story. It is a declaration of war. In the aftermath that is to come, I'll need better protection than a Celtic cross and a sheet of grievances in triplicate. What I'd require is a uniform: a military cap like the one Michael Collins wore, the braided brocade and stiff brim. If I had a military jacket I'd put that on as well, snug in worsted wool and great brass buttons. It flashes through my mind the cross will look good in the coffin if I happen to be wearing it when I'm shot. Nothing for it but to don the armour, the cross, the eyeliner. Sure I'll be looking grand for my assassination, for my three-day lying-in-state.

I march through the aisles of the bookstore. But at night floats the image of my ignoble end. Over and over again I wake up to sweat-soaked sheets and find myself half inside the dream and half without: the gunshot in the back of the head. An ambush on a tiny road in Cork. Béal na mBláth. In the mouth of flowers.

This man knew his way around a shooting range. His father owned guns and had taught him to shoot. This father still lived in Texas. One of the last things my ex had threatened as he hassled me down the bookstore aisle was that he was going back to Texas for Christmas and he was coming back loaded. I pictured it crossing state lines, the gun snug in a glove box, or else a rifle tucked inside the trunk, making its way along a blue vein of lonesome highway towards me. Nacodoches, Shreveport, Memphis, Champaign, Chicago.

Michael Collins on the signing of the treaty, on the fateful return home: Sure they won't kill me in my own county?

The last time I saw the man from Texas was in the Cook County Courthouse. The saplings that lined the traffic islands were leafless and stabby. That frigid morning, I checked for the car bomb, kicked the hubcap, and drove my blue Buick to the house of justice. The courtroom was an immense force field of polished chestnut. There was a massive American flag suspended in the back. The confines resembled a Department of Motor Vehicles with its throng of sad cases crammed together, the same stale air of prolonged waiting and depleted expectations. Disloyal wives and deadbeat dads, low-grade domestic abusers and petrified exes: we were all packed together, hashing out our harrowing tales in amplified monotone. The death threat, under fluorescent lights, had been reduced to a mere bureaucratic event. The defendant had showed up that morning with an entourage of a legal team. They swished down the hallway, slicked back and well-heeled, smelling of aftershave and money. I didn't look at him during the proceedings. A hassled judge presided, separating the wheat from the chaff, emotion from facts. In the end the judge said he was sorry for my trouble but he could not grant me the order of protection. He cited a lack of evidence. He rapped the gavel.

One week after the court date, I got the phone call. My boss from the bookstore was on the line. He repeated the news that had reached him from Texas. At his words I started to tremble uncontrollably. For a time I could not speak. I hung up the phone. What I'd wanted to say, had I been able to say it, was that there had been a mix-up. I was sure that the bullet at the hairline had been intended for me, not him. The bullet had my name on it. Only it had no narrative loyalty. You could say it entered the wrong skull. The assassination had happened. The man had used it to take his own life. I was still alive.

'I saw Death in a dream last night,' I'd said to him once, one day behind the counter when we were re-shelving books. He replied with a sly smile, 'Are you sure it wasn't me, poorly dressed?'

I'd wanted romance, and I'd wanted a story. And for what? At what cost? The day I got my story was the day I shut my mouth.

Today I am thirty-three. As I walk to my office in downtown Chicago I see girls fettered in army surplus wear. They pass me on West Madison Street, heavily lipsticked and wrapped in wool, flashing insignia, dressed for battle. On their chests they wear labels they did not earn. They bear the names of regiments they did not, and do not, belong to. Their battles are not recognised, have never even been declared.

I work at a historic preservation trust. My supervisor is an architectural historian whose basic attitude seems to be, 'That's a protected structure! Don't knock it down, just let it turn to shit.' Needless to say, I have a lot of respect for him. It takes a special type of person to speak his mind when the logical consequences of his theory, were it to be carried out, would be to make himself obsolete. Our days are spent on site visits or sifting through paperwork, applying for demolition-delay ordinances that are duly overturned after the ninety days. I spend a lot of time ruminating over ruins and cracked paving stones. I'm in awe of those blades of grass and spindly flowers that somehow find a way, those signs of life that in their humble growth and stubborn existence put us all to shame.

The other day as I was drawing up a draft of a preservation report, an invitation arrived at my office along with the afternoon mail. It was a postcard from my former Irish lover, the one who'd approached me in Grafton Street and shown me the bullet holes in the GPO. I don't know how he found my address. He was to deliver a special lecture on Michael Collins and his place in the Irish romantic imagination. Apparently he was some kind of a respected academic now, a lecturer at a university. This lecture was at a prestigious academic institution in Dublin. It would require me flying overseas. The lines he'd scribbled on the postcard were from a poem by W.B. Yeats. I recognised them immediately. He'd read these lines to me more or less verbatim one afternoon as we lay together on the grass of a rugby pitch, our limbs entangled, a rare blue slash of a sky over our heads. Under the lines from Yeats, he'd written two words: *Please come*.

When I got home I made the mistake of looking him up online. It is a terrible thing. There is no mystery. He lives in England with an English wife. Maybe he was planning an English child right now, an entire English brood. Now it was no longer a reverie, this springtime visit. I would have to employ seduction. Perhaps, if the seduction went well, he would leave his wife for me. Would I attend this lecture? He seemed to think I would, otherwise he would not have reached out across the span of a decade, across the reach of an ocean, to find me. I thought about what he'd say if I met him afterwards for a pint. I wondered if I could ever tell him the story, the one history of Michael Collins that he didn't know.

Historicising is its own violence. That's the kind of thing he might have said, he might still say. It's no stretch to see him standing at a lectern saying it, shrouded in the tweed he'd probably traded for his leather jacket: 'Historicising is its own violence.' Serious young ones in horn-rimmed glasses would write it down, taking his dictation. Would he say that about history or would that be admitting that his line of work was wrong? I don't know. I've lost him. The slagging, the singing, the taking each other down a peg, all the love-making and street-wandering, this romance is far in the past. Ten years is it now? Eleven? It doesn't matter. Today he furnishes his life with objects we used to scoff at: a sturdy desk, an office, a reputation to uphold. For my part, I live in a railroad apartment on Ravenswood with two women in their mid-thirties, not friends so much as young people I located in a newspaper listing. I carry a clipboard to falling-apart buildings and overgrown lots and draw up reports in strangled legalese. I argue for the cultural impact of these buildings, structures festering in blighted neighbourhoods that even aldermen want nothing to do with. I outline five-point plans for what should be done with these heaps of ruins though these reports end up, more often than not, in someone else's trash.

Was it too late to insinuate myself among the smart set, to fly to Dublin to accept his invitation, to carry to a lectern my own sheaf of papers and interpret the ruins? I could do it. Or else a poem. Surely I haven't lost touch with that side of myself. Surely a career has not rent that romance from me. There are verses and songs and language in me yet. I'd show him. I'd start the poem with the iconic, with the pillars he'd shown me one day in Dublin with such tenderness. I'd put into this poem all I knew about the bullet holes in the GPO, about the day he took my hand and we traced the gouges in the granite. This poem would say what the bullet holes had meant for the brave men and women who'd fought for Irish independence. It would not be historical per se but it would have facts, facts that he'd taught me, facts that had nothing to do with him, facts from the biography that had kept me alive. The words would bridge the distance that had separated us. They would explain what it had all been for. But the right question is not what do the bullet holes mean or even what is to be done with the bullet holes. The right question is always, do you see the bullet holes? Do you see what has been wounded and rent? That day on a flowered duvet in a rented Galway room I had wanted this fella in the leather jacket to look me in the eyes and tell me he saw the damage, the bruising on my back, the stain of purple yellow on the shoulder blade. He might have seen it. He might have tried to look me in the eyes. But if he saw, he did not say, or I did not hear. And I did not want to say, look at me, see how I am hurting.

I slipped the invitation into the recycling bin at work, though I think that was not enough. Reduce, reuse, recycle: it would come back. I should have burned it. I should have returned it to the ash from whence it came, the ash of our old acquaintance, with a fare thee well and please fuck off to my fair Irish lover. There was nothing left for the relics but to burn, burn, burn them all out—the letters, the pictures, the poems—to burn the relics as I'd burned the letters written for me by the man who, when I left him, would lose his mind. My Irish lover had not saved me from the other's violence, any more than he should have. How could he have? It didn't matter. I'd burn out the men, and the memories along with them, but they leave their own residue.

This is not a story at all but a shelf upon which I've lined up bits of sculpture, bits of history, here a blown-off head, there a pillar riddled with dents from old rifles. I should burn this story, too, and along with it my notion that I, a young woman of twenty-two, had any business doing myself up in the garb of an Irish commander-in-chief. I should do away for good with the notion that a book I'd read under the covers while I waited for my car to be bombed was anything more than what it was: a book about a man named Michael Collins that I happened to fancy. Fancy—that's a word I don't use. These words should be wrenched right from my mouth. I can't be trusted with a pen.

This isn't a story about Michael Collins. This is a story about damage. This is a story about two lovers: one who took me to see the bullet holes in the GPO and another who took his own life with a bullet. They crossed over in time but were so removed from one another it was as if I had two lives, was two people. I had one life in Ireland and another in the suburbs of Chicago. Everywhere, everyone was looking at violence, staring at it, looking around it, blinking, not blinking, and not a single one with any idea of what to do with it.

Hairy Jaysus

Donal O'Kelly

'The soul of revolt against man's inhumanity to man,
the ripest ear of corn that fell in Easter Week.'
—Sean O'Casey on Frank Sheehy-Skeffington

A solo play about Frank Sheehy-Skeffington, pacifist, feminist, socialist, atheist, summarily executed in Dublin, Easter Week 1916.

Lights up on a man begging, a sleeping bag like a cloak on his back.

So I'm sittin there beside the AT fuckin M
opposite the Swan in Rathmines with my styrofoam cup,
and this redneck bluebottle looks down at me and says
—I'm arresting you for beggin if you don't
get the fuck away from that AT fuckin M.

And I say—Is that what occurs to you to do
when you see an Irish bank ATM?
Arrest the guy who's beggin beside it!?
Do you realise how fucked-up that is!?
We the Irish people are paying 43% of European bank debt
because of the fuckin crimes of the people who run that ATM!
So there's no host in your fuckin tabernacle—whah!?

This makes the bluebottle agitated
and he says he'll fuckin pepper-spray me.
I stride away brushing me shitty sleepin bag against him.
All he sees is a crusty leper that needs clearing
ouha da way o da smooth runnin o da gaff.

C'mere to me, he shouts, I'm not finished with you yet—
I let on I don't hear but he's after me
and I start to leg it down the Rathmines Road,
but he's young and blood-up and me laces are loose
and a bit of pins and needles from the sitting down too long,
so I can hear his studded bootsteps catching up on me.
He somehow stamps on the tail of my sleepin bag,
that's become, by some fuckin weirdness,
an ancient cloak stretching way back up the road—
it's the clobber of fuckin history I'm always dragging along,
the nightmare James Joyce was always trying to awaken from,
and this gobshite's after making it manifest fuck knows how,
he's trodden on the fabric of the nation
I didn't know was hanging off my shoulders,
I fall back in slo-mo, choking on the zip
and I recite James Joyce's thunderword from *Finnegans Wake*
as an incantation to protect me against bluebottle aggression—
it's a trick I sometimes pick out of the old back pocket
when I'm caught in a tight spot—

bababaldagheraghtakamminaronnkonnbronntonneronntuonnthuntrovarrhou-nawnskawntoohoohoodenenthurnuk!

Bluebottle's shittin himself, thinks I'm after putting some kind of Satanic curse on him, which allows me a split second of respite to ponder the following:

Clip-clopping along to Glasnevin,
clip-clopping along to Glasnevin,
just a crate on a cart
from Portobello Barracks
to Glasnevin Cemetery.
What's in the crate, Mister!?
Head down, none of your business!

The bluebottle's recovered from his attack of superstition.
He tugs and I am enfolded in the shitty sleeping-bag of history,
as the Rathmines Town Hall chimes ten o'clock...
It's the 26th April 1916,
the Wednesday of Easter Week.
A volley of shots rings out in Portobello Barracks, Rathmines.

A crow gives a big long caw.
Another volley a minute later!
Frank Sheehy-Skeffington is dead.
The bluebottle twists the zip and triggers a flash of now—ow—
A million Irish voices roar: '*Frank WHO!?*'

Frank Sheehy-Skeffington!! See!!??
He's fuckin forgotten, ignored,
And by many who know who he was
he's ridiculed and laughed at. Why!?
Because in Dublin in Easter Week 1916
James Joyce's best friend, the little atheist
he called Hairy Jaysus,
was trying... to stop... the looting!
Isn't that a good one!?
Thousands putting their lives on the line,
occupying buildings all over Dublin
and firing shots all around them
for the freedom of fuckin Ireland,
and Skeffy was... trying to stop the looting!
What a fuckin gobshite he musta been!
A buffoon! A clown! Very fuckin hairy
taking such a Jaysusin figairy...
What possessed him!? What was he thinking of!?
Why, why, why!?
Here's Hairy Jaysus's cross and passion!
Francis Sheehy-Skeffington in The Stations of The—not Cross,
no—The Stations of The Crank!
Small instrument that makes Revolutions!

The First Station: Liberty Hall, Dublin, Noon, Easter Monday 1916.
The illustrious occasion is about to commence!

James Connolly musters the Citizen army and the Irish Volunteers the cause of Ireland is the cause of labour
And the cause of labour is the cause of...
Frank Sheehy-Skeffington hanging around the edges
—Comrade Connolly, on a point of order
by whose authority has this armed alliance been convened!?

I push him into the back lane til Connolly gives the order
and off they march around the corner to the GPO
and into the history books…
—James Connolly, friend, comrade, why do you deny me!?

On Palm Sunday in Liberty Hall we cheered for Skef-fy Skef-fy
if we had palms we'd have laid them down at his feet,
beside James Connolly after their doublebill of plays,
'In Ibsen's play *A Doll's House*, the heroine Nora
goes out the door to an indeterminate future.
In *my* pointed comedy, *The Prodigal Daughter*,
Lily goes out to campaign on the steps
of her local church for Votes For Women!
That's revolutionary action!'
Connolly clasps him as if he's going to kiss him.
Then he cites his own play, *Under Which Flag?*,
whether to fight for Britain or Ireland…
—There are guns in the hands
of tens of thousands of Irishmen
in the British Army in Flanders!
Why not guns in our hands
in Dublin city here today!?

And a company of the Citizen Army marches in the door,
and everyone cheers as the men and women drill on the floor.
Skeffy walks off the stage,
leaving Connolly to talk about channelling the rage
to make the maximum impact.

Second Station: City Hall, 1pm, Easter Monday.

A soldier gashed open at the side of City Hall.
Skeffy to the chemist on the corner!
Bayonet accident! Terrible mess!
Skip back with bundles of bandages clutched
to find the soldier's been dragged
inside the gates of Dublin's Castle. Cross! Fire!
Skeffy flattens up against a door.
Lucky he never put the weight back on
after the hunger strike last year…

—Silence in court! Francis Sheehy-Skeffington,
you are found guilty of sedition
for making forty speeches against recruitment
to His Majesty's armed forces…
—That's right… forty!
The Castle spy who followed me can count! Though he missed a fair few!
I wouldn't give him the full thirty pieces of silver if I were you!
Damn pity I didn't get to make another forty anti-war speeches too!
—Silence!
—Should I be silent while the slaughter of innocents proceeds!? And where articulate resistance to this organised murder is deemed to be a crime!?
Damn your war! Non serviam! I will not serve! I will not kow-tow!
I will not bow and scrape! Any sentence you pass on me is a sentence passed on British rule in Ireland. The Irish people do not subscribe to this imperialist war!
—You are sentenced to one year's hard labour! (*Aside*) See if you're as vocal in the stonebreakers' yard!
—Try as you might, you'll not shut me up! Long before the expiration of the sentence, I will be out of prison, alive or dead!
—Remove this unmanageable crank from my court!
—Damn your war!

Mountjoy Jail!
—Seán MacDermott, volunteer head honcho, you here too! For an anti-recruitment speech? Good man, sure one is a start! We'll hunger strike while the iron is hot!
A hunger strike by two such as we, relatively prominent in the public eye—
Seán don't be shy—would undermine their recruitment drive for the war!
They'll release us before the week is out!
The price of freedom is hunger! My wife Hanna did it!
For votes for women three years ago!
Why should it be left to women alone to hunger strike for rights!?
Now, stop even thinking about eating!

Of course, it'll be hard for you,
'cos they'll fry rashers and sausages outside the door.
They did it on Hanna, not realising she's vegetarian.
So am I. I'd appreciate it if you didn't illuminate them further
or they'll stink us out with scabby cabbage and burnt turnip pooh,
making it an even more miserable situation for everyone.
Mount of Joy how are you!!

Day one, day two, day three…
Day four, they say, is the worst.
Some instinctive reaction in the stomach that will not be quelled!
The days move slower, and the nights lie still.
The crows outside Mountjoy are deafeningly loud,
and the lovers walking home along the prison wall
seem to roar their sweet nothings as if they're in the cell.
Day Five, no word, they think they can ignore us…
Day Six, escalate to hunger-and-thirst strike!
Day seven, day eight—surely they're not going to just let us…
Door opens, set free. On a Sunday to avoid publicity!
Trousers won't stay up – button them to the waistcoat.
A car, I'm fine, absolutely f… the chug-chug…
Outside the garden gate, little Owen runs to meet me.
I try to say Owen but just manage Oh…
Hanna helps me walk the path,
step, in, dizzy, sit, water, and a little piece of toast,
wet it til it softens, slide it down the throat…

Third Station: Nelson's Pillar, 4pm, Easter Monday.

Hanna in a rush to the GPO, Frank says no.
—My place is on the outside, I won't join in!
—Frank, we're officially citizens of the Irish Republic!
The Proclamation guarantees equal rights to everyone, men and women,
what we've campaigned for is achieved! Worth celebrating!
—You go so Hanna…! Take care, don't stay long!
When the response comes it will be sudden and it will be strong.
Hanna…

Coming up to Christmas 1900, the wheezy Sheehy doorbell clangs
and I enter in my jaunty new plus-fours.
I'm a different kind of student
come all the way from Cavan via Down,
my knickerbockers scream.
James Joyce giddies in behind me.
—Get out of my way, Hairy Jaysus!
He makes a beeline for the wine
and the continental cheeses.

Ha-ha-ha-Hanna and her sister Mary Shee-hee lead the charades
But Joyce soon barrooms into Greek mytholohee-hee.
He pretends he's Aphrodite stepping from her clam-shell.
He coyly covers his pee-wee… tee-hee…
I become one of Boticelli's Three Graces twee
with Hanna and Mary Shee-hee,
hand to hand we twirl nimble nymphs so fay…
I see us nude with our berry-food at hand.
I sway my beard from side to side
to the roars of the loudy-crowdy.
Knickerbocker-kick!
Hanna's haunches and hips sheer I try not to leer,
and a pearl hangs from her neat Vermeer.
Hanna focussed, gaze straight,
no jokey, pupils dilate, oh,
fingers touch, the slightest stroke, oh,
I cough, trip, nearly choke. Hannaah!

But I won't follow you into the GPO,
for a gun-toting tête-à-tête with MacDermott and Connolly.
They've consigned me to the outside, so be it.
Shop windows shatter up the street,
people wearing fur stoles and silk top hats appear
—Would you look at the state of me now!!??
—Would you look at the state of me now!!??

The state of me now…
Marooned, in no-man's-land…
They call it the rock of Futility, an isolated shore,
where no rain falls, where no wind blows,
where no bird calls, where no plant grows.
Stillness, in a sea of cobblestones and glass.
Men I knew, chiselling loopholes in brick,
and rolling gigantic wooden print spools for barricades,
while I stand stuck, tied in the idle of futility.

Fourth Station: Grosvenor Square, Rathmines, 9pm, Easter Monday.

Silence. Huff.
Owen put to bed.
—Hanna. Stuff to discuss.
Her brow knits, her cheeks puff.
—You knew the rising was to happen and you didn't tell me.
Pause. Moon.
—I was sworn to silence, Frank.
—But not to me!
—Yes, especially to you!
—By whom?
—By James Connolly!
—Why did you agree?
—He asked me to be one of five members of a Civil Government to be declared if the rising leaders are killed.
A woman in government Frank! First time ever!
Even if it's theoretical, and anyway only nominal!
But still! Significant!

Betrayed? Too strong! Distrusted? Too weak!
Kept out of the action! Why? Too meek?
I feel like a little boy at my father's knee,
the schools inspector educating me at home,
manipulating my influences until I broke free.
—Connolly couldn't look at me today! Now I know why!
—I'm sorry, Frank.
—Not enough!
Silence. Huff.

Going home after that 1900 Christmas Hann-ahaha-hadvent
I stick a sprig of cherry-blossom in my hair.
—Is this love, Joyce… what do you think?
He says, 'a poet must write tragedies, not act in one.'
I'll act in the comedy, the tragedy, the work, the play…
whatever life-love makes it, come what may. Liove. I will liove.
Joyce found his way to liove too.
Went east with his Galway chambermaid.

Still together, last I heard!
He's put me in his book with the long pretentious title.
Portrait of the Artist as a Troubled Know-it-all.
I'm a boring character called McCann
full of his own conceit, who eats a lot of chocolate.
Hanna likes chocolate. The early days…
Hanna the light and Hanna the word,
me the pacifist, pen not sword!
Oh the debates, the teasing out, the tos-and-fros
in the basement cellars and rooms and back-bureaus,
them was days! Hannaargh! Liove! I will liove!

She had me sent to America after my Mountjoy slimming escapade.
It was liove that made it happen, her liove for me.
She put me out of the way of the Cat-and-Mouse act
or I'd have been in and out of Mountjoy like a jack-in-the-box,
an inch or two thinner each time.

Stayed with Joyce's old friend Byrne from 7 Eccles Street,
nice place he has in Brooklyn now, he's landed on his feet
and made a new life, full of bustling activity,
of the peculiarly Irish kind.
I went and met the Wobblies, socialists, communists, anarchists, feminists,
suffragists and the black rights folk.
But John Devoy-devoy-devoy had me shunted out of harm's way
at every hand's turn with my 'naïve divisive views'
by his cigar-toting wide-brimmed double-breasted cronies…
—Let's hear a song from the old sod!
Sentimental baloney!
Not one Clan na Gael platform did I grace.
Traded funny stories with Byrne about Jocax Joyce.
He kept me sane.
It felt futile pretending I was there at the Clan's invitation
while they pushed me out of sight with fervent application.
Back here for Christmas last, Owen grown a full inch taller!
He's taking after the other side…

A rifle shot! Not too far away!

An old geezer said someone's in the belltower of Rathmines Church,
sniping across into Portobello Barracks.
Wait till tomorrow comes. A response will arrive in time,
the bells will chime as the bullets rain.
Will it all be in vain…? Will we end up stuck
in Joyce's societal paralysis again?
He'd probably think so. But I don't know.
At least they've made a mark, put out a shout.
How do I participate, civilly, in critical…
if not support, let us say comprehension,
without becoming a willing party to military action?
There's not much room for a minority position.
With us or ag'in us… this is a defining time.
It's happened, and it must be dealt with.

Fifth Station: The Irish Women's Franchise League office, Westmoreland Street, 5pm, Easter Tuesday.

Frank on his hands and knees
charcoaling big squares of paper
NO LOOTING BY ORDER
ANTI-LOOTING COMMITTEE
Hanna rushes up the stairs
—Time to go home, Frank! Things are getting out of control!
—Well indeed, quelle surprise!
—Army reinforcements are encroaching on the city centre, tightening their grip!
—Well, your confidante James Connolly has said
organise, educate, agitate for years!
But the war reminds him of his British army days in India,
and the forthright methods sometimes required
to get *things* done.
So he starts training and drilling in the use of guns,
and now he's talking about 'our gallant allies' the Germans
as if they're somehow less imperialistic than our own John Bull
when if anything they're arguably even worse
in their treatment of Africans!

—Frank, our friends and comrades, including James Connolly,
have held the centre of Dublin for thirty hours
against the most powerful empire on earth!
Is that not a matter of considerable joy!?
—If it's joy, it's a dangerous joy!
All I can do is try to stop the looting,
so it doesn't look like hooligans run amok.
That's the only role left open to me now,
what I've been reduced to,
thanks to Connolly… and you!

—Frank! What's the name of the magazine James Joyce's novel has been appearing in? I forget! We laughed at the funny title! Remind me!
—*The Egoist*!
—*The Egoist*, that's it! Yes, we all must be careful not to think,
as James Joyce did and presumably still does,
that the universe revolves around us.
An historical event is taking place in which you're not,
at present, playing a central role.
But in which you will, in time!
That gunfire we hear is the sound of challenge, not compliance.
—But it's challenge the old way, the same methods
of armed aggression and blind obedience.
—Where there are guns there must be obedience!
—This is futile!
I'm on my bloody knees.
Nowhere I can stand. Nowhere I can speak.
Nowhere I can make the case against the military spirit that infects humanity.
I'm a pacifist journalist who can no longer make a living.
—I can. Just about! I teach.
We're equal, remember, Sheehy Skeffington?
—I haven't had a jot published since I went to jail!
London, Dublin, it doesn't matter they're agreed.
I've been expelled from the citadel…
to slow death in the stoney plain,
like Dante's doomed friend Cavalcanti.
—Melodrama, Frank, you know you have a weakness for it…
—Melodrama!? Farce!! There's nobody coming

for my anti-looting committee meeting,
because they think I'm a bloody buffoon.
—Bloody Buffoon!? That's what your dad called you
when you joined my name to yours, Sheehy Skeffington!
—As a consequence a lot of people think I'm an aristocratic
double-barrelled toff!
—Not the people who matter, you bloody buffoon!
—Don't crank me up, Hanna!
—Crank!? That's what the university's president called you
when you resigned your cushy job as registrar
over unequal treatment of women.
'Frank, there's no future in being written off as a crank,' he said.
'A crank,' retorted Frank Sheehy Skeffington...
—is a small instrument that makes revolutions!
Oh yes, by order, the anti-revo-looting committee!
—Frank, my crank! Hug?
—Not by a long shot, Hanna! Not yet!
—I still love you no matter what you think.
—A funny way of showing it!
—How long will you keep this up? I'm off home!
Don't dilly-dally! Liove! Time to call it a day!

Sixth Station: Kelly's of Portobello the first time, 6pm, Tuesday 26 April.

I'm Dickson with a cheque for a tenner in advance
from Kelly the loyalist councillor publican
who wants me to print and post up on walls
the King's proclamation of martial law
telling everyone to go home or get shot.
Kelly's been fleeced of his stock
of expensive cigars and fine wines
by the tenement-dwellers out the back of his premises.
Fair enough, I said.
I go running around trying to knock up every bloody printer I know
and it's getting a bit harem-scarem 'cos
I haven't a clue where the rebels are,
they're poppin up everywhere

and soldiers are making sorties out of Portobello Barracks,
when who do I see walking up the middle of the street from town
with a bucket of paste and a brush and a roll of posters but…
the man I used to report on for making seditious speeches…
Frank Sheehy Skeffington, Hairy feckin Jaysus!

—No looting, he shouts!
Sure everybody laughs and jeers.
—Leave 'im alone, a fat vintage wine-guzzler says,
he fed my childer during the Lockout, Hairy Jaysus is alright.
Sit down and give us an oul smacker, me gamey little Lothario…
—I don't care if you think I'm alright or not,
citizenship has its duties as well as its rights,
and one of them is to prevent theft.
—So what are you going to do about it, a loudmouth shouts.
—What'll I do!? Well, I may be five foot two,
but I'm not afraid of you or anyone else
who threatens my right to public protest.
I'm going to put up these anti-looting posters.
You don't want to be like the traders in the temple!?
You know what happened to them! Whipped and run out of it!
—Yeah, holy Jesus threw the head, but you're not holy –
you're hairy Jaysus the atheist!
—I'll give you a hand, I say, give me your posters there.
I take them and I walk up towards the Canal Bridge.
—Where are you going? he shouts.

Seventh Station. The Checkpoint 7pm, Easter Tuesday.

We just secured the canal bridge when we saw a crowd approaching.
—This man has been putting up rebel posters, says the first.
—My name is Francis Sheehy-Skeffington, I'm a militant pacifist,
I'm proud to say I've been jailed for it, but those are NOT rebel posters,
they are anti-looting posters.
I believe that property, as well as having its duties,
which it is far too often loathe to perform,
also has its rights, until such time
as due democratic process might wisely decree otherwise.

—Bursts of gunfire! Half-a-mile away! Take him in!
Martial Law has been declared! Get off the streets!
I fire in the air and off they scatter.
One small boy is smoking a giant Cuban cigar.
He gives my men a puff of it, and they have a hearty laugh
as they trudge back up to the barracks, prisoner in tow.

Eighth Station: The Detention Cell, Portobello Barracks, 8pm, Easter Tuesday.

Guard, could you ask someone to get a message to my wife?
She's in the garden flat in 10 Grosvenor Square, not far, ten minutes.
Maybe the little boy who followed us in with the fat cigar would
run around. I can hear him coughing his lungs up.
He can't miss it. It's got a big *Damn Your War* banner
stuck in the hedge outside.
I know there's a human being residing inside that uniform,
and I know he has a pair of ears and brains to comprehend,
and empathy enough to know that there's nothing seditious
about wanting my wife and child to know I'm safe.
Just ask the little boy if he'll do me a favour and my wife Hanna
will give him something nice like an apple or maybe a date,
I think there should be at least one left in a box on top
of the long press, tell him to tell her.
And perhaps you'd ask him to tell her I love her.
Life-love. Liove.
Em, no, forget about that,
too complicated, just love will do.

Ninth Station. The Guardroom, 9pm, Easter Tuesday.

Seven of us interrogate him, and he doesn't flinch.
—You were carrying rebel posters, admit it!
—The posters are nothing to do with rebels
or anything but me and the organisation I set up today
called the Citizens Committee against Looting.
That means me. I *am* the Citizens Committee against looting.

Because no one else turned up! I intended to put up posters,
but it was too dangerous, so I decided to go home.
I was not pleased, as I like to be at the centre of things.
—I saw two priests attack you in Kingsbridge Station
during the lockout a couple of years ago.
—Yes, they said I was doing Satan's work
by bringing some workers' hungry children
to be well fed in the safety of Kildare
until the lockout dispute was resolved.
When the children tried to stop the priests from kicking me to death,
this was taken as proof I was indeed the devil's advocate.
—I was the one who picked you up.
—Were you? Well thank you, belatedly.
I survived, as you can see, thanks to my padding.
—Padding?
—My father's cricket padding, fitted to protect the stomach and kidneys.
I wear it under my clothes whenever I'm at risk of a clobbering.
—Are you wearing it now?
—Yes. What bits of it are left.

—That's a rebel uniform.
We have spent two years risking our lives
and the lives of our men, many horribly slaughtered,
and you prance around in your homegrown uniform
and stab us in the back.
Lieutenant! Strip this hairy Jaysus of his rebel robes!

An order is an order.
When it's all stripped off
And the stupid bits of cork are scattered on the floor
I bend him over while we kick his legs apart
and we get him to sing God Save The King
but he won't so we have to make him…

The Three Graces twirl with their berry-food at hand…
Fingers touch, a gentle stroke…
there's Hanna the first grace
bringing sacks of flour to the rebels
at the back of the College of Surgeons.

Hanna, the time we went up the mountains to Tibradden
and lay down in the grassy gap in the secret clumps of heather
and looked at the smoky city below and pointed out the landmarks
Rathmines Church with its big green dome,
and the Wellington Monument in the Phoenix Park
and my Ibsen one… you laughed…
up here up in the Freudian heather…
And there's James Connolly, the second grace,
tucking into his rations in the GPO.
James, the meeting we spoke at during the Lockout was broken up.
We lashed the reins of the horse
and the platform we spoke from took off
through the lines of police—giddy-up!
How *you* laughed, Frank and James, James and Frah…
And there's James Joyce, the third grace, hobnobbing in Zurich,
regaling his companions with his latest risqué ballade:

Connaissez-vous l'histoire, d'un vieux curé de Paris,
d'un vieux cu-, d'un vieux cu-, d'un vieux curé de Paris.

Joyce, the day we carried our eighty copies of *Two Essays*
away from the printer in a borrowed wheelbarrow
and across the little bridge in Stephen's Green
our first published works:
'The Day Of The Rabblement' by J.A. Joyce and
'A Forgotten Aspect of the University Question:
The Unequal Treatment of Women' by F. J. C. Skeffington.
Everyone raved about your rambling piece
with hazy references to Giordano Bruno,
the heretic burned at the stake in Rome,
with a dagger through his cheeks,
and a dagger through his jaw and tongue…
a muting crucifixion!
Bru-no! Bru-No! Bru-!
Tie him up! Use your rifle pull-through!
That'll teach the pacifist!
Knickerbocker-kick! Get up!

Tenth Station: Rathmines Road, 10pm, Easter Tuesday.

We go out the gatepost and onto Rathmines Road.
Three men on the far side! Halt!
Captain roughs them up so they spread the word
the army are out and we mean fucking business.
One of them starts walking away…
—Halt! Name?
—James Coad.
—Martial Law is declared! Why are you out!? An altarboys' meeting!?
In Rathmines Church!? There's been a sniper in your church's belltower.
The captain shoots him in the head. Blood pours.
—That's what we do to our enemies. We smite them. So the Bible's Book of Isaiah says. God save the king!
Hairy Jaysus bursts free, but his hands are tied behind his back
so he kneels down and lays his head on the boy's chest
and he starts to howl an atheist prayer!
—Our father, who art in Heaven, will someone staunch the bloodflow!?
He tries to use his face to do it, the fucking clown!
The Captain wrenches him up by the pull-through.
—One more WORD out of you, Hairy Jaysus, and we'll call around to your wife in 10 Grosvenor Square. When she opens the door I'll plug you in the head like I plugged him and then we'll shoot her twice in the belly so she dies slowly in great pain, 'cos you're all up to your eyes in it. You are all our enemy and we will smite you! God save the King!

Eleventh Station: Kelly's the second time, 11pm, Easter Tuesday.

I keep prodding the prisoner 'cos the swollen bollocks
makes it hard for him to walk. The captain says if there's one bullet
fired at us to plug this rebel leader Sheehy-Skeffington!
Captain's thrown a bomb into Kelly's. He charges in with ten men.
—That pub is owned by the loyalist councillor Kelly. You're attacking the wrong premises!
—Of course you'd say that! You want all the cigars and wine for yourselves when you're in charge, securing your fucking assets!
—The captain's murdered once. Look at the blood on my face – that boy's blood! He'll murder again. Are you going to just obey!?

—You've spoken without permission. Now your wife's going to get the works.
—Hanna the light… Hanna the word…
—Captain's back! Found another pair of rebel leaders in there.
Tie the three of them together!

Twelfth Station: The road back to Portobello Barracks, Midnight.

—Skeffy! I'm Dickson. They think I'm your rebel accomplice.
I'm nothing of the kind! I'm the opposite in fact!
I took your posters to print the proclamation of martial law on the backs.
Listen to me! I'll say you gave them willingly… I'll say it was your idea, that way we back each other up! Fair deal! Nothing to lose! The state of you! Is that your own blood or someone else's!?
—I'm McIntyre. I know I've lampooned you in *Starlight*, Skeffy,
several times, but boss's orders, y'know!?
As a journalistic professional I know you understand.
This captain's mixed the *Starlight* the employers' paper I edit
with the bitch Markievicz's shabby rag *The Spark*.
Skeffy, tell him I'm no friend of *The Spark*!
I'd piss on it sooner. I'm the *Starlight*!
—Skeffy, I'm Dickson and I'm all for women's rights.
I got engaged last week. Tell them I'm no rebel!
—Skeffy, why are you walking so slow, man?
Speed up, they're prodding me! Why are you gone so quiet!?
—Leave him alone! He's been through the mill.
—Hanna my light… Hanna my word… Hanna my light… Hanna my…
—Frank? Where are you Frank my crank?

Thirteenth Station: Portobello Barracks, Wednesday.

At 10am the Captain told me to take Sheehy-Skeffington, McIntyre and Dickson to the stoneyard. I did it.
The captain told me to get seven men with rifles. I did it.
He told me to order the men to go to the wall. Go to the wall!
Ready! Present! Fire!
The three men fell. One of them still moved. Sheehy-Skeffington.

—I advocate no mere servile lazy acquiescence in injustice.
I want to see the age-long fight against injustice
clothe itself in new forms, suited to a new age.
I want to see the manhood of Ireland no longer hypnotised
by the glamour of 'the glory of arms',
no longer blind to the horrors of organised murder.
We are on the threshold of a new era in human history.
Nothing can be as it was before.
The foundations of all things must be re-examined.
Formerly, we could only imagine the chaos
to which we were being led by the military spirit.
Now we realise it.
And we must never fall into that abyss again.

I collected four of the men and I led them back to the stoneyard. I told them to aim at the moving man. He looked at me and said:
—liove!
—Fire!
And I fired a bullet in his head to make sure he was dead.

Fourteenth Station. Grosvenor Square Rathmines, sometime the next day.

—Missus, I was sent by a soldier to say to give me a date
they're in a box on top of the high press
for telling you that Hairy Jaysus is in Portobello Barracks.
That's all!

Clip-cloppin along to Glasnevin.
Clip-cloppin along to Glasnevin.
Just a crate in a cart from Portobello Barracks,
to Glasnevin Cemetery.
What's in the crate, Mister?
Head down! None of your fuckin business!

—Dear Colonel Maxwell,

It has come to my attention
that my son Francis Skeffington's body
lies within the walls of Portobello Barracks.
I request to be informed of the conditions requiring to be met

for the transportation of my son's body
for burial with Catholic rites in consecrated ground.
I assure you any conditions you might reasonably apply
will be met by me with discrete compliance.
For the sake of my son's immortal soul,
I undertake not to inform his atheist wife Hanna Sheehy.
Yours ever,
JB Skeffington,
Justice of the Peace

There he goes, clip-clopping along to Glasnevin,
the bloody buffoon,
the anti-looting clown of Easter Week,
Frank Sheehy-Skeffington,
pacifist, socialist, feminist, atheist,
buried forever in sssh…
sssh… shovelfuls of discreet compliance
and historical heaps of scorn…

As the clay thuds on the crate,
Hanna and Owen are held at gunpoint.
The captain orders forty men to rifle through the flat.
He raids Frank's study using the key he took
from the blood-soaked pocket of the jaunty plus-fours.

James Connolly, facing the firing squad at dawn,
asks for Skeffy to be made his literary executor,
he'd know how to sell the publishing rights…
to be told by Lily—They shot Skeffy, James.
Tears pour down his face, tears pour down.

And James Joyce regales his Zurich companions
poised to become the most celebrated writer of the age…
as the clods of Glasnevin clay
become a gigantic mound of collective forgetfulness.
And our overseers parade their glorious pomposities
with their medals of swaggering impotence
pinned in their stiff lapels,

we – are – the – gov – ern – ment –
and their someone's-got-to-do-it looks of dogged duty
if you only knew as we do the sacrifices made
by such as we of another time that we might be free to…
parade here in sanctimonious panto-fuckin-mime…

Where are the Skeffys to make them afraid?
Where are the cranks, small instruments that make revolutions?
Where are the hairy Jaysuses, the way, the light, the truth—
the frankness!?

The bluebottle has me shoved against
the railings of Rathmines Tech!
Where Hanna used to teach!
I see her there, at the door,
looking at me through her plain round specs!
The way she must have looked at Sylvia Beach
the publisher of *Ulysses*, when she sold her
Frank's twenty copies of *Two Essays*,
to pay in part for Owen's education.
James Joyce's heretical Bruno thunderwords are go!

The bluebottle rips the history sleeping-bag
off of me back and fucks it into a skip.
That's enough of that bollocksology he says,
as he cuffs me, and shuts me up,
and puts me away in a paddy wagon
for the greater security of all the AT fuckin Ms of Ireland,
that they may dutifully pay
the gambling losses of fuck-knows-who…
Ireland, unfree, a-fuckin-Boo!

NOTES ON CONTRIBUTORS

Kevin Barry is the author of the short-story collections, *There Are Little Kingdoms* and *Dark Lies The Island*, and the novels, *City of Bohane* and *Beatlebone*. He lives in County Sligo.

Joan Win Brennan recently moved to Deal in Kent from London. She has worked as an illustrator, education editor, further education tutor and university librarian. She has been shortlisted for many prizes and awards, including the Bridport, Fish, V.S. Pritchett, and Willesden Herald. *The Bean Farm* was a finalist in the Exeter Novel Prize.

Colette Bryce's most recent collection, *The Whole & Rain-domed Universe* (Picador 2014), received a special Ewart-Biggs Prize in memory of Seamus Heaney.

Lucy Sweeney Byrne has been published in *The Bohemyth, Banshee* and *The Incubator*. She is currently living in Berlin.

Siobhan Campbell won the 2016 Oxford Brookes International Poetry Competition. Her third book, *Cross Talk*, 'explores Ireland in the aftermath of its turbulent peace process' – *Poetry*. New work appears in *The Hopkins Review, New Hibernia* and *Magma. That Other Island* is forthcoming from Seren.

Evelyn Conlon's most recent novel is *Not the Same Sky*. Books Upstairs will publish *A Glassful of Letters* and *Telling* in 2016. She compiled the literary anthology, *Later On*, which was the basis for the Italian conference The Language of War. *www.evelynconlon.com*

A.M. Cousins' work has appeared in *The Stinging Fly, THE SHOp, The Honest Ulsterman* and *The Irish Literary Review*. Her collection, *Redress*, was shortlisted for the 2015 Patrick Kavanagh Poetry Award.

Therese Cox was born in Chicago and lives in Brooklyn. Her work has appeared in *The Brooklyn Rail, gorse,* and *Banshee*. She is pursuing a PhD in English and Comparative Literature at Columbia University.

Gavin Corbett's second novel, *This Is The Way*, is published by Fourth Estate. It was named 2013 Kerry Group Irish Novel of the Year and shortlisted for the Encore Award. His latest novel, *Green Glowing Skull*, was published in May 2015.

Catriona Crowe is Head of Special Projects at the National Archives of Ireland. She edited *Dublin 1911* (2011), and she is an editor of *Documents on Irish Foreign Policy,* the latest volume of which, *1948-51,* was published in November 2015. She is Adjunct Professor of History at the University of Limerick and Chairperson of the Irish Theatre Institute.

Kevin Curran's debut novel, *Beatsploitation,* was published in 2013. His short story 'Saving Tanya' from *Young Irelanders* was longlisted for the Irish Book Awards Short Story of the Year in 2015. His second novel, *Citizens,* was published in January 2016 by Liberties Press.

Martina Evans is a poet and novelist. *Burnfort Las Vegas* was shortlisted for the Irish Times Poetry Now Award 2015. *The Windows of Graceland: New and Selected Poems* will be published by Carcanet in 2016.

Aisling Fahey has performed in various locations across England, America, Ireland and India, including the Barbican, the Houses of Parliament and Glastonbury. She is a member of the Burn After Reading collective and Barbican Young Poets and was the Young Poet Laureate for London 2014-15.

Elaine Feeney has published three collections of poetry, *Indiscipline* (2007), *Where's Katie?* (2010) and *The Radio was Gospel* (2014). Her next collection, *Rise,* is due out with Salmon Poetry later this year.

Elaine Gaston is from Ireland's north coast. Her first collection is *The Lie of the Land* (2015). She received a Commendation in the Vincent Buckley Poetry Award 2015. She lectures at the University of Ulster.

James Harpur's latest book, *Angels and Harvesters* (Anvil Press), was a Poetry Book Society Recommendation and shortlisted for the Irish Times Poetry Prize. He lives in West Cork.

Anthony Hegarty is a poet and ecopsychologist who lives in County Galway. He has poetry in *Burning Bush 2*. He won the Culture Night Poetry Competition at Kenny's Bookshop and was a winner in The Poetry Ireland / Trócaire Competition in 2014. *www.hugofgaia.com*

Desmond Hogan has published five novels and six collections of short stories. His early novels, *The Ikon-Maker* and *The Leaves on Grey,* have recently been reissued by The Lilliput Press.

Seamus Keenan lives in Derry. He won the Hennessy Emerging Fiction Award and Overall Hennessy New Irish Writer of Year Award and is currently working on a fourth play. He is a father to three sons.

Lauren Lawler is a law librarian and lives in Portmarnock, County Dublin. She studied in UCD and holds an MA in Poetry Studies from the Mater Dei Institute. This is her first publication.

Dr Hilary Lennon received her PhD from the School of English, Trinity College Dublin, and is the Harriet O'Donovan Sheehy Research Fellow in the School of English, University College Cork. She is the editor of *Frank O'Connor: Critical Essays* (Four Courts Press, 2007), and the creator and editor of the UCC official O'Connor website, frankoconnor.ucc.ie. Her *Selected Letters of Frank O'Connor* is forthcoming from Cork University Press.

Dave Lordan edits the alt.culture website *bogmanscannon.com*. He teaches poetry as a multimedia art form in various second- and third-level institutions and researches for the RTÉ poetry programme. Find his poetry films on YouTube.

Paul Lynch is the author of *Red Sky in Morning* and *The Black Snow*. He lives in Dublin with his wife and daughter.

Patrick McCabe was born in Clones, County Monaghan, where he still lives, in 1955. He has worked a lot in fiction and drama and has published a lot over the years.

Mike McCormack is from Mayo and is the author of two novels and two collections of short stories. His novel *Solar Bones* will be published by Tramp Press in May 2016.

Iggy McGovern is Fellow Emeritus of Trinity College. He has published two poetry collections with Dedalus Press. His latest book, *A Mystic Dream of 4* (Quaternia Press 2013), is a poetic biography of William Rowan Hamilton.

Lisa McInerney is the author of *The Glorious Heresies*. Her stories have featured on BBC Radio 4 and in *The Long Gaze Back*, edited by Sinéad Gleeson, and *Town and Country*, edited by Kevin Barry.

Belinda McKeon's second novel is *Tender* (Picador). She is also the editor of *A Kind of Compass: Stories on Distance*, published by Tramp Press.

Eoin McNamee was born in Kilkeel, County Down. He is the author of *The Blue Trilogy*.

Patrick Maddock is a one-time Hennessy Award winner and featured on the shortlist of the Gregory O'Donoghue International Poetry Competition. His poems have appeared widely in magazines.

Aidan Mathews recently published *Charlie Chaplin's Wishbone*, a suite of stories some of which are set in the 1960s. He was ten years old in the fiftieth jubilee year of the Easter Rising. He is much older now.

Lia Mills writes novels, short stories, essays, reviews and an occasional blog. Her most recent novel, *Fallen*, is the Two Cities One Book festival selection for 2016 (Dublin and Belfast).

Patrick Moran is from Tipperary. He has published three collections of poetry: *The Stubble Fields* (Dedalus Press, 2001), *Green* (Salmon, 2008) and *Bearings* (Salmon, 2015). His work has appeared widely in Ireland and the UK.

Julie Morrissy is a poet from Dublin. In 2015 she was shortlisted for the Melita Hume Poetry Prize, and selected for the Poetry Ireland Introductions Series. Her debut pamphlet, *I Am Where*, is published by Eyewear Press.

Jimmy Murphy is a playwright. His most recent work, *Of This Brave Time,* was premiered by the Abbey Theatre as the opening play of their Waking The Nation programme and will tour the UK in March.

Stephen Murray is the author of two poetry collections with Salmon Poetry, *House of Bees* (2011) and *On Corkscrew Hill* (2013). His company Inspireland delivers Ireland's most popular and exciting schools poetry programme to teenagers across Ireland, Britain and Australia.

Doireann Ní Ghríofa is a bilingual poet writing in Irish and in English. She was awarded the Ireland Chair of Poetry bursary 2014-2015. Her most recent book is *Clasp* (Dedalus Press, 2015).

Val Nolan's definitive history of the John McGahern banning appeared in *Irish Studies Review* (2011) while his story 'The Irish Astronaut' was shortlisted for the 2014 Theodore Sturgeon Award. He lectures at Aberystwyth University.

Jessamine O'Connor is founder of The Hermit Collective and facilitator of The Wrong Side of the Tracks Writers. She is nominated for a 2017 Pushcart Prize and was judge of the New Roscommon Writing Award 2015. She has won several poetry awards and is widely published. Her three chapbooks are available from www.jessamineoconnor.com.

Donal O'Kelly is a Dublin playwright and actor living in County Leitrim. His plays include *Fionnuala, Little Thing Big Thing, Catalpa, The Cambria, Jimmy Gralton's Dancehall, Vive La, Running Beast, Asylum! Asylum!, Operation Easter* and the Prix Europa award-winning *Francisco.*

Glenn Patterson's latest novel is *Gull* (Head of Zeus). He has published nine previous novels and three books of non-fiction and co-wrote the film *Good Vibrations*. He lives in Belfast.

Grahame Williams was born in County Down and now lives and works in London. In 2014-15 he won a place as a fiction writer on the Jerwood/Arvon mentoring scheme.

Mary Woodward has an Irish and Welsh background (South Sligo and Ceredigion). She published *The White Valentine* (Worple Press) in 2014 and was highly commended in the Forward Prize 2015 and the Gregory O'Donoghue competition 2016. She also writes fiction.

~

Our guest editor:

Sean O'Reilly is the author of *Curfew and Other Stories, Love and Sleep, The Swing of Things* and *Watermark.* He teaches in the Irish Writers Centre and at the American College Dublin. He also leads the Stinging Fly fiction workshops. *Love Bites and Other Stories* will be published by The Stinging Fly Press later this year.